*This copy is dedicated to the memory of
Bee Cutler, Dr. Allan S. Cutler,
Hannah Braun, and Herbert S. Braun.*

*With deep love and gratitude,
Jerry*

Nine Nights with the Taoist Master

by

Master Waysun Liao

SECOND EDITION
Copyright © 2005 Waysun Liao
Taichi Tao Productions
433 South Boulevard
Oak Park, Illinois 60302

www.taichitaocenter.com

ISBN 0-9765454-1-1

cover design and layout by Steven Vasilakis

for "Prince KoYou"

About the Author

Master Waysun Liao spent his teenage years with a traditional Taoist master, learning the art of Tai Chi, meditation, feng shui, Chinese traditional medicine and healing, as well as the true philosophy of Tao and its applications to spiritual development, health and longevity.

Shortly after coming to the United States, Master Liao established the Tai Chi Tao Center at 433 South Blvd.,Oak Park, IL. 60302 (www.taichitaocenter.com). Since 1970, it has been regarded as one of the most authentic and informative schools in the world, teaching the true philosophy of Tao, Tai Chi, and its application to spiritual and meditation work.

He continues to spread the art of Tai Chi and the science of Tao by giving seminars, group and intensive training, as well as private sessions with sincere students. His previous books, *Tai Chi Classics,* and *The Essence of Tai Chi,* published by Shambhala, have been translated into many different languages and enjoyed by readers worldwide.

Master Liao has students all over the world, and enjoys sharing his teaching to help others who are longing for the wisdom of Truth.

Contents

Forword

This is a fictional story about Lao Tzu's masterpiece, the *Tao Te Ching*. For hundreds of years, its mysterious and beautiful words have enchanted and inspired millions of readers. It is my hope that weaving this fanciful tale will help readers hear Lao Tzu's words in a new way, and perhaps understand them more deeply.

Legend says that Lao Tzu became weary of the ways of mankind, and thus traveled west into the desert lands. A guard at the gate leading to the western wilderness stopped the sage and asked that he give a final discourse on his wisdom. That discourse is the *Tao Te Ching*.

We know that writing in those days, 2500 years ago, was no easy matter. It was a laborious process that involved carving characters on strips of bamboo with sharp knives. Very few had the resources to carve and preserve such a document. This fact alone might give us reason to assume that the story behind the legend is more involved.

The speculation that there is more to the legend of Lao Tzu's transmission of the *Tao Te Ching* is the foundation for this book. In our story, the gate to the west is an ancient trading city, and the "guard" is the prince of that city. When Lao Tzu visits the city, he encounters many adventures as well as the curious questions of both the prince and others. During his stay, Lao Tzu is able to teach many people about the truth of the power of Tao through his words and example.

In acknowledgement, many people contributed to this book with their typing, editing, research, design and computer skills. In that regard, I would especially like to thank Steven Vasilakis, Tracy Litsey, Mary Martin, Jane Andrew, Catherine Lange and my niece, Peggy Liao.

I hope you enjoy this book, and that its pages will shed new light on the *Tao Te Ching*.

Master Waysun Liao, 2004

Chapter One
Trouble for the Border City of West Peace

"General KoWu!" the breathless soldier gasped as he burst through the council doorway, bowing hastily.

"Report!" ordered a stately leader from the center of the council room.

2500 years ago, central Asia knew nothing of chairs. The prince, who soldiers often addressed as "General," sat on a plush cushion surrounded by smaller mats. On these mats sat several old warriors and key palace advisors. The group came to argue defense strategies against an imminent attack from northern barbarian tribes before the scout's abrupt arrival. The frantic scout brought critical news, since he monitored the advancing barbarian troops on the city's southern outskirts.

"Laotzu! The sage. He's coming…he's on his way up the southeast road!" puffed the soldier, out of breath from his run to the chambers.

"What? Now?" cried the prince. "Is he accompanied by armed escort? How many in his entourage?"

"He comes alone sir. Riding on an ox," the soldier reported.

Prince KoWu's square face usually offered the inspiring confidence expected from a leader. Now, however, that same face paled and furrowed, his mind wrestling with the impossibility of this news. How could Laotzu get here through the hordes of raiding barbarians? Did he not hear? Couldn't he see that this was no time for traveling through this troubled region? And riding alone on an ox?

"Dispatch an escort party of your best swordsmen, fast!" shouted the prince to the soldier who heeded the command by disappearing as quickly as he arrived.

"This is a worse situation than I thought," the prince confided to his counselors.

He heard weeks ago that the renowned sage Laotzu might be traveling through the region. Visiting sages and scholars rarely traveled this far west, and KoWu was eager for an opportunity to meet this legendary sage who talked about a mysterious "Tao."

But he assumed that any sage would be smart enough to stay off the main roads in late autumn when the northern looters gathered their annual plunder. KoWu figured Laotzu, like the traveling merchants coming westward, would bide time inside the walls of Bright Plain, the city lying three days journey southeast, until the raiding quieted down.

Because KoWu's forces protected miles of frontier land at the desert border, Bright Plain stayed safe and calm. But KoWu's city, West Peace, bustled with the coming and going of troops, and the influx of country villagers seeking protection from raging barbarians.

West Peace stood on the northwest border of what is now known as China. At that time, China had many small kingdoms much like the feudal states in early European history. Although states sometimes fought each other, their common and fearsome enemy was the powerful and unpredictable northern barbarian tribes. All interior states relied on the city of West Peace to provide a measure of protection from these invading northerners.

Stationed along the main north and west roads that vanished into the vast desert beyond, West Peace also served as a key stop along Asia's trade routes. Merchants from as far west as the Mediterranean and as far south as the flowering islands met in West Peace to trade. Here, dusty traders hoisted heavy silks rich with color, exotic woods, and pieces of stonework off the backs of camels and carts as they haggled for bundles of fragrant spices. In the local drinking houses, the traders gambled for gold coins bearing the faces of faraway kings Prince KoWu would never meet.

The flourishing trade drew many new people from faraway lands to permanently settle in West Peace. The mix of cultures and languages often led to squabbles between the foreign born and the West Peace natives, so KoWu kept a strong civil force and a network of local administrators loyal to him.

West Peace was indeed a challenging city to rule. But Prince KoWu was the logical choice for such a strategic military and economic outpost.

In ancient China, a separate family empire ruled each independent state. West Peace belonged to the larger kingdom of Ching. The King of Ching understood the importance of West Peace, not only to his own kingdom, but as a pivotal city among neighboring empires as well. West Peace gave him both diplomatic power and great wealth.

His oldest son, Prince KoWin, could not rule faraway West Peace. Tradition decreed that KoWin would rule from the central palace by his father's side until the king's death when KoWin would then become king himself. It was just as well that KoWin stay in the capital, since KoWin pre-occupied himself with the fawning attentions of village courtiers. He loved acquiring sumptuous robes, and presiding over pretentious feasts for even the smallest occasion.

But the king's second son, KoWu was brave, sober and smart. The shrewd king made KoWu governor of the vibrant border outpost, while he kept watch over the wasteful older son back in the capital.

As a king's son, KoWu grew to manhood under the influence of the brightest scholars and finest warriors. Well educated and disciplined, he earned the quiet respect of his teachers. Unfortunately, his teachers made more public displays of approval for the firstborn son, KoWin. The teachers knew it would be Prince KoWin who would stay in the palace and Prince KoWin they would ultimately serve, not KoWu.

Nevertheless, his teachers' secret respect won KoWu many favors. His tutors always invited him to late night discussions with visiting sages that came through town. These conversations about mystical arts and philosophies gave KoWu the chance to see the faces and see the power of legendary masters. The long nights with these unforgettable characters and their inspiring teachings increased both KoWu's wisdom and skill at dialogue.

KoWu's strong character, even his tendency toward pride, suited him well in West Peace. Now thirty years old, he could play all the roles he must: governor and general, judge and gentleman, husband and father.

Keeping the border city peaceful and stable was a formidable task. The endless comings and goings of merchant caravans, the sheer number of their animals, the petty thieves and robbers who followed merchants like flies, made West Peace a stewpot of trouble waiting to boil over at the edges if not carefully tended.

And while the city seethed inside its walls, outside the northern desert lands teemed with countless hungry tribes. With no means to feed themselves in their harsh world of endless sand, wind and rocks, these barbarians instead would ride south – usually just before winter – to loot the richer southland for the gold, silks, food and supplies they needed to survive.

The barbarians were strong and wild and led by an aggressive chief. During their seasonal raids, they mounted their best horses and often joined together with other tribes to attack and burn the smaller villages around West Peace. There might be as many as a thousand to five thousand strong in a bad year.

West Peace had close to one thousand well-armed men, and strong walls with virtually impenetrable gates. But it was also KoWu's task to protect the surrounding villages as best he could. Without the peasants' support and without their farms, West Peace would soon find that its own supplies of wine, meat and grain would be dangerously scarce.

The barbarians swarmed again this autumn like locusts. They usually went southwest of West Peace, not bothering to challenge the big city head-on. They preferred to bully the smaller towns. But this summer had been very dry, and due to the drought, the villages had poor harvests so there was less to loot. The raiders, forced to press farther south than usual, still hadn't stolen enough supplies to last the winter.

That spelled trouble for West Peace. It meant that on their way back, the tribes would risk more to fill their saddles closer to the city. They might well charge the city's own walls, since West Peace was the last town on their return to their desert home. Worse, having had their fill of wine but not their fill of gold, the barbarians were foolhardy and desperate.

According to KoWu's scouts, the enemy raiders rode over the plains toward the southeast road. If they turned northwest, that meant they planned to challenge West Peace directly and could arrive before the sun reached its zenith.

Soldiers already evacuated the caravan quarters and local settlements just outside the city wall, bringing the people safely inside the gates. But although the people were safe, they would undoubtedly lose homes, live-stock, and crop stores. Clearly many good soldiers would lose their lives deflecting the barbarians back northward to their desert hovels.

In years past, Bright Plain and other neighboring cities could send re-inforcements to help chase the hordes back. This summer's drought had been too harsh however, and those cities had nothing to spare for West Peace as they struggled to defend their own walls.

Under these ominous conditions, Prince KoWu called his war council together to agree on a last minute strategy to defend an important grain store-house on the southeast road.

That was until the scout's report about Laotzu's coming.

Barbarian Raiders Gather Outside West Peace

KoWu couldn't fathom how the sage made it this far unscathed. Others described Laotzu as an older man who traveled unarmed and unaccompanied on the back of a farm ox. But KoWu thought those stories were merely poetic tales. He didn't really believe that Laotzu would come this far on an ox. He assumed that Laotzu would travel with a master's usual score of disciples and a squadron of warriors or personal guards provided by wealthy patrons. KoWu heard that another master, Confucius, traveled through the city of Nan Do last year with seventy-two disciples and dozens of followers.

Although he puzzled over the question of how Laotzu managed to ride alone across China on an ox, there was no doubt in KoWu's mind that the sage currently faced grave danger.

If the barbarian leader did not recognize Laotzu as a holy master, he would certainly kill Laotzu and take his ox as spoil. When word got out that Laotzu, the most venerable master of a hundred kingdoms, died under his watch, KoWu would face the scorn of cultivated people far and wide.

If the barbarians killed Laotzu, he knew the local priest would play upon the superstitions of the people and blame any disasters for the next hundred years on KoWu's failure to protect Laotzu. While it wouldn't threaten KoWu's immediate power, it would make negotiation with the temple priest intolerable and give him undue leverage for years that KoWu might never reclaim.

There was a second more remote possibility. The barbarian leader might actually be wiser than his thickheaded tribesmen. He might recognize Laotzu as a sage and not kill him, but rather take Laotzu as a hostage. If that happened, KoWu would be bound to pay any ransom the barbarian chief demanded. It would then be a matter of marketplace haggling that could jeopardize a large share of the city treasury.

This was the first time in eight years that the barbarians dared to challenge the main city of West Peace head on. Eight years ago, KoWu, who'd been prince of the border city for only a short time, led a massive and deadly charge against the barbarians that earned him their fear. It was in that legendary autumn battle that KoWu won his nickname of "Martial Giant," for one meaning of "Wu" means "martial." That great war won him the enduring respect not only of the barbarian tribes, but also of all the citizens of West Peace. It was in that battle, too, that he rescued the woman who would later be his bride – Zhu Xiao Hua and her young son Zhu Chian. They'd been held captive in the barbarian caves for over two months after the murder of her former husband, General Zhu Ming.

But apparently, the barbarian's awe of KoWu wore thin, and the northerners were willing to test their strength against the "Martial Giant" today. The poor sage Laotzu stood in the middle of what would be an undisputed blood bath.

No, the situation couldn't be worse. Prince KoWu stormed out of the chamber followed by three military generals and a dozen advisors. As he turned toward the stairs and started his climb, they trailed and rippled behind him like the hem of a long robe as he strode two steps at a time to the top of the city walls.

Chapter Two

An Unprecedented Arrival

"There, General," squinted a watchman toward the southeast road made of hard-packed gravel and yellow dirt.

The prince could see his armed escort racing furiously toward a lone, tiny figure on the horizon. He could make out a small gleam of white that could only be the ox Laotzu rode. Yet from this high perch on the city wall, the prince could see what his armed escort could not. Both from the southwest and due west, two flanks of barbarian troops barreled toward the southeast road. In addition, to the south, behind Laotzu's very back, a gray cloud swelled up from the ground to the heavens. Undoubtedly the cloud was dust and smoke from a third marauding tribe galloping towards Laotzu.

KoWu's heart sank. He knew he must now watch the dire fate of his men and the old sage who blindly headed for the exact place where the enemy forces would converge.

With gates locked and the city surrounded by his best warriors, Prince KoWu stayed on the wall where his men could see him and take courage. From here he could dispatch orders to the archers, and watch the troops below.

Standing now with his chest thrust out, KoWu assumed a general's air. Silently, he held his breath as he watched Laotzu and the escort. Why weren't they hurrying? The white ox, now clearly in view, ambled along like it was a summer's day on the farm.

"Who is this crazy and mysterious sage that travels on an ox? And why must he be fated to die before my very eyes?" mulled the worried ruler of a city now at arms.

Six famous masters visited West Peace over the past ten years, providing KoWu welcome news from the inner circles of the big interior and coastal cities. He valued the long conversations with them that rekindled his curiosity about new philosophies, astronomy, and the mysteries of life. Such sages were the only men he could speak with as equals since their position allowed them to gently challenge and teach him. Their visits relieved and distracted him from the grueling politics around him, and came too seldom.

At least four of the previous masters had spoken of Laotzu. They spoke his name in hushed tones, acclaiming him the master of highest mysteries, and a worker of miracles. From the level of respect they accorded this Laotzu, KoWu wondered why the sage had no entourage. A sage, like a prince, often had courtiers of a different sort. While some masters were as wealthy as merchant kings, others lived like frugal scholars. Nevertheless, most had a score of disciples who followed them wherever they went.

KoWu looked on as Laotzu came closer into view. The royal escort troop finally spotted the barbarian forces, so they circled their horses in a perimeter of defense around the sage. The gray cloud to the south grew larger, another enemy horde getting closer…

But wait!

It was no dust and smoke cloud rising to the south as KoWu previously assumed. It was a burgeoning storm front brewing black and ominous, propelled by an east wind. Nobody on either side of the battle expected this! There had been no rain for weeks, and little at all since spring.

The cloud-cover softened the sun's glare, allowing KoWu to survey the full panorama of the plain. Just as he suspected, the barbarian troops converged on the plain less than a mile from the southeast road, and almost within an arrow's reach of Laotzu and the escort company. As the enemy armies spied Laotzu and the small platoon of soldiers, they shouted boasts to each other about which clan could take the pitiful group the fastest.

But their garrulous laughter and threats grew quiet as the barbarians surveyed the changing weather. They looked up to see clouds spilling up from the south like a black tide over the entire plain. The clouds rumbled their warning.

From the city walls, the prince could also see the clouds move over the plain. These were rain clouds like KoWu had never seen. The clouds grew from the south horizon like huge mushrooms. They covered the plain to the west, south and north as far as the eye could see.

Suddenly, the clouds began to twist, touching the ground. Gusty winds swept over the yellow earth, churning up dust and scrub-brush. The wind picked up speed while the devil clouds exploded into torrents of hail and lightening.

The barbarians' horses panicked and reared at the crack of thunder and the threatening weight of the dark sky. As their horsemen struggled to regain themselves, the barbarian army became a whirling chaos just like the whirling clouds circling above their heads.

Just then, two swirling fingers of black wind extended down from the angry heavens and traced a line of death through the crowd of invading horsemen. The twisting tornados sent bodies and spears, packs and carts, rocks and sand flying in all directions. Any barbarians not scattered by the winds now scattered in utter fear for their lives, riding north to the desert as fast as their wild-eyed horses could gallop.

And while the storm raged on the southwest plain, a stretch of open sky, blue and serene, opened to cover Laotzu and his escort. The narrow blue stretch extended northeastward over the city of West Plain. It seemed as if the sky split itself in two – a sky of terror and a sky of protective calm.

Down on the road, Laotzu's escort troop kept their weapons drawn and faces alert while riding to either side of Laotzu's ox. Untouched by the storm, they made their way slowly toward West Peace. The ox set the pace for the group, never quickening and never stopping through the whole ordeal. As they traveled, the patch of clear sky followed them. Laotzu, now in view, held no weapon, only a flywhisk that he occasionally swept over his shoulder or over the ox's ear.

KoWu and his men on the city wall watched in speechless awe as the nearby clouds enforced a horrific victory swifter than their own army ever could. Not only did the storm rout the barbarians, but it also left their plunder littering the southwest plain. Barrels of food, discarded weapons and treasure dotted the fields amidst the terrible carnage of severed limbs, barbarian corpses and dead horses.

The wind died down while the clouds thinned. The remaining clouds scattered to the north, along with what remained of the barbarian armies, until both disappeared from view beyond the northern horizon.

A military advisor rushed up the stairs asking "General, shall we follow the barbarians and destroy the last of them while they flee?"

"No," spoke KoWu, his eyes still riveted on the sage who now approached the gate below. "I believe we have more important matters to attend to."

Other counselors scurried along the wall to offer the prince congratulations on the stroke of good fortune. The watchmen from the North and Western walls came to confirm that the enemy had indeed fled.

Laotzu and the Tornado

KoWu barely noticed any of them and waved them off as he strode decisively down the stairs and through the market to the South Gate. People already buzzed with news of what happened. Heads peeked out of doorways and alleys. The lanes gradually filled with townspeople, curious for more details about the storm and the barbarians' defeat. As the prince walked the several blocks to the gatekeeper's post, the crowd parted to let him and his guard pass.

Arriving at the gatekeeper's post, the prince bellowed, "Open the South Gate." As the huge oak timber doors creaked aside, there was Laotzu's ox only a few yards from of the threshold. The animal had never stopped lumbering along, as if fully expecting the doors to open. The sage, who rode sidesaddle, nodded to the gatekeeper as he passed.

The people of West Peace flooded the streets and assembled along the side of the main road that stretched from the south gate to the palace steps. A line of civil guard held the crowd's curiosity in check and kept the center of the street clear.

Expecting a much older man, KoWu noticed that Laotzu appeared to be only middle-aged. Wearing a plain, yet sturdy dark cloth robe, the sage simply raised his hand silently to bid the ox to stop. Like his robe, his shoes were plain: meticulously woven of hemp, sturdy and evenly worn. His face, though unremarkable, had a kind and confident expression. The dust settling from the escort troop's procession did nothing to hide the gleam from Laotzu's eyes as he surveyed the prince and the welcoming townspeople.

"Do I have the honor of welcoming the great master of legend, Laotzu?" said Prince KoWu stepping forward.

"And you must be Prince KoWu," Laotzu smiled, still sitting sidelong on his ox. As he looked down on KoWu, he waved his flywhisk casually from right to left. It was two feet long, and made from the hair from a horse's tail woven around a sturdy stick. Some of the interior scholars and monks carried them. Whether masters carried the whisk as a ritual, a fashion, or simply to brush away flies, KoWu could only guess.

"Yes, I am Prince KoWu," KoWu bowed.

At the prince's cue, his counselors and guards bowed as well. A soldier stepped forward to tie a rope around the ox' neck. A young girl ran up to tie a red ribbon around the ox' tail. She took the rope from the soldier's hand and turned to Laotzu. The townspeople could no longer contain themselves, and cheered when the young girl bowed to the sage on their behalf.

From on top of the giant ox, Laotzu looked down at the young girl's beaming smile. "Excellent," replied Laotzu, with an uncanny and gentle tone that carried only kindness to the ear. Turning again toward the prince, the sage said, "I happen to pass your city on my way to Kunlun Mountain. If possible, I will stay here a few days."

"Of course, it will be our honor," answered KoWu. "May I have the privilege of inviting you as my guest in the palace?"

"That will do, if you could also invite my friend here. He also needs some rest," said Laotzu, throwing the prince an inquiring grin. The sage slid down the ox' ribs and patted the animal's neck.

"Certainly," said the prince. KoWu himself humbly took the ox' rope from the girl and led the hulking animal toward the palace. "He will stay in the royal stable with our finest war horses." The two men walked side by side up the city's main road toward the palace. Children broke free from their parents and skipped behind the white ox. They laughed and played as barking dogs joined the celebration to greet the new visitor. The whole crowd burst into a roaring cheer when the two men reached the palace gate. Clearly, this would be a day that the city of West Peace would never forget.

Chapter Three
A Royal Welcome for the Sage and His Ox

KoWu's palace gate opened to reveal a magnificent courtyard. Its elegant stonework and simple landscape of rare shrubbery and stone paths stood in quiet contrast to the busy market avenue outside.

Inside the palace gates, the young girl took the ox' rope from the prince's hands. Laotzu followed her as she led the animal to the royal stables at the side of the palace courtyard and into the largest stall. The ox' pen brimmed with fresh grasses and dry straw, and Laotzu nodded his approval to the girl. Knowing his friend was in good hands, Laotzu went back to rejoin the waiting prince.

Laotzu and the prince followed the courtyard path toward the huge polished wooden doors of the main palace. Through side windows, they could spy the bustle of household servants preparing for the arrival of an important guest on short notice. Two barrel-chested men pulled aside the heavy double doors and the two entered the main palace hall.

Two servants quickly stepped forward to take the prince's outer robes and offer him a new one. Others brought silver trays with basins of water and clean towels, offering to help the men wash the dust off their hands, faces and feet.

"Holy master, I have heard about you for a long time, but I was never blessed with the opportunity to meet you until now," said the prince as he led Laotzu over to the side of the hall where large cushions trimmed with tapestry and gold beads lay on the floor. Taking his seat, the prince continued, "It must be God who answers my prayers and brings you to my city."

While the prince spoke, several of his advisors came in and stood behind their ruler with heads bowed and hands folded.

"Master Laotzu," Prince KoWu turned to the sage, offering his guest a seat on a nearby cushion. "It is my highest honor and a true blessing to have you here. The whole city owes their deep appreciation for what you have done for us. We faced a dangerous siege, and you came to rescue us all. Please stay and make this city your permanent home."

Entering the Palace

"I did nothing. The power of Tao did what is right. I am just an average man passing by. I am actually on my way to Kunlun Mountain to meet with some sages. There is a prince there who needs help."

"Master, winter will be here in only a few weeks. Won't you stay until spring?" the prince asked.

Laotzu took a long and silent pause with his eyes closed, as if he waited for some inner instruction on how to answer his host. "Well, according to my ox, it is a very long journey to Kunlun Mountain. At most I can stay here a few days, then I must go. This prince I mentioned has been trying to connect to the spiritual power for years. He has given up everything and sought many teachers. I must go to him to teach him how to meditate. I can feel the utmost sincerity of this faraway prince. He has felt the pain of his people; he sees them suffer through birth, sickness, old age and death. He tries so hard to find the way to bring relief to the ever-suffering world, so I must go, even if winter comes," Laotzu answered.

"Master, could you at least teach me while you are here?" the prince implored. "After all, I am also a prince and I also need help. I have been looking for a true master since I was a young teen. True powerful masters like you rarely visit this remote city. I need your guidance."

"Why do you want me to teach you?" the sage countered.

"Because, if you do, then maybe I can become a more able and worthy ruler. My father, the king, brought me up with many prominent masters to tutor me to make me a good leader and general. Yet I still have a difficult time governing this tough frontier city, especially with so many barbarian raids. Master, I need to learn so that I may possess your level of power. Could you teach me to do what you can do so I can protect this city?"

"I cannot do anything. I am just an average person riding an ox, going wherever the ox takes me to. It is the power of Tao doing its job, not me," replied Laotzu in gentle defense.

"Master, I suspect you are far from ordinary," said KoWu. "You know, I worship too. I was taught to pray to the gods, but it never works. Could you teach me this power of Tao?"

"My teaching is simple and easy, it only takes a few words to share it and to know it – that is, if anyone is willing to actually practice it. However, I see that you are sincere in your desire to learn. This is what I can do: I will stay nine nights and will answer nine questions from you each night of my stay. You may ask me what you like. Is this agreeable to you?"

The prince nodded, then embraced his hands to his heart as he bowed deeply to the sage in silence. Rising slowly, KoWu replied, "Your offer relieves my disappointment that you cannot stay longer. We will meet this evening then. We will dine in the main palace hall so that other guests and my advisors may also be enlightened by your great wisdom."

KoWu stood up, resumed his commanding posture, and with a hearty voice concluded, "In the meantime, please be my guest and enjoy all the palace has to offer. Every servant here is your servant and I am your devoted disciple for as long as you will stay."

Laotzu just smiled quietly and nodded. As the sage rose from his mat, he wandered toward a nearby window. He looked outside and waved his whisk back and forth in time to a tree branch swaying in the breeze.

While the sage enjoyed his reverie, KoWu clapped twice. At this cue, servants brought in golden platters of meats, fruits and delicacies. Laotzu turned around in time to see half a dozen beautiful girls draped in gold and purple make an enchanting entrance. They performed an exquisite dance to wooden flutes and strings of golden bells while another line of servants followed offering delicate jars of aged wine. The fragrance of the drink and food mingled with the sounds of music. Pleasing visions and palatial splendor wove a feast for every sense. The celebration offered an important guest of West Peace a regal welcome.

Laotzu glanced briefly at the procession and turned back toward the window. He resumed his play with the whisk, waving it in time with the branch that now tapped at the window's edge.

Advisors and servants alike seemed puzzled that the sage preferred to remain aloof from the festivities. Nevertheless, since the sage was preoccupied, the courtiers took their opportunity to pull the prince aside one by one. Each conveyed urgent bits of official news and business that needed attention. Although the prince responded to each advisor briefly and succinctly, he never took his eyes off of the mysterious sage at the window.

KoWu's head servant Dai Dong came in to ask the prince's wishes for the evening meal and Laotzu's guest quarters. After giving Dai Dong his orders, Prince KoWu invited all the advisors present to attend the evening's session and share in Laotzu's wisdom. Then to Laotzu, the prince concluded, "Teacher, stay here for awhile and enjoy our hospitality. The servants will prepare the best room in our palace for you. I need to leave for just awhile to attend to business matters. I will return before long to personally escort you to your room so that you may rest before our first evening time together."

Turning on his heel, the prince left the hall to tend to the business of restoring order after the morning's astounding events. The barbarian bodies and horses left on the plains required burning before their spirits became restless, and returning soldiers would expect the prince to welcome them.

Laotzu watched KoWu leave. Then, he surveyed the servants and the food around him, and pondered the face of each advisor. Everyone stood still, too dumbfounded with awe by the day's events to approach him.

The sage then turned again toward the window, where the branch that he previously fancied now hosted a small blue bird. Laotzu smiled at the bird, extending his flywhisk toward the branch. The little bird hopped onto the whisk and started to chirp a beautiful melody. To everyone's amazement, Laotzu began to hum along in perfect cadence and harmony. Everyone watched and listened in speechless wonder. When the odd pair finished their duet, the blue bird cocked its head at Laotzu with a whistle and then flew off.

Chapter Four
Suitable Lodgings Found

While KoWu was gone, Laotzu passed most of his time gazing out the window. He took only a bit of water and fruit to refresh himself. Two of the prince's advisors finally mustered the courage to make small conversation with the sage, mostly about the seasonal weather in various regions he'd traveled through.

True to his word, the prince returned before long. At the prince's return, servants made a swift and noiseless exit with trays, jars, and cushions, while the advisors made polite farewells leaving KoWu and sage alone.

The prince motioned for the sage to follow and led him through the rear doors of the reception hall into an inner courtyard between the official palace and the royal family's residence. The inner courtyard differed from the outer courtyard. This one had a large open area surrounded by delicate fruit bearing trees. Along the periphery lay comfortable alcoves for painting or conversation. As he followed the prince along a luminous stone pathway of smoothed and polished agate, Laotzu spied three young girls among the pear trees, undoubtedly the prince's daughters. The little princesses sat at the feet of an aging governess who patiently showed them how to wrap ribbons of silk into brightly colored bows around stems of ripe fruit. KoWu didn't seem to notice them, although they waved and smiled as the two men passed.

They turned along the path through a side opening into a long interior hallway. At the hallways' end, an elegant doorway of carved cedar boasted tapestry curtains pulled aside by two ropes that appeared to be woven from gold itself. Two tall servants bowed to Laotzu and the prince and stepped aside, allowing them to pass.

"I want to honor you with our best quarters," said Prince KoWu. "Only visiting kings and our most important guests may stay here."

The room was truly astounding. Tapestries embroidered on heavy silk lavishly draped each wall. The scenes depicted victorious battles and splendid palaces of ancient kings. Small tables held precious statues of pure gold.

On a special pedestal in the center of the room sat an exquisite vase of jade filled with flowers made of intricately cast metal. The curious petals held a rainbow of inlaid jewels. The king himself entrusted this rare and priceless gift to his son KoWu. The king of Ching gave each of his four sons a rare treasure to guard in their respective palaces. It was more than a specimen of immeasurable beauty; it was a symbol of faith and trust from the king to his son.

The prince opened wooden shutters carved in intricate latticework to reveal a window that overlooked a small pond hidden in the inner courtyard. Servants rushed in to bring basins of warm scented water for bathing and trays of refreshments. Rare fur trimmed the enormous sleeping cushions filled with soft down.

"This is Dai Dong, my chief valet. He will be attending you while you stay," said the prince.

Dai Dong added, "Anything you need or wish for here is yours. I hope this room will be acceptable to you." The pale servant bowed with exaggerated propriety.

"You do me a great honor in offering me this splendid room," replied Laotzu. The sage raised his flywhisk to his chin and turned to survey the tapestries. He paced along each wall, admiring the priceless works of art. After a few moments of appreciation, Laotzu turned toward KoWu and said, "You know, I once visited an eastern king who did me an even greater honor."

Prince KoWu blushed. Taking the bait, he begged the sage, "How so? What can we provide? What greater honor can I offer?"

"This king did not give me a guest room in his palace, but rather gave me the authority to choose whichever room I wanted – even if I chose the king's own chambers!" said Laotzu. "Now that king gave me a great honor, don't you agree?"

"Consider it done! If this room is not as you wish, you may choose whichever room you will. The palace is yours and you may stay in whichever quarters you choose. Although I will confess that even my own quarters are not furnished quite as well as this," the prince apologized. He felt ashamed that this sage expected greater luxury than his palace could offer.

"I have an idea," said the sage. "Why don't you give me the two golden cords that hold this room's curtains aside from the doorway. I will place one cord across the door of the room I choose, and I will give the other cord to the honored guest who shall stay in this room in my place."

"If there is a guest in our city who deserves this honor, please give him this room with my blessing. Dai Dong will take the cord from whomever you choose and give him these quarters during your visit. And you may place the other cord on the door of any room you choose. We will send you a team of servants when you choose where you will stay."

"Oh, no thank you. I only need a young boy who can show me around and run errands. My needs are few and I'm unaccustomed to servants," answered Laotzu.

"As you wish, Master." Prince KoWu instructed Dai Dong to bring Laotzu the golden cords from the doorway curtains. These Laotzu looped casually around the waist belt of his robe.

Laotzu gave the room one last glance of admiration, then rested his fly-whisk across his shoulder as he turned back toward the hall. The prince now followed behind Laotzu.

Laotzu looked over his shoulder. "No need to accompany me, you can go back to your work. I'm sure you are very busy today. Don't worry. I will be fine. I'm sure the boy you send me will tell me when dinner is served." Laotzu flicked his whisk at the prince as if to dismiss him.

Laotzu walked down the hall alone, leaving the prince and Dai Dong to stare down the corridor after him.

"Ah, it's curious," the prince spoke softly to his valet. "I try to honor this man and no honor I can give finds a place to rest in him!"

At a loss for what to do next, the prince did exactly as Laotzu commanded, and returned to his business. He knew his palace was safe, and the sage would find plenty of servants wandering the halls if he happened to get lost. Whatever room he visited would not match these guest quarters, so the prince expected Laotzu would give up soon and return to this very spot for a rest. He told Dai Dong to keep a servant posted near the guest quarters for when the sage returned.

Laotzu, meanwhile, wandered down the corridor and back out through the inner courtyard. This time he stopped to smile at the little princesses under the pear trees. He squatted beside them and admired the fruits in their baskets. Each of the girls offered him their ripest pear. Laotzu, with exaggerated gusto, bit into each pear in turn. He closed his eyes and relished the fruit with great drama. "Mmmmmm." As the juice ran down his chin he exclaimed loudly that these were certainly the sweetest pears he had ever tasted and made so much more delicious by the lovely bows on their stems. He winked and the girls giggled as they ran back to their governess to report on their successful gift.

Laotzu didn't bother to check the other hallways leading out from the courtyard and had no interest in exploring the palace. Instead, he strode straight back through the palace hall where he first came in, out the palace doors and through the outer courtyard. Once outside, he looked toward the stables where the stable girl led Ox.

The stable girl was nowhere to be seen, and the stable was relatively quiet, aside from an occasional stomp or bray from one of its occupants. Laotzu could see that each animal was exceptionally well cared for. The clean stable betrayed no odor of soiled straw. Each horse's coat gleamed as if it had just been freshly brushed. Feed baskets layered with fresh and dried grasses rested on special hooks built into the side of each stall. In the empty stalls, undoubtedly for horses yet to return from the day's battle, the feed baskets offered bits of apple or a carrot on top of bundles of fresh hay. The water pails held cool, clear water freshly drawn from a nearby well. A feeling of peace and order and a sense of affection for these animals pervaded the air.

He went to the largest stall, and patted Ox. Welcome banners now festooned Ox' stall since Laotzu last saw it, and Ox still sported a red ribbon on his tail from their parade through town. Obviously Ox was as well cared for as each of the horses around him.

Laotzu heard someone whistling a tune from the back of the stable. He walked noiselessly toward the music only to startle Lo Han, an old stable hand who was busy scraping dried mud off the hoof of a horse just brought in from the battlefield.

"Oh! I didn't know somebody else was here," Lo Han looked up. He dropped the hoof he was cradling, and bowed in the manner of peasants. Laotzu apologized for interrupting him and bade him to continue his task.

"Oh, I do this for all of them that come back. I figure they've been out in the dirt and mud to save our lives at least they deserve some respect when they come back home. The cavalry chief and his men, they're the ones that choose the horses to buy and breed, and they train them good. I just take care of them, that's all."

Lo Han moved around to the side of the horse and patted her on the neck. "This one, she won't eat apples. I never heard of horse that didn't like apples. I think they hurt her teeth. So I try to get her a ripe pear now and then. They're softer and she likes them." Lo Han rambled on as he fussed over the rusty brown mare.

"Do you work all by yourself?" asked Laotzu.

"Oh no, I have my daughter, Lo Yintz. She's the one that tied that red ribbon around your ox' tail when you came in. She's always doing that kind of thing. Lo Yintz likes to dress up the horses and tie ribbons on their manes. She doesn't have any brothers or sisters to play with, since her mother died giving birth to her. So she stays by me and plays with the horses when she's lonely. She says they're just as good as human friends. She's even given them all names."

"So you raised your daughter all by yourself? How long have you worked here in the stables?" Laotzu questioned.

"All my life I guess. My brother and I were both born here. Funny though, we've never even been inside the palace itself."

Just then a lovely young girl peeked around a back door and smiled at the stable man. Laotzu recognized her as the very girl by the town gate who'd tied the red ribbon on Ox's tail and led him to his new home. It must be the stableman's daughter, Lo Yintz. She couldn't be more than thirteen.

Her father nodded and Lo Yintz came in with two pails of fresh water and set them in the corner of the horse's stall while the stable man's rough and calloused hands rubbed down the horse's hind legs.

"Where do you live?" asked the sage.

"Oh we have a small place at the back of the stable. It's nice enough. See it's just out here." Lo Han pointed out the doorway without taking his eye off the horses' knee.

Laotzu wandered outside and spied a small stone hut. He peeked in the doorway and had a look around. The Lo home had two rooms, both as neat and tidy as the stable he'd just left. Furnished simply, but comfortably, the larger room had a small stone fire pit for a stove and heat supply. Two beds of straw covered in soft wool edged the corner walls.

While Lo Han and Lo Yintz tended the horse's leg in the stable, outside, Laotzu unfastened one of the golden cords from his waist and quietly tied it across the simple latch on the hut's door. Neither the girl nor the stableman saw him.

When Laotzu returned to the stable, Lo Han boasted about his home with a hint of pride in his voice: "It has a window in the back so that you can smell the fresh cut grass when they bring it in, and it's just a few steps to the well. It's close enough to hear the horses if there's a fuss. It's quite comfortable really, and big enough for the two of us."

"Can I make a trade with you?" asked Laotzu, returning to the stall where Lo Yintz helped her father by wrapping the horse's ankle in oiled strips of cloth with her nimble young fingers.

"Oh we don't have anything to trade. We've got enough, but we don't have anything a highly placed man like you would want," smiled humble Lo Han in reply.

"Oh, but you do! I need a room to stay in for ten days, and I'd really like to use your home. In exchange I can give you and your daughter another room. It may not be an even trade, but you'll have to live there for the ten days, with no complaints, no matter what. And it will be a much longer walk to tend to your horses," explained Laotzu.

"I don't know, I don't think the cavalry chief would allow it. He's nice enough, but he knows the horses. They need me close," the stable man looked worried at the offer.

"Somehow, I think in this case it will be fine. The cavalry chief will not be any trouble to you," the sage spoke kindly to reassure Lo Han and his daughter. "Take this golden cord to the palace door, and tell the servant that Laotzu said you must personally deliver it to the prince's valet, Dai Dong. He will give you and Lo Yintz a room to stay in while I borrow your home."

The man and his daughter stared at the gold cord Laotzu offered them and looked at each other, a little confused. Laotzu again assured them that they need only follow his instructions and all would be well.

Lo Han shrugged his shoulders and agreed. He took the cord from Laotzu and gave it to Lo Yintz to hold while he finished tending the mare in front of him. With his task complete, Lo Han guided Laotzu back to the doorway of his stone hut. "Here sir. Please be our guest. But I am awfully embarrassed to have such a visitor stay in our humble place."

"Actually, it is a lot like a place I used to live. I like it. It will be perfect for my stay. I need this fresh air, and Ox would be lonely if I don't visit him often," Laotzu concluded and bowed to the stable hand. Knowing that the sage dismissed them, Lo Han and Lo Yintz bowed in return and walked out of the stable.

Laotzu pretended to head toward the cottage, but instead stopped to watch the two. He watched as they conferred with each other in the stall. They whispered as they looked down at the golden cord. Finally they both shrugged their shoulders and left the stable.

The peasant man and his daughter, who had served the palace all their lives, walked through the courtyard and approached the palace stairs slowly, holding the golden cord together, each with an end in hand. Leaning into each other for support, they both looked and felt quite nervous.

Timidly, dressed in coarse wool dusted with bits of straw, they took the curious bit of rope to the palace doors as Laotzu instructed. After a short exchange between Lo Han and the doorkeeper, Laotzu could see from afar as his two new friends walked inside those palace doors for the first time in their lives.

Chapter Five
A Servant for the Sage

"He did what?" cried the prince in disbelief.

"He's staying in a stableman's hut in the outer courtyard, and has sent the stableman and his daughter to stay in the royal guest quarters," answered Dai Dong, aghast at the whole situation.

"What a curious and frustrating old man," the prince mused as he rubbed his chin.

If news of this odd arrangement got out, KoWu worried he might be accused of dishonoring Laotzu by consigning the master to a peasant's hut. But he did make an agreement with Laotzu, and so he must allow the sage to stay where he will. And as for the stable hand and his daughter, they would have to remain in the guest quarters during Laotzu's stay, since that was also part of the agreement.

Dai Dong waited anxiously for an order from his master that would put things right again—undo this breach of propriety that even now scorched through the halls as the servants whispered among themselves. He watched in earnest while the prince, head down, paced back and forth.

All of a sudden KoWu stopped pacing. "I have a clever idea! I will honor that sage if it is the last thing I do! He did say he wanted a young boy to help him find what he needed around the palace. Send me KoYou!"

Dai Dong's world, far from being restored to its pristine and predictable order, now spun out of control completely. The prince made his own son a servant now? Tornados on the plains, peasants in the guest quarters and now he must bring that rascal KoYou to serve a sage who rode an ox?

Dai Dong bowed deeply to the prince, thankful to hide his face, now red with confusion. He quickly scurried down the hall to find KoYou, muttering to himself all the while about this strange state of affairs. He fidgeted in his sleeve for a dried lizard charm the queen gave him for protection from evil spirits.

KoYou was a nickname for KoChian, KoWu's adopted son.

Years ago, barbarians killed KoYou's real father when they ambushed his small family on their way to a neighboring village. After KoWu rescued the boy and his mother from barbarian captivity, he made sure the widow and son were taken care of out of respect for the slain general. When his own wife died a year later in childbirth, he married the widow and adopted Chian.

Eight years later, KoWu grew to admire and think of the boy as his own son. Since KoChian's adoption, KoWu and his queen had three of their own children, all daughters. KoWu believed a fortunate stroke of destiny allowed him to adopt Chian, for he might otherwise never have a son. Over time, even KoWu called the boy by his nickname KoYou.

At fourteen, KoYou stood poised on the brink of manhood. Soon he would assume a rank within West Peace's civil guard. Although KoYou was a smart boy and well-liked, his father KoWu was stern with him and took every opportunity to keep him humble. KoWu feared that as his only son, KoYou might grow up pampered and arrogant like his own older brother KoWin. To prevent that, KoWu personally supervised much of KoYou's military training, and assigned him strict and demanding tutors.

KoYou was mischievous like most boys and had the fresh confidence of youth. Although he might be described as cocky, none could fault him for true arrogance. He never flaunted his position, although he might flaunt his skill with a sword from time to time.

Those who knew KoYou soon forgot that he was even part of the royal family. He had a contagious laugh and a keen sense of humor, and he never put on airs.

Bright enough to finish all of his lessons quickly on most days, KoYou relished his free time to do what he loved best – practice with his sword or ride horseback around the farmlands that encircled West Peace.

KoYou could only go riding outside the city gates during spring and summer when no barbarians threatened the region. This restriction led to a few arguments between KoYou and the gatekeeper.

One day in early spring, when the gatekeeper had strict orders not to allow him to leave the safety of town, KoYou could stand his confinement no more. He mounted a quick young horse, and grabbed his sword to head to the country. When the gatekeeper stopped KoYou's horse, KoYou unsheathed his sword and deftly cut through the sash that held up the gatekeeper's pants.

As the poor gatekeeper clutched at his private parts and grabbed for his pants, he hurried to hunch behind a bush to avoid the stares of villagers now roaring with laughter. When he rose to shake his fist at the boy, KoYou was already a hundred yards down the main road waving to the gatekeeper from over his shoulder.

Although KoYou earned formidable skill as a swordsman, and loved his studies of the martial arts, he cherished a love of nature and bore a free spirit. KoYou liked to visit a nearby riverbank and watch the birds dip for fish. He loved to stay out past sunset and see the stars come out over the full horizon – with no city walls to block the view. He dreamed of what the Western mountains looked like and when he would have reason to visit there.

At fourteen, KoYou would marry on his next birthday. His mother and KoWu had arranged the engagement to the daughter of a prominent merchant's widow.

Most young boys barely knew their brides to be. KoYou was different. When he was eight years old and his parents announced the betrothal, he snuck out of the palace late at night to meet Yin Lian. He threw pebbles at the wall by her window until she woke up. He needed to find out what sort of person she was. If he didn't like her, he was going to run away. But when Yin Lian leaned her head out of the window, he saw she was pretty. They talked for a long time through the window that night. The youngsters discovered they had a mutual love of horses, shooting stars and joked together about fat caravan leaders.

Best of all, Yin Lian's father, who died of a seizure only four years after KoYou's engagement to her, had insisted that she learn martial arts. The wise man knew that a beautiful girl might need a way to defend herself from the rough crowd that often haunted the merchant quarters late at night. Yin Lian's special talent was the double-sword dance. She moved so swiftly and gracefully, even KoYou couldn't duplicate her unique skill.

After their engagement, Yin Lian came to the palace frequently to visit KoYou. Sometimes, KoYou was too busy with his studies to play, so Yin Lian passed the time visiting the beautiful horses in the prince's stables.

Yin Lian was just a few years older than the stableman's daughter, Lo Yintz. Despite the vast differences in their social class, they became and remained good friends. Since Yin Lian's family made their wealth trading in fine silks, Yin Lian often brought Lo Yintz small scraps and strips of ribbon the family couldn't sell. She loved to watch how Lo Yintz wove beautiful bows into the horse's manes while they played together in the stable on cold winter afternoons.

KoYou and Yin Lian soon became the best of friends. She was like a sister to him, and they both laughed at the thought that they were to marry and grow old together. Neither one was particularly nervous at the prospect. The whole arrangement just seemed so serious and far away that they didn't talk about it much and preferred instead to talk about other things.

Yin Lian was an intelligent girl, and with her family's vast wealth, she had tutors of her own. Nevertheless, she appreciated it when KoYou told her all of the interesting facts that he learned in his daily lessons. He even taught her some of the fighting tactics he'd learned with his father and the generals. They argued once in awhile about geography, since KoYou believed that Tianzu lay to the west, and Yin Lian thought it lay to the south.

They also argued about the existence of the gods. Yin Lian held the same view as her mother, that greedy temple priests invented the gods as an excuse to get their fingers in everybody's purses. KoYou didn't especially care for the temple priest either, but on quiet days alone in the countryside, he felt something in his bones that spoke to him like a whisper and winked at him from the glittering streams he passed on his horse.

KoYou felt grateful toward heaven because he knew he led a charmed life. His mother always told him it was her constant prayer to their local deities that brought KoWu to rescue them from the barbarians. From that time on, his mother was quite devout. She told KoYou that she made a bargain with the gods that if she and her son were rescued, she would remain loyal to the temple forever. She was not only rescued, but one year later, when KoWu's wife died in childbirth, she married a prince!

KoYou went to temple ceremonies with his mother, but somehow he felt the heavens held more than what the priest disclosed. Without any prayer or bargain with the gods, KoYou still felt some power protected him. He'd experienced several close calls on his rides outside the gates: once with a wild bear that dashed at him from behind a bush, another from a stray barbarian pair scouting local farms for livestock to steal.

On the first occasion, KoYou tied his horse to a tree so that he could shimmy down an embankment by the river and look for good skimming stones. He had to push aside branches from a clutch of bramble bushes and unknowingly startled a young male bear. KoWu jumped a full four feet when the bear's nose poked through the bush. On foot and an easy target, he backed slowly toward the river and away from the bear. When KoYou stepped into the shallow stream, the bear burst from the bush with a loud bellow. But just before the bear broke for a run at him, KoYou's horse almost magically appeared at his side in the river. Apparently, KoYou tied the harness too hastily and the horse found a way to slip out of the tether and made its way to the river for a leisurely drink. The fortunate mistake allowed KoYou to quickly mount and get away just as the bear charged.

In the second incident, KoYou was again on foot. He left his horse in the stable of a local farmer he knew, so that the horse could be fed and watered. It was a beautiful day, and KoYou wandered along a hidden path that wound behind the farms. Suddenly, he saw a pair of barbarians slinking from tree to bush. They thought KoYou was a farm boy. Since they didn't want the local farmers to know they were sneaking through the village stealing chickens, they planned to grab him and quietly slit his throat. KoYou knew that they could probably outrun him if he fled, and he had no weapon of his own since he'd left his sword tied to his saddle.

Just as KoYou's eyes met the eyes of the thieves, he heard a faraway neigh over his shoulder. His horse! The sleek black stallion charged over the field toward KoYou, and came to a stop at his side. The barbarians stood stunned by the horse's gallant arrival, and before they gathered their wits to draw their knives on KoYou, the boy mounted his horse and galloped away.

When the boy and horse returned to the farm, the poor farmer was lying prostrate in the dirt. He feared KoYou's punishment for losing the horse. He wept loudly, "Young prince, please forgive me. Do not punish a poor peasant. I could not control the horse. I led him to the stream to drink and he went mad! He pulled and tugged and finally broke away. There was nothing I could do."

KoYou comforted the man and told him the whole story, assuring him that the fact his horse ran away was actually a stroke of good luck that saved his life. The man then prostrated himself again in the dirt – this time in gratitude to the gods for such a miracle.

KoYou knew he was lucky: probably as lucky as that visiting sage, Laotzu, who arrived this morning.

"Certainly luck saved Laotzu's life today," thought KoYou, "when that storm came through and chased away the barbarians". KoYou sat by the storeroom in the back of the kitchen. He'd wandered back here after the sage's arrival to get what gossip he could from the kitchen staff on what festivities his father planned for tonight.

Dai Dong hunted high and low for the boy in all his usual haunts. When he finally found him in back of the kitchen, the valet told him to report to his father immediately. KoYou followed at once. He knew it must be important. He'd assumed his father would be too busy to even think of him today with all the commotion. He followed Dai Dong to his father's council chambers.

"Hello father," KoYou bowed.

Prince KoWu looked serious. He always did with his son.

KoWu puzzled over this boy. He wished he'd known his son's real father, General Zhu Ming, better. Perhaps it would have helped him understand KoYou's character. KoYou learned the arts of war easily, but seemingly had little interest in government itself. He memorized the lessons the scholars taught him, and could recite many classic verses, but had no bent toward becoming a scholar. Handsome and strong, KoYou had little interest in other girls, but had a strange friendship with the one girl he was betrothed to – the kind of friendship one has with another man, not a pretty girl. He'd even seen them practicing swordplay together. It was odd!

KoWu knew KoYou caused more than his share of trouble. The boy's mother worried herself sick when KoYou didn't return after dark some nights. The prince would have servants frantically combing the town, only to find out that the boy had left the town gates to ride alone across the country-side and had lost track of time.

KoWu looked at KoYou's square face, so much like his own if it weren't for that upturned corner of the boy's mouth that always hinted at a smile. He could have easily been mistaken for KoWu's natural son. KoWu wondered to himself: Where was this boy headed? What kind of position would suit him? Could he be a ruler?

One thing in the boy's favor was his winning way with people. Just about everyone liked KoYou, especially for his contagious laugh and his quick wit. But this also worried KoWu. Could the boy be serious as an adult when he took his place as a leader of the civil guard?

KoWu admired his own idea of sending KoYou as Laotzu's servant. It would give the boy exposure to a great master who might help develop his character. It would also allow KoYou to play the role of a servant – certainly that would reinforce humility in the boy and dampen that cockiness. But mostly, KoWu enjoyed the fact that he finally found an honor Laotzu would not easily squirm out of – having the prince's own son as his servant.

"KoYou," barked KoWu, "I want you to leave your studies for the next ten days. I have a special job for you."

"Oh, Father? What would you have me do?" asked KoYou, surprised that there would be a break in the rigid schedule of training his father usually demanded.

"You are to put on plain clothes and report to the house of the stable hand that has a golden cord tied at the door. There you will find our guest, the famous sage Laotzu. He has requested a young boy to serve him during his stay and help him find his way around the palace and attend to his needs. You will be that boy and I expect you to serve him as you would your grandfather the king."

The news confounded KoYou. Laotzu staying in old Lo Han's house? How did this come to be? He himself as a servant? He would have to find out the full story from the servants' gossip in the kitchen tonight.

"Yes, Father." KoYou bowed and left his father to do as he'd asked. He knew better than to ask his father any questions after receiving directions. Advisors and servants might ask for details or even give the prince an opinion, but not his son. KoWu wasn't interested in KoYou's questions or opinions; he was interested in making a ruler out of him.

But KoYou didn't care why his father looked so stern today. This was an adventure!

KoYou fairly skipped to his room to change out of his robes and into riding clothes to report to his mysterious assignment. "A servant to a real live master," he thought. He couldn't wait to tell Yin Lian the news!

Within a few heartbeats, KoYou dressed and walked over to the stable. He knew the little stone house and the man and his daughter who lived there very well. Lo Han had let him help with the horses when he was small and helped him understand the animals and how to talk to them to win their trust. The girl, Lo Yintz, spent many afternoons with Yin Lian and him. But where were Lo Han and Lo Yintz now? How could such a small house host a guest?

As he walked toward the door of the Lo's cottage, KoYou had a clever idea. Since he hadn't been introduced to the sage, Laotzu wouldn't actually know who this boy was that showed up at his door, would he? He wouldn't have to tell Laotzu that he was the son of the prince. He could be any town boy as far as the sage knew.

What a great joke to play. Of course Laotzu would find out sooner or later, but what fun in the meantime. KoYou took off his gold cuff and tousled his hair to look less important. Thank goodness the riding clothes he chose hadn't been washed since his last outing, and were suitably scuffed.

KoYou approached the small stone hut with the golden cord that looked so curiously out of place on the weathered little door. "Hello, sir. Anybody here?"

"Who's there?" answered a small kindly voice.

"Someone at the palace said you needed a boy to serve you, and they sent me. I am here."

"Who are you and where are you from?" Laotzu now opened the door and smiled at the boy. A very strong and tall boy, he noticed. Almost a man.

"I'm Chian from the city. They sent me because I knew where the stable was."

"You don't look like you're from a city at all, Chian," replied the sage. "You look like a country boy who should be out riding through fields and streams herding sheep, not penned inside some city walls. Come in, come in, you can start by finding me some kindling for the fire pit and drawing a pail of water from that well."

KoYou liked this odd master already, and followed him into the little stone house to fetch the pail.

After drawing water up from the well, KoWu set the pail down to rewind the rope over the well's frame. He stooped down to pick up the pail of water but stopped when he noticed something very strange. The surface of the water should have been still, but instead, ripples formed little waves across the surface. The pail looked like a restless miniature sea, although there was no breeze to cause the ripples.

As he watched, the small waves slowly died down until the water was smooth and clear again. He looked into the pail expecting to see his face in the water's mirroring surface. But instead of his own reflection, he saw the face of Laotzu in the water! Quickly he looked up expecting to see Laotzu behind him, but the old sage wasn't there.

"Are you finished?" called Laotzu from inside the hut. "Stop playing with the water and come in then, boy!"

Chapter Six

The Palace Plans a Party

The afternoon couldn't have been busier for everybody in the city of West Peace. In town, merchants pried boards off of shop windows when the word quickly spread that they were safe from barbarian raids. The drinking houses and entertainers prepared for a citywide victory celebration to welcome the soldiers back when they returned later from clearing the plains.

Every available soldier worked out on the plains all afternoon. They gathered and burned the enemy corpses and their dead horses. Horses with injuries too severe to heal were slaughtered for meat. Other soldiers led the few barbarian horses that were still in good shape back to the palace cavalry yards. Most of the weapons strewn across the field looked crude compared to their own, but they collected them nonetheless. The valuable metal could be melted down and retooled later.

Hwang Yi, one of KoWu's most highly placed generals, supervised the scavenger mission. Literally hundreds of dead northerners lay strewn in pieces across the plain. Hwang Yi had seen many battle scenes in his life, but this was by far the most haunting for him. Although the bodies were twisted and mutilated, not one weapon had been drawn against them. The thought gave him chills. He couldn't imagine facing an enemy like the wind where a man couldn't even defend himself with his sword.

A line of soldiers stretched across the road to hold back would-be looters. Many villagers wanted to help themselves from the stolen treasure that covered the plains like a carpet. Without the soldiers holding them back, the situation would have turned into a free-for-all.

Hwang Yi had a better idea. Hwang Yi instructed a young captain to have all interested villagers form a line. He conscripted each willing worker for a wage of one-tenth the value of whatever they gathered. When someone had gathered all they could carry, they turned it in at a special post where wagons lined up to haul the goods back to the palace treasury for sorting. Military scribes kept a ledger for each villager's work on a plank of wood. Hwang Yi announced that the citizen workers could report to the treasury three days hence to collect their ten percent share in either gold or supplies.

Some people groused at the arrangement, but they realized that with so much treasure to gather, everyone stood to earn a handsome profit. Less than honest folk slipped a coin or ring into their shoe just to be sure.

Back at the palace, not one person sat still. Butchers carefully selected and slaughtered the animals chosen for the evening feast. A few cooks collected vegetables and spices from the palace storehouses. Others shouted orders at the kitchen help to fill pots with water and large pans with oil. The house servants scoured and polished every surface, while others decorated the corridors and main hall in anticipation of guests.

Zhu Xiao Hua, KoWu's wife, sent her attendants to convey personal invitations to the town's elite to join the palace banquet. KoWu made sure he invited any foreign dignitaries staying in town as well.

Back in the stone cottage next to the stable, KoYou swept out the fire pit and stacked pieces of wood in the shallow stove so that Laotzu could start a fire. While he swept the hearth, Dai Dong, his father's valet, knocked on the door.

"Excuse me, Master Laotzu," bowed Dai Dong to the sage resting on the bed, "but the prince sends me to ask if you will need any special arrangements for your teaching this evening?"

"Come in, come in," beckoned Laotzu.

Dai Dong lifted his robe off the dirt floor and stood stiffly in the corner. When he noticed KoYou over by the fire pit, he bowed out of force of habit. When Laotzu turned his back, KoYou held his finger to his pursed lips and then waved it back and forth to warn Dai Dong not to bow.

At first Dai Dong wondered why the young prince would disguise his identity, but then he remembered the boy's penchant for playing practical jokes.

"Master, would you be needing any special food or drink? Any special attendants during this evening's talk?" Dai Dong asked the sage.

"Well," thought Laotzu, "now that I think of it, I usually teach my students in an outdoor courtyard. But since it is cold, we'll be indoors. Hmmm...."

"Is that a problem sir?" the valet inquired.

"Well it's just that sometimes I like to draw pictures in the dirt to help me explain things, and if we're indoors...."

"Oh that's no problem Master!" KoYou interrupted. "My fa...I mean the prince always draws pictures with his generals when they plan their war strategies. All they do is fill a wood frame on the floor with sand. Then they use a long bamboo twig to trace their plans. Uh, at least that's what I hear."

"Yes," Laotzu looked at KoYou. "Young boys like you are always interested in armies and generals aren't they? Very well, if the prince has such a contraption, can we have one where we gather?"

"It shall be done. Will there be anything else sir?" asked Dai Dong.

"When shall we arrive?" asked Laotzu.

"Dinner will be served after sunset."

"Can I come along then?" asked KoYou.

Dai Dong's face grew smug. "Well, servants will have to stand in the back and not disturb the guests."

KoYou knew the valet enjoyed the fact that the prince's son was now, for all practical purposes, a servant. KoYou had played plenty of practical jokes on Dai Dong over the years. Dai Dong was so high-strung and predictable. He made an easy target.

"Good!" clapped Laotzu. "Then at least my young friend Chian can keep an eye on me."

Dai Dong bowed his farewell to the sage, and almost bowed to KoYou before he caught himself. Armed with the sage's requests for the evening, Dai Dong excused himself and walked briskly back to the palace, where the staff required his direction.

Through the stable and across the courtyard, Dai Dong stopped first at the palace records room. Record keeper Wei Lon met him in the doorway. "How may we serve you today?" asked Wei Lon.

"I need Pen Hei," ordered Dai Dong. Pen Hei was the chief scribe. The prince made it clear that the scribe must record each of the nine nights' teachings so that all of Laotzu's wisdom could be preserved.

In these ancient days, before Asia knew of parchment or paper, writing or drawing was a laborious process. Writing entailed carving with sharp knives vertically into long strips of bamboo. The elite often employed specially trained scribes. Once the scribes completed their etchings, they strung the bamboo strips side by side on a rope and hung them between two posts to read. This is why the Chinese, even today, still read and write in vertical columns.

To illustrate important points while teaching, or to diagram military strategies, generals and teachers sometimes used twigs to trace in the dirt or a tray of sand to illustrate important points.

"Pen Hei already heard about the guest Laotzu. He has gone to the marketplace to purchase extra bamboo so that we will have enough to record each of the nine nights," Wei Lon answered.

"Good. The prince wants Pen Hei to know that the sage's words must be his top priority. If Pen Hei is behind in his carvings, he must remember to carve the sage's words first."

Dai Dong stressed this point. Whenever a scribe took notes at a meeting, he always paid special attention to the most ranking official in the room. Because the laborious process of carving the characters into bamboo required abbreviating a large part of any dialogue, the scribe always strove to capture the prince's words first. Dai Dong's order conveyed an important deviation: otherwise the scribe would ignore carving Laotzu's remarks in favor of whatever Prince KoWu said. These new orders essentially reversed Pen Hei's accustomed priorities.

"Oh? I will be sure he knows," assured Wei Lon.

Wei Lon was also a scribe, but not as good as Pen Hei. Wei Lon's job was to take all official carvings on the bamboo slats and prepare them for preservation. This entailed stringing them in order with special rope, and rolling them into neat scrolls. Wei Lon then wrapped the scrolls in heavy silk to store them in special vaults that kept out insects and moisture.

Dai Dong made a small nod to Wei Lon, indicating that he expected everything to go as the prince ordered.

Dai Dong spun on his heel and made his way to the far side of the palace. He headed for the military quarters. On his way, he inspected every table and every rug, arranging all the palace accoutrements properly.

Once he reached the military gates, he summoned the servant who attended the generals in their quarters. The generals' gatekeeper let him in.

"We need your men to assemble a sand tray, like the one in the military counsel chamber, only larger," explained Dai Dong. He always hated asking favors of the military staff. The military were not under his authority and did not have to pay him the same respect as the household servants.

"What? Where?" asked the crusty old soldier. Missing an eye, and too old to fight, the generals gave the old war hero the post of gatekeeper to support him in his old age.

"The prince commanded that the visiting sage, Laotzu, is to have whatever he needs to give his evening lessons in the palace hall. The sage indicates that he would like to draw. This is why we need the construction of the tray. I need it done by sunset, and furnished with the necessary tools," said Dai Dong, brisk and to the point.

"Oh, well I guess that would be a few long pieces of bamboo twig and a small rake, and uh, let's see, one half wagon of sand. Hey wait a minute! Everyone is out on the plains today. It will be hard to assemble all of this so fast!" complained the old man.

"Listen," said Dai Dong, clearly and forcefully. "The prince believes that if Laotzu hadn't come when he did, those barbarians would be pounding down our walls right now. If you wish to keep your job, you'll find whatever help you need and get this done by sunset."

"I didn't say I wouldn't. I just said it would be hard, that's all," the old soldier replied. "I got some young kids I can put to work from out in the cavalry yard."

"However it's accomplished..." trailed Dai Dong who already turned and left to attend to the next task on his mental list.

"So much to do, so much to do," he muttered in time to his quick steps on the marble tile.

As he headed for the kitchen, a familiar voice hailed him from the servants' entrance. "Ho brother!"

There stood Dai Lon, Dai Dong's older brother.

"I thought I'd stop by today and see if you needed to hire any extra help with all the special plans needed for the new visitor."

Oh bother, thought Dai Dong. His brother, who had always been irresponsible and dull-witted, continually begged him for a job at the palace. Dai Dong never pursued the matter for he feared that Dai Lon would most likely botch any task given to him. Dai Dong always managed to find an excuse on how the palace had more servants than they could use.

"Dai Lon," said the valet, "I am far too busy to even think about that right now."

"That's right. You're busy because you need more help here. I can make things easier for you. I can clean or cook, or haul things back and forth. C'mon Dong-dong," his brother invoked a childhood nickname to win his brother's sympathy.

"You know you should really be out on the plains. I heard that they are paying able-bodied men a percentage of all the treasure they can gather from what was left after that horrible windstorm," Dai Dong urged. "You could be making a nest egg for yourself, and for mother."

"Too late. They have as many men as they need, and besides, I decided to offer you my services first, 'cause you need them more."

"Did you even go check the plains, Dai Lon? How do you know it's too late if you say you came here first?" Dai Dong caught his brother in one of his typical lies.

"C'mon Dong, don't you need my help this week?"

"Well Dai Lon, I don't right now. I have a million things to do, and to hire a new servant, even temporarily, requires a visit to the queen. I can tell you right now that she is far too busy to be bothered," Dai Dong argued.

"You know, mother would be so happy if we could work together," Dai Lon pled.

"Lon," Dai Dong fumed. "Don't blame me for mother's anger at you." He flashed eyes of impatience and disdain at his older brother.

"Fine," Dai Lon said.

Dai Lon turned abruptly, and walked back toward the delivery gate. He stopped to make a mocking bow to his highly placed brother, and ended the bow with an obscene gesture.

Dai Dong's cheeks burned red with frustration and rage. He'd worked his fingers to the bone to rise from a lowly kitchen boy to the most highly placed servant at the palace. Dai Lon on the other hand, spent his youth with a rough crowd in the streets.

As Dai Lon got older, he found that his reputation as a mischief-maker barred him from getting apprenticed to a trade. As an adult, Dai Lon made a copper here and there fixing carts and doing minor repairs for merchants at their shops. Most of what he made, he spent at the drinking houses where he boasted about how successful he would be someday. Why just look at his own brother, he would say. Dai Lon could only wave his brother's status around to defend his own worth.

At home, Dai Dong was his mother's pride and joy, naturally. When Dai Dong started working at the age of eight, he brought home enough money to help the family survive. When the palace hired him at ten, his brother's life became a living hell. "Dai Lon" his mother would shout. "When will you get a real position like your brother." Her nagging drove a wedge between the two brothers that would never heal. Her harping seemed to make Dai Lon even lazier just to spite her.

Dai Dong only went home once a week. He could barely stand a whole evening of his mother's worship, and chafed at his brother's jealousy. It was a heavy and unnatural burden to be a family hero. He gave them what money he could every week, and hurried back to his own world at the palace.

This week, that world needed Dai Dong more than ever. Servants in every quarter of the palace waited for direction from him, for only he knew what the prince wanted. Nine banquets in a row on short notice! He must get to the kitchen quickly to review the supply chief's plans.

*   *   *

Back at the stone cottage, Laotzu decided to rest before the night's festivities. He asked the boy Chian to sit beside him and chat.

"So what do you do all day, boy," asked the sage. "Do you have a job? A family?"

"Uh....yes. Both. I am a sword teacher for other boys, and my family makes swords," KoYou replied. He tried to spin a good yarn for the sage.

"Goodness! How exciting! Perhaps some day you can show me your skill. How is it that they picked you to attend me?" asked Laotzu.

"Well they knew you'd need protection, so they picked somebody who could watch out for you as well as show you around," said KoYou.

"Protect me? Well that's odd. You didn't even bring your sword," observed Laotzu.

"Oh, that's right. I must have forgotten it," KoYou's face started to turn pink.

"Well that's no problem, let's go get it," said Laotzu. "Then I can meet your family."

"What?"

"Your sword. Let's go get your sword," repeated the older man.

"Oh that's impossible. You see on the way here it broke when I used it to pry a heavy cart off of a dog. You see the cart fell on the dog during the parade when you came, and I just happened to be there and it was the only way to help…" KoYou dug himself deeper into a fanciful tale.

"Ha, ha, ha…" Laotzu couldn't resist bursting into laughter. "You'd better come up with better stories than that if you want to fool an old storyteller like me!"

"What? You don't believe me? I'll get a sword and show you how good I am." KoYou grabbed a twig from the kindling pile next to the fire pit and deftly swung and twirled it in the air.

"Oh, I believe you can use a sword. I can see that in your eye and in your well trained arms," agreed Laotzu. "I believe only a prince's son would be able to learn sword skills as fine as yours."

"Rats! How did you know?" stomped KoYou.

"I have my ways. Besides, that stiff servant gave it away when he bowed to you. Is your real name KoChian?" asked the sage.

"Yes, but they all call me KoYou," the boy confessed. "I hope you don't think I'm a liar. I just wanted to play a little joke on you today. Besides, everyone always treats me differently once they find out the prince is my father. I wanted to see how you'd treat me if I were just a normal average boy."

"Normal average boys aren't sword teachers, and they don't usually come from families who make swords," replied Laotzu.

"But wouldn't that be great? It would be so much more fun than my real life. Here I spend all day with tutors and generals learning boring old history and how old wars were won or lost. Who cares?" scoffed the young prince.

"It's a life of privilege. You should be grateful."

"Grateful? It's a prison!" cried KoYou. "I want to be a hero and ride alone in the countryside, rescuing people from bandits and barbarians. My horse and I would ride like the wind with only my sword by my side. I'd sleep under the stars and fish for my food in the stream," KoYou's eyes brightened as he shared his dream with his new friend.

"Oh, I don't know. A boy like you will probably have many adventures in life, no matter where you live. Isn't there something you like about the palace?" asked the teacher.

"Sure, I guess. I suppose there are lots of things – like this house right here. I have lots of memories of this cottage from when I was small. Lo Han, that's the stable man, he used to let me come and watch him take care of the horses. That's where I learned most everything about animals. And then there's my fiancée, Yin Lian."

"Fiancée?" the sage repeated.

"Yes. But she's great, I mean, for a girl. You see, next year I will be fifteen. I'm expected to marry Yin Lian and take my place as head of the civil guard. When I am eighteen I will help my father rule and take his title when he is too old to lead," KoYou explained.

"Oh, so you are growing up fast," said the sage.

"Too fast sometimes, and not fast enough other times," KoYou replied.

"I feel that way too, most everyday," Laotzu agreed.

KoYou liked this visitor more and more. He felt so relaxed around him, like he could tell the old man anything without fear of rebuke or reprisal. He wished he could talk to KoWu like this.

"Do you want me to show you around then?" KoYou asked.

"No, that's okay," said the sage. "When you've seen one palace, you've seen them all."

They both laughed, sharing a secret moment of irreverence.

"I'll just rest here," said Laotzu. "You go spend some time with that fiancée of yours and come back to tell me when it's time to go to the banquet."

"Okay. Thank you, sir." KoYou bowed and did as Laotzu told him. He left the cottage and ran out of the stable and through the palace gate.

KoYou didn't stop running until he reached the door of the largest house on the merchant's avenue. When the servant answered the door, she seemed shocked to see KoYou so disheveled. He quickly brushed himself off, and replaced the gold betrothal bangle from his pocket. He couldn't wait to tell Yin Lian about his new job as servant to the visiting master, and everything else that happened today.

Chapter Seven
The First Night with the Taoist Guest

Finally, after a long and eventful day, the sun set over the western desert. With great ceremony, a gong sounded from the main palace hall. Servants lined the palace corridors as guests, one by one, entered the sumptuous banquet room. Plush cushions lined three of the walls in a horseshoe. Low burnished tables in front of the cushions offered silver trays heaped with the region's finest delicacies. At the center of the horseshoe sprawled a six by six foot sand tray constructed by military servants. A servant knelt beside the sand to assist with the drawing implements. He held long and thin bamboo twigs for the sage to use for drawing and writing.

Behind the drawing tray, and facing the rest of the crowd, a large cushion and a smaller table waited for the guest Laotzu. Facing the horseshoe tables, Laotzu would be plainly visible to all of the guests.

KoYou joined the row of servants who stood at attention in the back of the hall. KoYou was thankful that at least he could hear what the sage taught, even if he could only see Laotzu's back. Just to be sure, KoYou nudged through the line of servants with his shoulder so that he could stand at the front and center of the line to hear the evening talk better.

After the guests took their seats, the prince and his gracious wife, Zhu Xiao Hua, entered together with Laotzu. Servants assisted the prince and his wife to their central spot at the magnificent table, directly facing across the room toward Laotzu's seat.

Pen Hei, the palace scribe, sat at his own worktable to the side of the room. He did not eat or chat, but sat up straight and quiet, like a soldier at attention. He took his post very seriously, and this assignment was a solemn duty.

Dinner finished quickly, the guests' conversation lilting with excitement and anticipation. Everyone eagerly waited to hear from the man who seemed to command nature itself to save West Peace. As the prominent citizens and courtiers finished their food and wine, servants took the platters away.

Laotzu rose from his cushion with his hands folded in front of him. The clamor of chitchat died down and hushes whispered up and down the tables. Clearly, the sage wanted to begin.

Prince KoWu stood and made a short, polite bow to Laotzu. He opened the evening's discussion with a warm welcome address:

"My honored citizens and guests of West Peace. Before us tonight is a most legendary master – one whose reputation for heavenly wisdom is known throughout our country. We would be honored if he merely visited. But Master Laotzu's arrival brought such favor from the heavens, that this very day a storm annihilated the barbarians from the north. Such miraculous favor of the gods follows this holy man. That he would agree to teach us his wisdom is an honor greater than any we can imagine.

"Although I invited him to make West Peace his home, and to stay and guide our royal household and its advisors, our dear guest has declined. Instead he has granted me the honor of nine nights here in the palace, in the company of our most honored citizens, and valued guests. On each of these nine nights, Master Laotzu will allow me nine questions. He will answer other questions too, from any of you who care to offer one."

Guests nodded their heads in appreciation that they, too, would be included in the evening conversation. After a short pause, the prince introduced his first question:

"In gratitude and humility, I welcome Master Laotzu and will give him my first question. As I stood on our city wall today and saw black clouds swallow our enemy, I saw how the very skies protected this master who now stands before us." Although KoWu's address began with confidence, his voice soon quivered as he remembered this day's astounding events.

"Master, you are so powerful and mysterious. You can do so many wonderful things. You must be a god!" KoWu announced with hands outstretched.

"I am not a god, I just follow the almighty power, the Tao," Laotzu replied calmly and humbly.

"What is the Tao?" asked the prince, finally able to collect himself and offer what would be the first of his eighty-one precious questions.

The sage cocked his head and smiled. Instead of answering, he rose from his cushion and moved toward one corner of the grand table. Slowly, he walked the inside perimeter of the horseshoe, carefully surveying each guest.

He looked each in the eye with a nod. As he did, each guest in turn seemed to relax. They found that his gaze cleared their mind and softened their heart.

When he finished, Laotzu returned to his place at the center. Facing the entire assembly, the sage finally answered the prince: "1-1 *If the* True *Tao can be talked about, it is not the ultimate Tao.* 1-2 *If the* True *Name of the True Tao can be referred to, it is no longer the real name* for the True Tao. Why? Because men can only use true feeling to feel the power of Tao. They cannot use an artificial name to name the almighty true power.

"Why are artificial names useless? Because 1-3 *the nameless* power of Tao *is the beginning of heaven and earth.* It was mankind who started to give names to everything. Soon afterwards we find that the 1-4 *the named is the mother of ten thousand things.* Everything people think they know about, they just give a name to. Actually, they know a lot of nothing about everything!"

Guests laughed.

"To see the power of Tao," the sage continued, "one must 1-5 *always observe from formless viewpoint, then one can see the wonderful changes* of the Tao's power. And, too, one must 1-6 *always observe from the viewpoint of forms, so one can see the manifestation* of Tao's power. 1-7 *Both* form and formless, *though differing in name, are made of the same source:* the Tao's power. 1-8 *From the same source, it appears fathomless.* 1-9 *Ever fathomless, it is the gate to wonderful changes.*"

The scholars present looked at one another. Merchants and monks raised their eyebrows. The other guests cocked their heads in wonder. Here was a teacher who didn't talk like the other scholars and priests. He spoke of mysteries in a way that drew them in. Though confused by the sage's words, the guests nevertheless yearned for more.

Pen Hei, the scribe, leaned forward over his table full of bamboo in earnest. In the shorthand of scribes, he tried to carve the main points first. When he recarved them later, he would fill in what he remembered.

There was no time to carve the prince's second question when KoWu asked: "Master, I have never heard of this Tao you speak of. How can one see and know this power of Tao, since from your description it is so vague that it can't even be named?" The sage's unusual words left him brimming with curiosity. He rose to the challenge of pulling the mystery out of the master.

Laotzu, appreciating KoWu's hungry mind and eager heart, looked him directly in the eye. "Before you can see the power of Tao at work, you must observe and understand how the Tao works. Tao works with two complete yet opposite powers."

The master grabbed his flywhisk from the floor and pointed it first to the left and then to the right, as he explained, "You see, everything appears in opposites: 2-1 *Under heaven all can see beauty, for there is already ugliness.* 2-2 *All know there is good for there already is evil.* 2-3 *Therefore, having and not having,* though in contrast, *emerge together.* 2-4 *Difficult and easy,* though in contrast, yet *lie opposite to each other.* 2-5 *Long and short compare* and contrast each other. 2-6 *High and low* in contrast *lean upon each other.* 2-7 *Voice and sound* are various but *harmonize each other.* 2-8 *Front and back* are different but *follow each other* in order."

Laotzu no longer stood motionless next to his table. Instead, he wandered slowly around the room as he talked. "Everything in this world is driven by the power of Tao, regardless if it is good or bad. It is very important to recognize the fact that everything has its opposite side, yet the contrasting forces complement each other.

"In the beginning, what we call the origin, the power of Tao in action, formed everything with two equal yet opposite forces. Through this process,

Pen Hei the Scribe at his Table

56

the power of Tao, also called the One Chi, created everything else. In effect, it created something 'more' than just itself. By turning into something 'more' than the pure power of Tao, what was 'more' started to decay and escape back to the Tao. Because of this, the objects disintegrated and died. That is why, even now, everything in creation disintegrates and dies.

"In the case of a human life," Laotzu continued, "A human being has the highest amount and most pure form of the power of Tao, the One Chi, of any other life form, trapped inside him. Human life is made of two equal but opposite powers, the male and female. Yet as a human grows, this power is diverted to brain activity and then decays. So the life energy, the Chi, starts to decline immediately after the thinking activities begin. There is no way to hold back the power of Tao from escaping."

Pen Hei raised his palm to signal that he needed a pause to complete his carving. It was easy to record the drivel of other scholars, for they always talked about the same old things. This teacher spoke in completely new ways, with new words and concepts Pen Hei had never heard. Pen Hei needed time to think of the appropriate characters to use. The whole process demanded his maximum attention and skill.

Laotzu and the prince paused a moment so Pen Hei could finish. During this short break, KoWu's spiritual advisor, Fa Tingtz, leaned across the corner of the table and begged KoWu's permission to ask a question. KoWu nodded.

When Pen Hei signaled he was ready, Fa Tingtz cleared his throat and asked, "Master Laotzu, how do you come to know so much about this Tao? You sound very learned, but I've never seen this Tao mentioned in any written records before?"

Fa Tingtz read a lot, but he rarely traveled. His isolation and conservative attitudes insulated him from any new philosophies springing up in the interior cities. He felt it important to keep his prince focused on traditional moral conduct as recorded in many well-worn scrolls. New ideas made Fa Tingtz nervous.

Laotzu answered Fa Tingtz patiently: "Here in China, the wise have been studying and practicing the Tao for over three thousand years. But what they know was only passed down verbally. The few times ancient saints of the Tao interacted with kings are the only occasions when scribes may have recorded bits of their wisdom: just as your scribes are recording me now. It is told that the famous Yellow Emperor consulted with a powerful saint, Guan Chentz, on how to absorb the power of Tao, the One Chi, so he could learn to live as long as he. You see, Guan Chentz was over one thousand years old! Guan said, 'Just put the opposite powers back together, then one can live forever.' Certainly you have read that passage?"

Fa Tingtz nodded.

"Likewise, I tell you that the power of Tao is invisible, powerful, ultimate and conscious. But when the power of Tao is at work, it becomes two opposite yet equal forces. By meditation, fusing those two forces back into the absolute One Chi, you may restore your Te power, which will be able to broadcast to the world with or without a message. It is the so-called 'non-action power.' 2-9 *Therefore the saint exercises 'non-action' to do things, and exercises 'non-talking' to teach.* He does this with the power of Te."

"Master, what do you mean non-action? Non-talking? How does this work?" asked Fa Tingtz, who put into words the same quandary on the faces of most guests.

Laotzu happily offered Fa Tingtz a description: " When a saint uses this power, 2-10 *he initiates nothing, and allows ten thousand things to grow.* He lets the power of Tao do the job. 2-11 *Raising* ten thousand things, *yet not possessing,* he sees that it is the power of Tao that's at work. 2-12 *Working, yet not considering he did it;* the task is 2-13 *achieved. Yet he does not consider that he completed it,* for he knows the power of Tao completed it. 2-14 *Therefore all the work he did lasts forever,* for he never considers that he did it on his own power."

Fa Tingtz bowed to Laotzu and the prince. He settled back to muse on these new notions.

In the meantime, KoWu took command of the discussion again, asking: "Master, I find myself in this place - a frontier city, with aggressive barbarians from the north, merchants of all sorts traveling through, even foreigners from the far south and west. I have an enormous task on my hands as prince of West Peace. You talk about the power of Tao, but how should I use the power of Tao to rule this city?"

Laotzu responded, "All of your problems will be helped by following the principle of the Tao. Apply the power of Tao and know that: 3-1 *Not exalting the elite dampens quarrels.* 3-2 *Not collecting precious things prevents stealing.* 3-3 *Seeing nothing attractive, there will be no disturbance in peoples' minds.* 3-4 *The saint therefore rules by making people empty their thinking and stuffing their bellies;* 3-5 *by weakening their ambitions and strengthening their bones.* You should 3-6 *make people lack knowledge and desire.* This will 3-7 *make smart intellectuals dare not try to interfere.* Remember to 3-8 *exercise 'non-action' to rule and all will be well.*"

KoWu shook his head, "Master, believe me, this is a very complex city. It is going to take more than just an attitude of non-action to rule West Peace. If there is power in this Tao you speak of, then what is Tao and where do these powers of Tao come from?"

"4-1 *The Tao is invisible, but its power is infinite.* 4-2 *Though it appears unfathomable, it appears as if it is the source of ten thousand things.* The term 'ten thousand things' means everything we can see and know," Laotzu replied.

"But Master, what can the power of Tao do to help a man like me?" asked KoWu.

Laotzu pointed his hand toward KoWu and answered, "The power of Tao can 4-3 *blunt the sharpness, resolve the tangles, soften the glare, and settle the dust.* 4-4 *The* power of Tao, as *immense* as the deep ocean, *cannot be sure of its own existence, and cannot tell where it comes from.* 4-5 *It is as if it existed before there was God.*"

Fa Tingtz leaned over and whispered in KoWu's ear. KoWu nodded to his trusted spiritual advisor and then asked Laotzu, "Master, if I practice kindness, will God bless me even more?"

This composed the essence of Fa Tingtz' dogma. Fa Tingtz always counseled that good action brought good results. He goaded KoWu with endless variations on this simple morality.

But Laotzu shocked both the prince and Fa Tingtz when he answered, "No. 5-1 *Heaven and earth appear to have no kindness; and* the power of Tao at work will *treat everything as if it were just a sacrifice.* 5-2 *The saint,* since he practices the power of Tao, therefore also *appears to have no kindness. They, too, treat people as merely sacrifices.*"

"Why so? If the Tao is as powerful as God, why must it become unkind?" challenged Fa Tingtz abruptly. The guests hummed around the table. They realized there would be controversy between the prince's spiritual advisor and their visitor. Everyone knew Fa Tingtz' dogma of good begetting good, and how vigorously he defended the sharp line between good and evil.

To the guests' surprise, Laotzu did not argue with Fa Tingtz at all. Instead, his voice grew kinder. He spoke to Fa Tingtz as a good friend might. "The power of Tao is the ultimate origin of the universe. It exists even before God. Good and bad spirits are both made of the power of Tao. But Tao always prevails. You see, it made everything, and gives life and takes away life in a returning cycle. It is the way of nature. Because everything that the Tao gives life to, even humans, eventually may suffer, decay and die, it seems as if the Tao plays an unkind role."

Laotzu continued, "Yet human life is made from the Tao's force. The nature of Tao's force is tenderness, kindness, and love. It is a force that is soft and weak. Therefore the Tao supports and gives favor to everything that manifests tenderness, kindness, love, softness, weakness and mercy. Otherwise, when these qualities are gone, the Tao withholds its favor. It then becomes not what we call good, but what we would call bad or evil." As Laotzu spoke, Fa Tingtz' slowly sat back down again. His stiff shoulders softened.

"When you know this, you can observe that when this great spiritual power moves in an opposing way, people regard it as the devil or the enemy of God. Each person possesses the second hand power of Tao, the Te, within his body and his mind. He must therefore understand the fact that if he stands on the side of force, he is an incomplete being that is doomed to decay and die." Laotzu clearly wanted his listeners to understand the fundamental nature of this mysterious Tao, and searched for more analogies.

"The power of Tao enters everything and everyone equally to help them play their designated role. You are better off if you empty yourself to allow the power of Tao to enter.

After all, 5-3 *isn't the space between heaven and earth like a bellows?* 5-4 *The more the empty space, the more it offers;* 5-5 *The more it moves, the more it generates.*

"Why do I describe the universe this way? Because you must know that the universe is made of the power of Tao. It is as hollow as a bellows. Although it is empty inside, when it is in motion, energy comes out. The more it is in action, the more energy it yields. It is never exhausted. Think about this in your own life."

Fa Tingtz seemed satisfied for the moment. He would have to think about this carefully. If this Tao was above all other powers and was as kind and merciful as Laotzu said, perhaps Laotzu's views weren't too different from his own, or at the very least tolerable.

Laotzu returned to his cushion and stooped to take a cup of cool water from a small platter on the floor. After Laotzu finished his drink, he gave the cup to a servant.

At that moment, all heads turned toward a giant man who rose from the side table. A foreigner from the far western land of Dazos, Abudamancus stood a full head and shoulders above any man in the room. He wore the crimson sash of his people around his barrel waist. His curly black beard made his white and toothy grin look even wider.

Everybody liked Abudamancus. A wry smile passed from face to face as the dignitaries wondered what their unpredictable Dazos friend might say.

Since Abudamancus was foreign, they pardoned his booming laugh and his gregarious ways. They even suffered his hard slaps on their backs. Because of his size and his good nature, he was in a class of his own everywhere he went. Everyone knew he brought rare treasures from the most exotic foreign lands. The wealthy of the town curried his favor.

Normally, caravan leaders would be excluded from royal functions, but Abudamancus rarely missed one. Almost a government official in KoWu's eyes, his word carried weight among all the caravan leaders that came and went from West Peace. They all looked to Abudamancus for his verdict when disputes bubbled up in their tents.

Abudamancus' status owed partly to the fact that he enjoyed a special friendship with the prince. When young KoWu first came to the palace, Abudamancus befriended him and taught him the wiles and ways of the caravan world. His advice saved the inexperienced boy prince from being taken in by tricky contracts or bad goods. Moreover, Abudamancus' friendship gave KoWu immediate respect from the caravan leaders who traveled through West Peace on their regular pilgrimages.

Abudamancus was big but not stupid. In fact, the well-educated Dazos trader could speak several languages. He'd conversed with sages and scholars from many lands in his travels. He had his own questions for this master.

Abudamancus turned to Laotzu with his trademark smile and gave Laotzu a sweeping one-armed bow. As he rose, he began, "Master, for generations people have tried to figure out how and why God works. I myself have received many teachings and advice from sages the world over. I have talked at length with men who called themselves holy. I've argued many scriptures with priests. They all have much to say and much to teach. They all seem like good men, even though each teacher contradicts the next one. I attend evening lessons such as this one in every town I visit. But sadly, Master Laotzu, I find that my own prayers are rarely answered and I am still confused. Why?"

Although the giant stood well above him, Laotzu showed no shyness in facing him squarely as he answered: "5-6 *Saying many words* to try to explain the true Tao's power *is like counting numbers backwards only leading to exhaustion.* The saint will 5-7 *hold fast to the center* issue of Tao's power instead of playing with words"

"Why do I say this? Because people all over the world try to figure out how God works: they worship God, analyze God and discuss God. It is all in vain because they chase the shadow and not the object. The power of God comes from the power of Tao. Exercising the power of Tao is like driving the opening and closing force of a bellows. Observing and discussing how the bellows works will never bring wind. Likewise, talking will never bring you to the power of Tao, and never give you the ability to communicate with God. Such empty talk is like counting down numbers, 9, 8, 7, 6, 5, 4, 3, 2, 1 and gives you zero." Laotzu dropped his flywhisk to the ground, holding forward his empty hands as he said the word "zero."

Abudamancus seemed impressed at the honesty of the sage. "Master if you say talk is not the answer, then I will not talk much. But I will give you the same question I ask every sage. Very few can answer me. Master Laotzu, where does our life come from?"

Laotzu looked up to him and replied, "Our life comes from the life energy, Chi, and our life energy comes from the original reproductive life energy of the universe. This is why 6-1 *the spirit that turns food into life never dies.* 6-2 *It is called the original reproductive life energy.* 6-3 *The gate connects to the original reproductive life energy.* 6-4 *It is the root of heaven and earth.* 6-5 *This* original reproductive life energy *is barely noticeable, yet it yields its energy inexhaustibly.*"

"Master, now you give me just words! How can one feel his life energy? Can we find this gate of life energy you talk about?" asked Abudamancus, leaning forward to get closer to the sage.

Laotzu chuckled at the giant man's straightforward manner. "The gate to life is the dividing line between where life energy initiates, from the action of reproduction conducted by life energy. As human beings, no one bothers to look into or try to feel his life energy much less connect his mind and his feeling back to life energy.

"The ability to use your purest mind to feel your original life energy, the gate between life energy and non-life energy, is the most essential work you must practice and master. Your true life energy is the very source and gate whereby you came into life. When your pure mind comes in touch with your true life energy, you will be able to feel this true energy. This is the energy derived from the Tao's power, the One Chi, and forms the core power of your life energy – the power of Te. This Te is a piece of the power of Tao."

"Master, could you show us how to feel this life energy gate?" Abudamancus was always practical and to the point. If there was a gate, he wanted to know exactly how to find it and what it did. He allowed no tricky words from traders or scholars.

Laotzu admired the Dazos man's persistence. "Of course. You first calm down your artificial thought and pay undivided attention to your breath. Inhale and exhale gently and naturally. Guide your breathing to begin and end from your lower stomach. Not too harshly, not too sluggishly – as if you were still in your mother's womb. You'll feel the gate to life energy."

KoWu enjoyed watching Abudamancus and the sage talk. The prince could follow his big friend's train of thought. He saw that Abudamancus pressed toward the heart of the issue. Following his friend's lead, the prince leaned forward and asked his own direct question, "Master, you mention a gate of life. If there is such a gate, how can we preserve our body and life to live longer?"

Laotzu looked pleased that KoWu jumped in, and happily answered him. "Because the power of Tao prevails, 7-1 *the Universe is everlasting.* 7-2 *Why does the Universe last forever? Because it does not bear itself, therefore, it is ever existing.*

"7-3 *Therefore, the saint stays behind his body* and allows the power of Tao to enter his body first; it's *as if his body goes ahead of himself.* 7-4 *And since he stays out of his body,* allowing Tao's power to run his body, *his body lasts longer.* 7-5 *It is because he is rid of his consciousness of self that he gains his true self.* Therefore he lives, by the power of Tao, a much longer life."

Then KoWu asked, "Master, you seem to say that I must turn even my body over to this power of Tao. But if I ever learn to practice so that the power of Tao enters my body, how then will my body function in daily life? I must rule and defend this crucial city, and so many things can go wrong. I need full use of my wits and my body at all times."

Laotzu bent over to retrieve his flywhisk from the floor next to the cushion. He waved it back and forth to emphasize key points as he answered the prince. "Just practice until the power of Tao enters your body, then let the power of Tao run the whole mission for you. Don't worry; it will take care of everything in the best way. See, 8-1 *the highest good,* the power of Tao at work, *is just like water* at work. Why? When water works like the power of Tao, 8-2 *it benefits the ten thousand things instead of competing with them.* When necessary, 8-3 *it even flows into places people reject. So* when you envision water working at its best, *it is almost like the Tao* at work.

"Likewise, when you are positioned by the Tao's power, 8-4 *it chooses the right place to stay.* Let the Tao's power guide your heart for 8-5 *its good heart is big and deep.* Follow the Tao's power to 8-6 *deal with others with gentleness and kindness.* Speak with Tao's power and you 8-7 *speak with truth.* When governing with Tao's power, you will end up 8-8 *governing everything well.* Follow the great Tao's power and you are 8-9 *ever capable.* Act by Tao's power and you 8-10 *always act with right timing.* 8-11 *Only when* applying the power of Tao do you find that *there is no need for conflict,* and *then there is no fault.*"

Many of the guests rubbed their chins, trying to follow what Laotzu said. They had always thought of gods and heaven as powers that were quite separate from the human world. One might implore them for favor, or anger them and be cursed. But this Tao was an even greater power that could come into a man's own body and affect affairs around him. The notion astounded everyone.

KoWu followed quickly with his ninth question, "Master, after I am able to follow this Tao completely to accomplish my aim in the way that you describe, can I then be both a saint and a successful Governor?"

"Beware the power of Tao, for even after the job is well done, it is easy to forget the power of Tao and fall back into the illusion of human life. If you want to keep within the power of Tao, there are truths you must keep in mind. You should 9-1 *rather* prefer to *disclaim than possess in full.* You should remember that 9-2 *when the point is sharp, it will soon become dull.* You must know that 9-3 *a house kept full of jade and precious jewelry is impossible to guard from theft.* 9-4 *Claim wealth and titles, and trouble will follow.* You should 9-5 *withdraw when the work is done.* Why do I tell you these things? Because 9-6 *this is the way heaven's Tao works.*"

Everyone grew quiet. Laotzu's answers seemed to be at the same time riddles and the clearest wisdom they'd ever heard. The guests reeled with the power of new notions that had never entered their minds before. They had no way to digest these ideas, no category to place them in. They were in a new world now – the world of Laotzu's Tao.

Prince KoWu sensed his guests were sated with wisdom for the evening. The scribe Pen Hei sighed from exhaustion, while his fingers ached from the knife.

KoWu, in his enthusiasm, could have gone on until dawn. Yet he realized that not only was everyone tired, but also that he'd also reached his limit of nine questions. There was nothing left to do but to bid his guests good night and invite any who were interested to return the next evening.

When everyone left, KoWu and Zhu Xiao Hua retired to their chambers, leaving KoYou to escort Laotzu back to his stone hut.

When Laotzu and the boy reached the stable yard, KoYou bowed to the sage. "Sir, what do you need tonight?"

"Nothing, son," replied Laotzu. "I'm glad you listened tonight, even if you had to stand all evening with the servants."

"I don't mind, although it was a little hard to hear sometimes," said KoYou. "Can I bring you anything tomorrow morning?"

"I don't need much," he answered. "Perhaps you can find some licorice herb and ginger, and maybe some buckwheat to boil for breakfast. And bring me a little bit of dried fruit to boil with it."

"That's all?" KoYou asked, surprised the sage would request only peasant food.

"That will be plenty," said the sage.

KoYou bowed and left the sage to his night's rest.

Chapter Eight
A Boy Learns from His Master

At sunrise, KoYou scrambled out of bed and down to the kitchen. He grabbed a cloth sack and stuffed four bowls of dried buckwheat, a jar of dried ginger strips, a small bagful of dried licorice root and three handfuls of jujubes inside.

The morning cook bowed and tried to take the sack from KoYou, thinking the prince's son craved a big breakfast. KoYou waved the cook away, explaining that he would take the parcel to Laotzu's guesthouse so the sage could cook for himself. The cook flailed both arms across his face furiously, declaring it a scandal to allow an important guest to cook for himself. But before he could protest any further, KoYou leapt through the door and into the courtyard.

KoYou thought he'd surprise the sage by coming early, but instead, found Laotzu already awake and outside his cottage performing a mysterious standing meditation. Laotzu's eyes were closed, but nonetheless the master raised his arms and turned with seemingly little effort in circular patterns. His feet stepped lightly as he moved. It was like watching the slow flight of a bird or the swirl of eddies along the riverbank.

The young boy paused to watch, not knowing whether to interrupt or not. As if to answer his question, Laotzu's mysterious dance came to a slow finish, and the master's eyes opened.

"Ah! Breakfast!" he cried, and stretched out his hand to take the sack from KoYou. "Come inside, boy."

Once inside the hut, KoYou saw that embers from a small fire already burned in the fire pit. Laotzu threw some extra kindling on the fire and looked around for a pot to boil the grain.

"I'll cook the grain, son, you just go fetch some water," directed the master.

"But I am to serve you," KoYou replied. "Shouldn't I cook you breakfast?"

"Have you ever boiled grain and jujubes before?" asked Laotzu.

KoYou looked down towards the ground.

"I didn't think so," chuckled Laotzu.

KoYou blushed. His life of privilege was sometimes a handicap. The young man grabbed the wooden pail and went out to the well for water as directed. When he came back, Laotzu took the pail with a nod and beckoned KoYou to make himself comfortable.

"Tell me about yourself, son," Laotzu asked, as he filled a stone pot with water and brown-hulled buckwheat. "I heard tell that you did not always live in the palace."

"No sir, that is true," said KoYou. "The Prince adopted me when I was only seven."

"Seven? What happened to your natural father?" asked the sage.

"My mother's first husband, my father, was General Zhu Ming. Barbarians ambushed our family one day and then they murdered him. They took my mother and me as prisoners for many weeks. I was only six years old.'

"Old enough to remember," the sage remarked.

"I remember some things, but not all," KoYou reflected. "I remember my mother's bravery. She kept telling the barbarian chief that she would bring a high ransom from the city, but only if they didn't harm us. She was very firm and persuasive. By some luck, he believed her and didn't touch us for the entire time. The chief couldn't decide whether to return us to collect the ransom, or keep my mother for himself. He never had the chance to make up his mind."

"Oh? What happened?" asked the sage.

"Prince KoWu led troops into the mountains and found our cave. It shocked the barbarians that the prince himself and his best guards would leave the city, much less come up into their hiding place. The prince caught them by surprise." KoYou retold the story of their rescue.

"I remember that day best! KoWu, now my father, had a huge broadsword. When he saw my mother and me in the back of the cave, and could see they'd already killed my father, he was furious! He and his men slaughtered every barbarian in those mountains. Nobody had ever seen such skill with a horse or a sword as they saw from Prince KoWu! The neighboring barbarian chiefs saw the massacre and hurried to sign a truce with KoWu to spare themselves from his fury. Many other servants, slaves and captives were set free that day by the barbarians and returned to West Peace.

"That is why they have been too afraid to attack my father's city for eight years. That is until the day you arrived."

"So he took you and your mother back and married her?"

"No. Not right away. The Prince already had a very young and beautiful queen. He treated us well though, and admired my mother's strength and cleverness in how she protected herself and me for all those months," KoYou continued. "He gave my mother a rather large sum of money so that she could live out her years with honor and raise me the way my father would have."

"So when did they marry?" asked Laotzu.

"One year later," answered the boy. "KoWu's young queen died in childbirth shortly after KoWu's return from battle. The midwives said her body was too fragile to withstand the strain. So after a few months of mourning, KoWu started to visit my mother from time to time. I guess he remembered her so well from our rescue. They had a lot in common, since they both suffered loss."

"Your mother is quite a gracious and refined lady," Laotzu assured him.

"Yes she is. Even when the barbarians held us in their miserable cave, my mother insisted that she and I behave with dignity and manners. She never lost her ladylike ways, even after they killed her husband."

"I can see why KoWu felt she'd make a good queen, he undoubtedly loves her very much," said the sage.

"KoWu had to make a special petition to his father the king to marry her. It was even more difficult to receive permission to adopt me. By adopting me, I now carry the Ko name and will be KoWu's heir."

While he talked, KoYou unconsciously picked up a twig and jousted it in the air like a sword.

"You really enjoy playing with the sword, don't you?" asked Laotzu.

"Yes," KoYou answered. "Ever since the day they killed my father, I have always picked up sticks and tried to practice the sword arts. Even as a little boy I thought that I could protect my mother if I had to, and I swore I would learn well so that I could protect my whole family when I grew up."

"Do you only practice with sticks?"

KoYou laughed. "Oh no. Well I guess I did until Prince KoWu saw me playing under a tree one day. After he adopted me, he soon assigned me tutors in the martial arts. I have several fine swords given to me from my tutors. Like this one here," KoYou parted his robe and revealed a scabbard tied tight against his waist. He didn't forget to bring a sword this day.

"So how did your name become KoYou instead of KoChian?" asked Laotzu.

"Oh that!" laughed the boy. "My name is still KoChian. Everybody just calls me KoYou because of the pun. Since my father's name is 'Wu,' some people joke that it means 'nothing' or 'void.' So they decided to call me 'You' since it means 'to have something.' I think, in a way, it is a strange way they honor us. It's like wishing your son to be even more successful than you are."

"There's a lot to a name," Laotzu nodded. He could see the boy really did have many talents. He inherited great talent in fighting and swordsmanship from both his natural and adopted father. His mother's grace and diplomacy helped teach him how to build goodwill with all of the palace advisors and the town elite. He could also tell that Prince KoWu invested much in the boy, giving him the best tutors and the finest training. KoWu obviously knew that KoYou might very well replace him one day.

"Teacher," KoYou shifted the topic from himself, "what was that meditation you were doing outside when I arrived?"

"That KoYou, is the Tao's work, some call it Tao Gong," answered Laotzu.

"Is it something you practice like a martial art?" asked the boy.

"Not exactly, although it takes devotion and some work with the body to change its nature, its way of functioning," explained the sage.

"What do you mean?"

"In the martial arts, you can only learn to become faster, stronger or more skillful. But it is still limited. If you are very strong, there will always come a day when somebody is stronger than you. If you are fast, you better watch out that your opponent is not faster than you, or you will lose," explained the sage. "So when you practice the martial arts, you are just trying to become a better 'you.'"

"Isn't that so with meditation too?" KoYou replied.

"With some meditation, you merely try to calm your mind. But in Tao meditation, you can actually change your whole self and become unlimited," said the master. "Let's pretend you are a rabbit. You are about as long as a forearm, and fluffy, and you are an animal. You can become strong, or fast, or you can meditate to become bigger, but you will still be a rabbit. You will just be a strong or fast or bigger rabbit," the teacher illustrated. "But with Tao Gong meditation, you seek to become something different entirely. With Tao Gong, it's as if you, a rabbit, change into a cat. Sure you might still be as long as a forearm, and covered with soft fur, but your nature has fundamentally and permanently changed."

"Wow," wondered KoWu. "But how can we do that? Why do we need to change?"

"To connect to the power of Tao, we must change. The Tao will not come down and reach us in the state that we are in; it is we who must change ourselves to come closer to the Tao. We do this by coming closer to that piece of Tao inside us called the Te," said Laotzu.

"I heard you talking about that last night. Teacher, I wish you could show me more about this power of Tao. All the others at the banquet, they talk so eloquently, but I am still so young and awkward. Would you mind if I ask you some naive questions?" KoWu bowed politely.

"Speak your mind," the sage invited.

"Well, I can't tell this to anyone, but really, inside, I don't care if I become a king or not. I would much rather be a spiritual person like you. I enjoy my talks with the visiting monks and scholars, and I think about such things

A Rabbit Transforms Into a Cat

often when I ride my horse out in the countryside," KoYou confessed.

"There's a reason for that, young friend," the sage smiled. "Every one of us carries a tiny piece of the power of Tao inside and therefore we each have a mission. We are moved to do what we are designated to do. We might try to go down other paths, because of ego or outside pressure from family or society, but the power of Tao, the original power implanted in each of us will continue to shine with the true message we should follow."

"Yes, Master. I am glad you tell me this. I always wondered what path I should follow to help the world ever since the barbarians kidnapped my mother and I when I was six. I feel it is very important to protect and help others, and I know everyone expects me to grow up as a prince or general or a great warrior. I even think I could be good at those things. But Teacher, something inside me is calling me to do more than that."

Laotzu gently encouraged, "What is it, my young friend? Say it."

"I want to be a spiritual monk, like you. Please don't tell anyone. Master, it would break my mother's heart, and my father's and everyone who knows me. If they heard my real intention, they would not be able to accept it. I've only mentioned such things to Yin Lian. Even though she understands, she never thought it would be possible for me. But now that you are here, it seems more than possible," said KoYou, whose head bowed as he spoke his heart.

"I understand, KoYou. It is the true energy, the Te, implanted inside your life energy. It gives you the true message that if you become a spiritual leader you will help more people than if you become a king. But the world is not ready for you yet."

"Why, Master? Why can't I become who I really am? Can you help me?"

Laotzu got up and checked his pot by the fire pit. The buckwheat and jujubes bubbled thick and sweet. He scooped some into two bowls, and set one in front of his young friend. After they both paused to blow the steam off the porridge, they enjoyed a few quiet bites together, as Laotzu continued: "In Tao, the first principle is to follow the flow of the power. It's like swimming in a rapid river. You must flow with the current, not fight it. Flow is the natural way: to fight is artificial and stems from man's ego."

"How does that work in life, Master?" asked KoYou.

"Look at yourself right now. How did you come to be in this cottage eating cereal with me this morning?" asked Laotzu

"Gee. Well my father asked me to be your servant because you only wanted a boy. I thought it was a great adventure and so I agreed, and here I am!" said KoYou.

"Right!" Laotzu exclaimed. "You followed the flow. What would have happened if you had refused your father and had become indignant at being made to serve like a commoner?"

"Well, I would have saved some pride. But I wouldn't be sitting here with you," answered the boy, now smiling with understanding.

"I think you're catching on."

"Master," KoYou seemed anxious and hesitant now. "I know I could be very good as a governor. I study hard, especially philosophy. I am also very good at martial arts and sword fighting. I am only fourteen, but I can fight adult warriors with equal skill. I know I am qualified to be a prince, a governor, a general and even a king someday, but I…"

"But what? Go on."

"But…."

"I know what it is, so you don't have to be afraid," Laotzu smiled. Being a master of the Tao, he knew other people's very thoughts. "You say it yourself though, it is better that way."

"Master, I hate killing." KoYou looked down, embarrassed. "I know I shouldn't say so, and I shouldn't feel so. I'm expected to be strong, merciless, powerful and determined, like my father, Prince KoWu. My father can give an order to kill without blinking an eye. I saw him kill literally hundreds of barbarians in one charge when he rescued my mother and I. He didn't flinch. Yet, I still cannot accept the idea of killing people. I just can't, Master. What should I do?"

Laotzu patted the youth on the shoulder, "My friend, there is never any embarrassment in what you said. Quite the opposite! It is an honor to say you cannot kill."

KoYou looked at him with surprise. "Master? You don't think I am born a coward?"

"Not at all. I think you are a true, brave young man. Only a man with courage and honor admits his true feelings. Those who pretend to be brave and hide their true feelings are cowardly and weak. You said what you truly feel and so are strong and honorable." Laotzu stood up and motioned to the boy, "Come, son. Let's go take a walk in the courtyard."

They walked through the stable and out into the gardens. They strolled slowly, admiring the stonework, the bushes, and the placid ponds stocked with fish. Together they formed an idyllic picture: a young prince with a wizened icon, talking together about truth.

"You see this beautiful garden," Laotzu began. "It is groomed and tended so well by the gardener with tenderness and love. This is true human feeling. But this garden can be destroyed in the blink of an eye by a barbarian troop if they attacked this city and broke through the gate.

"The killing is artificial and learned. The love and care is a natural occurrence. Love needs patience and care. Hate and killing only need rage and anger. Love needs true feeling and wisdom. Hate and killing need only brutality. It is true and normal to say you cannot kill. Why should you feel embarrassed that you feel that way?"

"Master," KoYou asked, "if I do not learn how to kill, then someday when I am attacked or my family is attacked, I would not be able to defend and protect them. My father always taught me that you must kill first and make your other enemies afraid of you. I know he is right, but I cannot kill."

"What your father says is true on one hand, but every situation has more than one solution. Unfortunately, most rulers don't take the time to find a better solution so they take the easy way out. In the case of ruling a border city, it is easier to enforce order by killing an offender. This scares the others who might also seek to upset order; but it is a hard and brutal way to take care of things." The sage shook his head slowly.

"But how do we find a better way to keep order without such killing?" asked KoYou.

"You attended last night's session, but you sat there quietly and said nothing. I know what you are thinking, and it shows you still don't understand what I tried to tell everyone about the power of Tao," scolded the sage.

"I confess. I didn't understand most of what you said," blushed KoYou.

"What I tried to tell everyone is to use their most sincere mind. We must focus and dedicate our awareness toward our body. We must use our body like a broadcast tower where the bugler trumpets his message to the entire city. We must broadcast a positive message to impact and influence others. If one can achieve this, he need not kill."

"I like that idea, Master. Could you teach me how to do it? If it would save me from having to kill, I am willing to learn."

Laotzu smiled, "It is not a trick, young man. Neither does it require learning."

"Why so? If I do not learn, how can I do it?" mused KoYou.

"Because everyone is born with it. But when we grow up, we trade our true and powerful life energy for fake, 'man-made' ideas and tricks. It is in us – the ability to broadcast the signal and radiate outside our body – but we lose it when we grow up," Laotzu explained.

"Did I lose mine?" asked KoYou.

"Yes, but not totally. It is because you still possess quite a good amount of true life energy in you that you feel you cannot harden your heart and kill. That's why you can easily practice the Tao's work and restore your true ability," Laotzu said as he stared directly into KoYou's brown eyes.

"Can I really?"

"Of course," said the sage. "As soon as you practice the Tao's work and restore your true energy, you can broadcast your message to impact others. If you have an enemy in sight, you can send a message to him and make him no longer want to be your enemy, without having to kill him."

"My father KoWu would rather order his army to kill, and whoever escaped would never want to be his enemy again!" countered KoYou.

"When KoWu orders 'kill,' he sends a message of fear with a lot of action: slaughter, killing, merciless deeds. Of course the message is delivered, but it is through much action, trauma, fear and horror. It is a hard way to take care of trouble.

"However, by non-action, one just has to project his message by using his mind, life energy and body. Like a broadcasting tower, he learns to radiate and deliver the message of peace. This message impacts his enemy-to-be, canceling out the enemy's thoughts. The enemy thereby changes his mind and becomes no longer an enemy. This is what I called non-action. It means taking action without any action. Ha, ha, ha..." Laotzu laughed to himself at the simplicity of the proposition.

"Master, can this truly be done?"

"Try this," Laotzu beckoned. "Look at me." The sage pointed directly toward his own eyes so that KoYou stared into them with his.

"Now," ordered the sage, "try to pull out your sword. Try hard!"

KoWu reached across his waist with his right hand and grasped the hilt of his sword. He tried to draw the sword but couldn't. He felt a strong force glued to his brain, making him feel that his hand was frozen. The sword he tried to pull seemed as heavy as a horse!

"Go on, pull," encouraged Laotzu.

Regardless how hard KoYou tried, his sword handle got heavier. He looked at Laotzu with awe and disbelief.

"All right, you may draw your sword now," said the master. To his amazement, KoYou could now easily pull out his sword.

"Master, this is awesome! How did you do it? Can you teach me?" cried the boy.

"Like I said, you do not have to learn. All you have to do is rid yourself of artificial thinking, purify your mind and concentrate on a particular part of your body in a particular posture. Then you can easily broadcast your mind to impact others," the teacher assured him.

"Look at that bird," continued Laotzu, pointing up to a redwing sparrow in a tree branch. "Calm your mind and look at the bird. Meanwhile, stand in this posture and form your hand this way. The bird will stay there and go nowhere." Laotzu positioned the boy's arms just so, and stood back to model the proper posture for him.

KoYou tried, and indeed the bird stopped chirping and jumping around. It just stood quietly on its branch.

Then Laotzu told him to look away toward the other sidewall of the courtyard. As soon as he took his mind off the bird, the little sparrow woke up from its stillness and flew away.

"Wow! I can do it, Master!" KoYou beamed with excitement.

"Indeed, anyone can do it," smiled Laotzu encouragingly.

"Now I know what you mean by non-action," KoYou nodded.

"Good. If one can practice sincerely and diligently, he can improve and increase his ability. He can expand his impact power and extend the range.

For one who wants to be a king," Laotzu winked at him, "he must practice very hard to reach out to all his subjects to let them receive his majesty's message. Otherwise, he will be a very busy king, and work very hard like your father, taking so much action to rule his kingdom."

KoYou instinctively kneeled down and bowed deeply to Laotzu. "Master, please take me as your disciple. I want to follow you to learn your wisdom. I want to live with the truth. I don't want to kill or use brute force. That's not what I am. I want to learn this non-action power. Please help me."

"Do get up young friend," Laotzu replied. "You already know how to practice. Just keep practicing and you will be able to exercise your Te power to broadcast through the networking power of Tao."

"Master, I give you my heartfelt thanks."

"Here, let me show you more things you can practice," said Laotzu.

As they walked back to the stone cottage, Laotzu stopped from time to time to show KoYou different postures and movements to encourage what he called the Tao's work, or Tao Gong. He stressed to KoYou that the motions and postures needed to be practiced with a calm mind and a relaxed body.

When they arrived back at the stone cottage, Pen Hei the scribe sat against the wall next to the small hut's door, waiting. The scribe rose and brushed himself off as he bowed to both KoYou and Laotzu.

"Master," said the scribe, "I've come to ask you some questions so that I may accurately carve my notes from last night's teaching."

"Certainly my friend," said the sage. "Come inside, and we'll talk." Laotzu motioned for Pen Hei to join him inside. He winked over his shoulder at KoYou, signaling that they'd finished their time together for the day.

KoYou's head filled with wonder and overflowed with new understanding. As he walked back to the palace, he stopped from time to time to practice the Tao Gong movements his new Master showed him.

Chapter Nine
The Second Night with the Taoist Guest

On the second evening, many of the merchants from the previous night stayed home. Such high-level philosophies lay far beyond most of them. Likewise, many of the scholars' wives, anxious to make their appearance at the first palace banquet, had satisfied their curiosity about the mysterious visitor. They had enjoyed one evening of palace splendor, but didn't wish to endure nine whole evenings of listening to men talking in circles.

KoWu's own wife made her apologies for the evening. She had done her duty to the palace by graciously appearing and sitting at the table during the entire first night's talks. However, these arguments of scholars and masters didn't interest her. She didn't understand why people argued about religion. She'd lived in West Peace all of her life. As the daughter of silk traders, she'd grown up among the local customs. She and her family made offerings to the local gods at the temple.

Her first husband was also born in West Peace. He earned his place as a great general, and the king appointed him regent until KoWu came of age to rule here as prince. Shortly after KoWu's arrival, marauding barbarians kidnapped the general, Zhu Xiao Hua and their son Chian while they traveled by carriage to visit an aging uncle in a neighboring village.

She didn't see them kill him, but she heard her husband's gasp outside the cave as the barbarian chief plunged a sword through his heart.

For months, she and Chian lived in captivity in a cold mountain cave. The barbarian chief wouldn't let any of his men violate her, for he couldn't decide whether to keep her as a wife for himself, or hold her for ransom.

Every one of those terrible dark nights, she chanted endless prayers to the gods. She pledged that if by some great miracle she and her son were rescued, she would give her undying loyalty to the West Peace temple.

KoWu didn't share her faith in the same gods the citizens of West Peace knew from childhood. As a dutiful husband, he would go to the temple ceremonies and allow her to pay her vows. But because he was raised in a sophisticated capital city, his views of spiritual matters were far more philosophical.

Zhu Xiao Hua considered her husband's interest in matters of philosophy an impractical but harmless hobby. She appreciated his intelligence, but thought he wasted it on empty notions. He'd accomplish more by spending the night with the civil guard and solving real problems, not imaginary problems of the mind. Certainly the favor of the gods could not be found in such endless talk, she thought. He would do better to offer sacrifices to the temple with her.

Not only was the queen gone, but also most of KoWu's generals were absent. They'd missed both nights due to the heavy work of cleaning up and sorting the barbarian plunder. The task took more time than anyone expected. They wouldn't be free until later in the week.

But although several noteworthy citizens stayed home that night, new faces made their way into the hall. A few were foreign faces, some from the south judging by their dress. Rumors around town reported trouble in the southern city of Nan Do. A political matter led to a change of power in Nan Do's palace. A handful of advisors and well to do from Nan Do arrived late last night. They'd made a hasty flight from the city to West Peace. In these small feudal territories, changes in power often led to widespread execution of those loyal to the previous ruler. The more prominent of the Nan Do visitors, lucky to escape such a fate, would seek asylum at the palace of West Peace.

A meal, just as lavish as the night before, awaited the guests at the long horseshoe table. Quiet talk about the situation in Nan Do, and whether KoWu would have an opinion on the matter, dominated the conversation.

Laotzu came in late, and sat down to quietly enjoy a small plate of food in the corner of the room. Finishing this, he assumed his position at the center of the table's wide opening.

On this night the prince looked serious and prepared. He'd reviewed Pen Hei's carvings of the night before and carefully considered the best question to start the evening's talk. As he stood, all others ceased their private exchanges.

"Master, what is the proper procedure to prepare myself, my body, my mind and my life energy to let the power of Tao enter my body?" KoWu began.

Laotzu nodded and the teaching of the second evening began.

"When Tao's power is at work in a person, it is called the Te. When it works at its best it is called the Great Te, which is almost like Tao.

"To practice the power of Tao, 10-1 *while carrying body and consciousness and embracing the only One Power, can you avoid the separation of body and consciousness?* To practice with the Chi, 10-2 *flowing life energy and becoming supple, can you be like a newborn baby?* This life energy that we can learn to flow is one step down from the One Chi, the original power of Tao.

"To practice, you must work with your mind so that it may become absolute, purest mind. 10-3 *Washing and cleansing your mind to obtain the true original vision, can you be without contamination?* One needs an un-contaminated mind to feel the power of Tao, and the power of Te, or to work and pull in the power of One Chi."

At this point, Laotzu rose and walked around the tables as he did the night before.

"I emphasize the One Chi because the power of Tao begot the power of One, the original pure force, the One Chi. The One Chi is omnipresent. Every person is born with the One Chi, the power of Tao, to form the energy of life, to become a human being. But the One Chi inside the human body is already 'used.' Because of this, it degrades, turning into a declining One Chi – decaying and escaping back into the void to join the power of Tao. This is called returning to the mother since the power of Tao, as a whole, is a conscious being."

By the blank stares that greeted Laotzu from all directions, the sage knew he should elaborate even further.

"To be a saint, an average person must engage in the effort to bring in the original pure energy of the universe, the power of Tao, the unused Chi, the absolute Chi, the One Chi. He must first turn his mind back to the absolute pure state with no artificial contamination. Then, he must dedicate his absolute pure mind toward fusing back to his life energy, his body, his breath, his heart beat, his physical demands, his sexual drive, etc.... Third, as soon as he settles into the state of harmony, fusing his purest mind and his physical movement, he turns his body, an energy field, into a weaker cavity. This attracts the One Chi to flow into his body, as if he were forming his life at the stage of an embryo. He then must do his best to 'hold the One Chi, and avoid it separating from his body.'

"Our consciousness cannot feel the power of Tao, the only One Chi, in our body. This is because our conscious mind is already polluted and distorted. Also, the power of Tao, the Te, or the One Chi that is in our body when our life begins, is already 'used'. It is no longer the almighty power of Tao. It is only life energy that is destined to decline and die in its process of returning. Any feeling of the power of Tao, the One Chi, must therefore come from the outside and enter our body."

Laotzu picked up his flywhisk and used it as an extension of his arm as he gestured. He shook his flywhisk toward KoWu like a scolding tutor: "10-4 *Loving all people and governing the country, can you apply no cleverness?* Instead, broadcast the power of Te with the signal of love, not manmade knowledge.

"While following the rule of Tao, nature works with changes and opposites, like the 10-5 *opening and closing of the gates of heaven.* The original power of Tao works with passive, subtle, yet unitary force. Everything else is made of two separate and opposite powers and thus possesses only the used power of Tao. You may sense the force in its active phase, but *can you also coordinate the female power* and reach stillness?

"10-6 *Understanding and reaching to everything in the universe, can you exercise non-action?* Can you bring in the power of Tao and broadcast out to the whole world? Are you able to achieve it with non-action power?

"10-7 *Allowing a thing to emerge, to grow, to nourish it yet not possess it, to work at it yet not control it, lead it yet not dominate it –* 10-8 *this is so called the Great Te* or the great power of Te."

Prince KoWu was still very confused about the idea of the power of Tao. He had personally witnessed the awesome power released by Laotzu. The sage could change the sky and manipulate the weather, but kept saying it was the power of non-action. Indeed, it did appear that Laotzu did nothing, but nevertheless, somehow he put the ultimate power of the universe into motion.

Laotzu seemed to sense the prince's frustration and continued with more analogies about the power of Tao.

"The void and emptiness is invisible, but it is substantial. The True Tao includes the power of 'have' and 'have not'. Unfortunately, the usefulness of nothingness is ignored in our daily life," explained Laotzu.

He continued, "11-1 *Thirty spokes share a wheel's hub; it is the center hole that makes it a useful vehicle.* 11-2 *Mold clay into a pot; it is the hollow space within that makes it a useful vessel.* 11-3 *Cut out doors and windows of a room; it is the enclosed open space that makes it useful as a house.*

"11-4 *Therefore, to benefit from having something, one must also employ having nothing to achieve its usefulness.*"

Laotzu tried to explain that the nothingness is the origin of "something-ness," and that inside the emptiness there is a useful essence. This subtle, yet very powerful force is the Yang or positive power. Adepts who practiced the science of essence referred to it as the original fire force of One Chi.

"There are two ways to access the power of One Chi," continued Laotzu. "This original Chi is different in quality from the life energy Chi we posses from birth. One method is through the direct effort of meditation to absorb the One Chi from the emptiness into our body to replenish our body's ever-decreasing Chi. The other way is practiced by those who know how to apply alchemy to extract the One Chi from the emptiness into a chemical element that they swallow to replenish their Chi."

KoWu, now thoroughly overwhelmed and confused, threw open his hands and asked humbly, "Master, to obtain the power of Tao, how do I prepare? How do I start?"

Laotzu poked his flywhisk like a long finger into the prince's chest. "Rid yourself of false thinking, and hold on to true feeling. While we are growing up, our Chi quickly migrates to our brain and turns into thinking activities. We exhaust our Chi by thinking too much and spend no time to feel. Our mind is distracted by false sense that further complicates the thinking process and, in turn, further weakens the true feeling of our life energy. As you lose more of your life energy, you age, sicken and die prematurely."

Laotzu stepped back from the prince and wandered in a big circle, raising his voice to warn all those at the table: "12-1 *The five colors blind your eye. The five sounds deafen your ear. The five flavors ruin your taste.* 12-2 *Too much hunting and games confuse your mind.* 12-3 *Precious things lead one to steal.*

"12-4 *Therefore the saint is guided by what he feels and not by what he sees.* 12-5 *He rejects the other way and chooses this way.*"

The prince, wanting to change the subject back to one he could more easily understand, asked about the possibility of using the power of Tao for more personal applications. The guests listened intently when KoWu asked his third question. "As a governor, Master, I do care greatly about my reputation and my honor. I try very hard to keep up my name. Can I gain honor and esteem from practicing the power of Tao?"

Laotzu shook his head "Oh no, 13-1 *honor and disgrace are fearful.* 13-2 *Treat misfortune equally as you treat your own body.* 13-3 *Why be fearful of honor and disgrace?* 13-4 *Honor and disgrace arise from a false sense.* 13-5 *Gaining honor or disgrace makes one fearful. Loss of honor and disgrace also make one fearful.* You exhaust your life energy on something made of false sense. It is wasteful to apply the power of Tao to false sense. 13-6 *Therefore it is fearful to have honor and disgrace.*"

Fa Tingtz interjected, "But Master, our parents taught us to win honor and avoid disgrace at any cost. How can we avoid the fear of gaining or losing honor?"

"You should turn your body into a vehicle for the power of Tao instead of treating your body as your own, which only leads to suffering. 13-7 *Why should one treat misfortune as part of his own body?* 13-8 *The reason I have misfortune is because I have a body,*" answered Laotzu.

"How is our body related to misfortune Master?" KoWu knew he was using up his precious questions too hastily, but he wished to follow this train of logic.

"13-9 *If I do not treat my body as my own, why should I have any misfortune?* Do honor and disgrace affect me anymore?" the sage questioned in return. He further explained, "Apply the power of Tao to your body, and then extend the power of Tao to the whole world. 13-10 *Care about the world as you care about your body, as if you can be trusted to care for the world.* 13-11 *Love the world as if you love your body — as if you can be trusted with the world.*"

With that, Laotzu motioned that he would take a break. He'd spoken for quite a long time and felt the need to return to his cushion to soothe his throat with a cup of water. Pen Hei took advantage of the short intermission to catch up on his frantic carving. He sent servants to bring him a second carving knife since the blade on his own was wearing down.

The prince motioned for Fa Tingtz to approach him. The two men raised their sleeves and whispered to each other, obviously trying to further understand the sage's words. Just then, the gatekeeper appeared at the door and motioned for the prince to come. He wanted to report on a new caravan that had just arrived. The prince went to the doorway to confer quietly with the gatekeeper, while his guests took the opportunity to stand and stretch or talk among themselves.

On this night, there sat a new guest in the hall who had a keen interest in the sage's words. It was Chong Zen, a scholar from the troubled interior city of Nan Do. Chong Zen joined the prominent refugees who'd escaped to West Peace. As a scholar, he held hope of gaining new employment with KoWu. The Nan Do prince he recently served fell out of favor with his king only a few days ago, after plotting a coup. The scholar was shrewd enough to escape in the night with a small band of advisors. He'd heard rumors that an execution party was headed from their capital city to enforce the king's displeasure on the errant prince. Many heads would fall. He didn't want his head to be one of them, and left in the dark of night.

Chong Zen could tell from KoWu's questions that he'd missed much during the previous night's dialogue. He looked for somebody who could fill him in on this concept of Tao so that he could better follow the master's logic.

Sitting next to him, he saw a monk who kept to himself during dinner. Like Chong Zen, the monk had a southern complexion. Yet the monk hadn't arrived with Chong Zen's group. From the monk's satchel and from the fact that nobody seemed to pay the monk any mind, the scholar guessed that the monk was probably just a solitary traveler, a passing visitor through West Peace. Chong Zen lifted the sleeve of his robe so that he could inconspicuously lean over behind it to ask the quiet monk, "Hello, I am so sorry to trouble you. My name is Chong Zen. If I may ask, please give me a summary of this sage's teachings to the honored prince. I've just arrived from Nan Do and I wish to understand enough so that I may hear the sage's teachings with a clearer mind."

The monk whispered back to Chong Zen: "I would be happy to do so. My name is Dao An. However, if you are from Nan Do, I would recommend you not return for a while. There has been some trouble there of late, and Prince Kah Chan and his household have all been killed."

So it seemed everyone in West Peace knew Nan Do's troubles, Chong Zen thought. He was thankful that he had escaped just in time. This monk must have heard the news from other travelers.

Dao An continued, "I, too, have traveled from the south. My temple is in the hills a half-day's journey northwest of Nan Do."

Chong Zen exclaimed "Ah, Minglian Shan! I know it well. You do look like a Nan Do monk."

"It is unfortunate that you weren't here last night. Laotzu's awesome power and wisdom impressed the prince. KoWu is desperate to find out how he, too, can gain what Laotzu calls the power of Tao. But it is hard to understand. KoWu isn't really sure what the power of Tao is even after asking Laotzu again and again," Dao An explained.

"To Laotzu, the power of Tao is the most original, the absolute, the only One Power. The power can only be felt, but cannot be described or talked about with something like language, which is artificially concocted," continued the monk.

"Laotzu mentioned the first night that everything is made of the power of Tao, and shaped and formed by two equal but opposite powers. As soon as the power of Tao turns into things, they contain the power of Tao, but it is no longer the absolute power of Tao. Instead it starts to disintegrate and escape from the thing, including human life. This is why everything ages, decays and dies.

"From what I understand, the only way something can avoid aging is to replenish its power of Tao. Once the power of Tao is turned into a subject, it is not the pure power of Tao. Even if it is consumed by another object, it only turns into another object, and cannot restore the integrity or replenish the original power of Tao. The original power of Tao, the One Chi, has no negative (Yin), and no positive (Yang), and never decays or changes.

"But look now, the prince is away from his mat receiving word from his gatekeeper about some trouble with an arriving caravan. Some other guests may take this opportunity to ask their own questions."

The scholar lowered his sleeve whispering to Dao An, "Thank you for the excellent report, but again, if I may ask, what exactly is the power of Tao?"

Chong Zen whispered this so quietly and privately to the monk, it would have been impossible for anyone else in the room to hear. Laotzu, however, looked up from his cup of water and stared directly into Chong Zen's eyes.

"14-1 *Look, but you cannot see it – it is formless,*" started the sage, abruptly. He rose from his mat and slowly walked toward the scholar and monk's corner, saying "14-2 *Listen, but you cannot hear it – it transcends sound.* 14-3 *Grasp, but you can hold nothing – it is intangible.* 14-4 *These three are unfathomable: Therefore they are merged as one.*" Laotzu paused in front of the two startled men, then turned again to address the whole assembly. The guests fell silent and took their seats.

"14-5 *From above it reflects no light; from below it casts no shadow.* 14-6 *Impossible to comprehend, it cannot be named.*" Laotzu voice seemed to deepen with power as he spoke about the Tao in grand terms. "14-7 *Eventually it returns to nothingness.* The power of Tao made everything. Although that power decays inside things, it is still inexhaustible and, as it escapes, will seek to return to rejoin the wholeness of the power of Tao."

"**14-8** *So it is called a form without form, a shape without shape. It is called vague and subtle.* **14-9** *Encounter it from the front and you can't see its head. Follow after it and you can't see its back,*" the teacher continued. "You should not consider it subject to rules of distance and width. It is not matter with dimensions. **14-10** *Hold onto the ancient origin as you deal with the present.* You should not consider it subject to the rules of time. **14-11** *Knowing the origin is the law of Tao.* The only thing that really matters is connecting back to the origin, the mother consciousness of the power of Tao."

KoWu returned from his private conference with the gatekeeper in the doorway. Anxious that he might have missed something, the prince quickly took his seat. Not wanting the conversation to run away without him, KoWu grabbed hold of its reins again. He asked, "Master, while practicing Tao's power, what should one feel like?"

Laotzu turned to the prince and nodded, "Let's look at how the holy masters felt in the past. **15-1** *The ancient masters were subtle, mysterious, profound and aware. The extreme depth of their knowledge is hard to understand.* **15-2** *Since they are unfathomable, allow me to try very hard to describe their appearance in this way:*

"**15-3** *Watchful,* he follows with Tao's power *just like a man crossing a winter stream.* **15-4** *Ever alert,* he circulates with Tao's power *like* men *aware of surrounding danger.* **15-5** *Courteous* while facing the power of Tao, he behaves *like* he is *facing very important guests.* **15-6** *Yielding* with Tao's power — he yields *like ice about to melt.* Tao's power fills his body and he finds himself **15-7** *appearing so simple and real, like an uncarved block of wood.* **15-8** *So hollow and deep,* he is *like a big canyon.* **15-9** *So unclear,* he is *like muddy water.* **15-10** *Resting, won't the mud settle and the water become clear again?* **15-11** *Can't he rest knowing that stillness will again awaken into action?*

"**15-12** *Knowing the way of the Tao, he never seeks to be full.* The saint first learns how to pull in the power of Tao to replenish his ever-diminishing One Chi, then he continues to allow the power of Tao to flow into his body by being non-resisting and yielding. **15-13** *Never full,* he will always be replenished with the power of Tao, *even if he is worn out* he *need not be renewed.*"

For the first time since he entered the hall, Dao An, the Minglian Shan monk sitting next to Chong Zen, spoke up from his corner. He couldn't resist. Whatever this master offered pulled on the center of his chest irresistibly. He asked, "Master, how can I start to practice so that I may receive the power of Tao?"

Laotzu Answers Guests

An unknown monk interrupting the assembly without asking permission might normally offend KoWu. However, the prince appreciated the important and well-phrased question, and was happy Laotzu would answer it without he himself using up one of his nine.

Laotzu smiled at Dao An. "Excellent question. You must know the correct way to begin. It is very easy. It is also very hard. You need to start by calming your mind, relaxing your body, and breathing slowly and smoothly. Then, 16-1 *attain to the utmost inward weakness.* Dedicate your mind to such an extreme state that it seems you no longer exist. You forget your body and you are so weak that you finally become emptiness.16-2 *Focus firmly in the purest state of stillness.* Hold fast to the extreme state of calmness as if nothing changes.

"When you reach that state, someday, after repeated effort, and guided by a true master, 16-3 s*uddenly, the ten thousand things will appear in circular sequence* in your vision. 16-4 *And then everything will develop and flourish and then return to the source of the void.* 16-5 *Returning to the source is the stillness.* 16-6 *The stillness is unchanging; the unchanging is the constant.*"

Laotzu continued, "16-7 *Knowing* the source of *the constant is wisdom. Straying from the* source of *constancy leads to disaster.* 16-8 *Knowing constancy, you will then be able to be tolerant. With tolerance, you will be openhearted.* 16-9*Being openhearted, you will lead. Being a leader, you will attain heaven.* 16-10 *Attaining heaven, you will be at one with the Tao. Being at one with the Tao is eternal.* You and your whole body will turn into pure power of Tao and reach the state of *never dying.*"

Dao An, who'd asked the original question, felt deep within his heart that Laotzu had honored him with a precious key to open the treasures of the Tao. He immediately slid from his mat and knelt with his head to the floor in gratitude.

KoWu heard Laotzu's answer to the foreign monk, but it was still so hard to understand. He felt embarrassed that this monk from the south seemed to grasp what he, a prince, had not.

"But I do not live the life of a monk," said KoWu. "Can those who live in the world of regular men do what you describe?" asked the prince.

Laotzu now turned to the prince to elaborate further: "You must first prepare your body. It helps to prefer to be in nature and maintain your health. Then you must also prepare your mind to be in the purest condition. The way to purity is to go backward. Go back to where you came from. As an infant you knew nothing, but you used your feeling. You judged nothing, interpreted nothing, but you felt the truth of everything."

Prince KoWu confessed to the sage, "I am in good shape physically, generally speaking. However, my mind is busy with the demands of city affairs. I must always be on alert and can never drop my defenses. My mind is constantly mulling problems that come up and how to rule without making mistakes. I am a long way from the purity you speak of."

Laotzu's face became even gentler as he encouraged, "One step at a time. A thousand mile journey starts at the first step. You could just spend some short bits of time during the day to be alone, to calm down, to relax your body, to gather your mind, and to temporarily forget your daily affairs."

"That I can do," reflected the prince.

"Then you can take another step and develop the ability to feel your body, to feel your heart beat, to feel your stomach, to feel your breath," encouraged the master. "Of course, the most important part is to continue to calm and purify your mind. When your mind reaches the purest state, like that of a newborn baby, you apply that mind to feel your body. Once you can do that, the life energy will come into play, followed by the inflow of the power of the Tao."

As the sage patiently enumerated these steps to the prince, he kept one eye on the quiet monk. Dao An respectfully closed his eyes as if to better carve each word into his memory. Here is no ordinary monk, thought Laotzu to himself. He is not visiting this city by accident.

"Can I feel the inflow of the power of Tao?" asked the prince.

"Definitely!" Laotzu signaled KoWu to come forward. He whispered in the prince's ear "You will feel like this…" Laotzu held his open palm toward the top of KoWu's head.

The prince's face froze in an expression of utter amazement as he gasped "Oh!"

Laotzu withdrew his hand, and the prince looked around to see if anyone else felt the rush of energy that he had just felt. Everyone simply stared at him blankly.

After his wide eyes relaxed, he turned to the sage intently, "Master, can I direct this inflow of Tao's power back to my people and make them follow my wishes?"

Laotzu folded his arms across his chest and answered, "I'd rather see you lead them with the power of Tao, which requires the exercise of mercy, tenderness, weakness, softness and yielding instead of harsh force. As you know, 17-1 *the best ruler is hardly recognized by the people.* 17-2 *Then come those who they know and love, then those who they fear, then those who they disdain.* 17-3 *He does not have faith in them, so they have no faith in him.*

"17-4 *A true leader can accomplish his aims without too much talking. When his goal is achieved, people will say, 'We did it!'*"

KoWu shook his head, "If I try as hard as I can, but still fail to reach the power of Tao, what would happen?"

"You then can't apply the power of Tao to rule because you wouldn't be able to broadcast the power of Tao. Everything you rule would require the maintenance of man-made artificial systems and the force of action," replied Laotzu.

He continued,"18-1 *When* the power of *the great Tao ceases to prevail,* the people in your state receive no blessing of Tao's power. 18-2 *Then people can only count on* so-called *kindness and justice* to get along with each other. 18-3 *Then wisdom and intelligence are born,* so people compete to get ahead of each other *and the great hypocrisy begins.*

"18-4 *Then there is no peace within the family.* People care not for the family members. Instead, they start to value false sense such as success, fame, honor, title, and the value of jewelry, money, and gold. They discount the value of natural family feelings, *so* instead *people are asked to display filial piety and devotion.*

"18-5 *Then the entire country is in a state of confusion and disorder, thus many loyal ministers appear.* They try very hard to set rules, laws and regulations to enforce order. They keep changing and increasing the number of laws, but in vain."

KoWu opened his mouth to ask another question, but Laotzu raised a warning finger, signaling the prince had already asked his nine for the night. KoWu sighed and nodded.

"Ladies and gentlemen," he concluded, "I am afraid we will have to continue our conversation tomorrow evening."

Guests around the table rose and made their bows to both Laotzu and the prince.

Outside in the hall, the scholar Chong Zen found Dao An and thanked him again for his help. Dao An replied, "It was just a brief report on what I heard. I have yet to fully understand this great master's words."

"Nevertheless," said Chong Zen, "If I can ever return the favor…"

"Well, you may have a better chance than I will of securing a position with the West Peace Prince," said Dao An. "When you do, remember me."

"I will," promised Chong Zen.

Several other guests lingered in the corridors to discuss what they'd learned with each other that night. The hallways filled with the din of intellectual dissection and debate. Laotzu squeezed through the crowd and made his way out of the building.

He walked back through the starlit courtyard to his stone cottage. KoYou had returned to the hut before he did, and already had a fire crackling in the pit to welcome the sage.

"How'd it go, Master Laotzu?" asked the boy. "I left before the last question."

"Fine, son. Be glad you're still young and don't know too much yet," the sage shook his head in dismay. "Pardon me while I rest now. I often rise early before sunrise to meditate." Laotzu didn't even bother to undress. He stretched out on his straw mat and soon slept like a babe.

KoYou covered his new teacher with a blanket, and quietly closed the door on his way out. He wanted to meditate with Laotzu in the morning. He promised himself to wake up early and come back to the stone cottage to join the sage before sunrise.

Chapter Ten

Spying on the Sage Leads to an Early Morning Lesson

On the third morning of the sage's visit, Yin Lian rose early to meet Lo Yintz in the courtyard to practice a sword dance together. Lo Yintz had no means to afford the tutors and training Yin Lian enjoyed, so Yin Lian shared her sword techniques with her.

Yin Lian and Lo Yintz remained good friends even though their different positions in life might normally tear them apart. When Yin Lian's father died, it was Lo Yintz who comforted her and let her come to the stable to find solace with the company of the animals. Lo Yintz, who'd lost her mother at birth, somehow always knew the right words to comfort Yin Lian. And when KoYou was too busy with his training, Yin Lian could always find a friend in the Lo cottage.

On this morning, Yin Lian giggled as the stable girl Lo Yintz peeked out from behind the main palace door. It was so exciting that Lo Yintz was actually staying inside the palace guest room. Since nobody else was awake, Lo Yintz pretended to walk like the queen as she lifted her chin and dramatically swept her simple robes to the side. She lifted her hand and walked down the palace stairs as gracefully as Zhu Xiao Hua herself. Yin Lian covered her mouth, now full of laughter at her friend's play.

The stable girl and her father enjoyed their brief lodgings in the splendor of the guest quarters. When Lo Yintz reached the bottom stair, she rushed to hold her friend's hands and describe the new luxuries she'd enjoyed for the first time.

"...And the servants actually cover you at night with soft silks, and they light lamps of pure gold while flutes play in the hallway. You can eat as much as you like and there is always more. They bring fragrant oils and water to bathe in and fresh clothes every morning!"

Yin Lian smiled and grew warm inside enjoying the thought that her simple-hearted friend could finally enjoy a bit of the luxury that Yin Lian had known all her life. Although she didn't know Laotzu well, she loved him like an uncle for how he gave the simple Lo household this great gift.

Yin Lian brought her two swords with her like she did every morning. This allowed her to share one with Lo Yintz. As the young friends walked arm in arm tittering like magpies about all of the week's adventures, they could see across the courtyard that Laotzu was already awake. In the clearing by the stable, he danced his own strange sword dance with his flywhisk.

He inadvertently took over their own favorite practice spot. He danced in a corner of the courtyard that lay protected by a hedge on one side and the outer stable wall on another. They were surprised he was up and around given the late-night teaching at the prince's banquet.

The old sage seemed quite absorbed in his slow and airy movement and oblivious to them. The girls eyed each other knowing that they had the same thought. They crept slowly along the side of the courtyard and huddled together behind the hedge to watch in secret.

Laotzu's mock sword dance with his flywhisk seemed very different – different from any style Yin Lian had seen, and she'd seen plenty. Instead of moving fast, he moved very slowly with his eyes half-closed. Sometimes he appeared to be meditating or praying while he moved. It looked odd! So odd that the girls couldn't stifle their giggling, even though they tried to cover their mouths.

"Shhhhhh...." hushed a low voice from behind the other corner of the hedge. Apparently they weren't the only two in the palace who'd snuck up on the sage's dance that morning. Chong Zen, the scholar from Nan Do and the record-keeper Wei Lon peeked their heads around the other corner of the hedge and frowned at the giggling girls. They signaled the ladies not to disturb Laotzu. The two girls bent down and crept quietly over to join the two men.

"What is that, Uncle Wei Lon?" whispered Yin Lian. "Is Laotzu still drunk from last night?" They all watched as the sage weaved back and forth slowly stretching one arm and then the other. His head bobbled and each part of his body seemed to float gently from one posture to another.

"No, he is not drunk," Wei Lon whispered. He'd spent the last two days in the records cellar, carving and preserving the bamboo notes from the scribe who'd recorded each of Laotzu's evening lessons. The notes made him curious enough to use this rare moment of free time to catch a glimpse of this curious master. He was not disappointed, and now watched with awe at Laotzu's strange dance. "He is meditating, praying and exercising his body and spirit by the power of heaven. It is the most beautiful and powerful dance I have ever seen, and the most eloquent prayer I have ever heard."

"Let's watch," Chong Zen reminded everyone, urging them to stay quiet.

Chong Zen was overwhelmed by the sheer volume and breadth of Laotzu's teachings the night before. After everyone left last night's gathering, Prince KoWu summoned Chong Zen and asked the visiting scholar to prepare his opinion of the sage's teachings. The prince invited him to give a presentation later in the week for him and his own spiritual advisor Fa Tingtz. Chong Zen was very anxious to make an impressive report, since this first request would undoubtedly decide whether the prince would offer Chong Zen a position as a scholar at the palace.

Wanting to prepare his report, Chong Zen woke early to find the palace records-keeper so that he could review the previous nights' notes. A servant pointed to Wei Lon across the courtyard, and Chong Zen could see the records-keeper crouching, watching somebody from behind the hedge. When Chong Zen saw that it was Laotzu himself doing some sort of morning - ritual, Chong Zen delightedly joined Wei Lon in the bushes.

Before the girls arrived, the two men watched Laotzu emerge from his stone hut and perform his strange motions. But after only a few minutes, Laotzu returned back to his hut.

"Maybe he just came out to stretch and allow a cup of hot cereal to cool," thought Chong Zen. The scholar tiptoed up to the small house's window. As he peeked inside, hoping to catch the sage at breakfast and perhaps ask him a question or two, he could see the sage instead napping on the bed cushion against the wall.

Chong Zen dared not disturb the sage, so he tiptoed back to find Wei Lon. No sooner had he rejoined the records-keeper than Laotzu emerged again from the hut. Back he came to the courtyard to do more mysterious dancing. Wei Lon and Chong Zen again crouched behind the hedge to watch. Shortly afterwards the two giggling girls increased their hidden audience to four.

Finally, as the early sun rose high enough to cast its first gleam on the tall trees, Laotzu stopped his slow dance. Laotzu waved his whisk toward the corner of the stable wall. "Okay, son, you may come out now." Out stepped KoYou, Prince KoWu's son. He, too, rose early that day and had come to the courtyard looking for the sage. He also stumbled upon Laotzu's mysterious morning exercise and had hidden behind the stable door to watch.

"And you too, you may all come out now," Laotzu turned and waved the whisk toward the hedge. The four embarrassed faces rose in a row over the flat top of the newly trimmed bushes. All five spies filed into the clearing. The sage motioned for them to take seats on the ground around him.

Once they all sat down, Laotzu squatted effortlessly against the stable wall and surveyed the voyeurs. He broke into a wide grin, and his small audience laughed at themselves, realizing they could relax with the teacher without fear of reprisal.

"Master, what is that exercise you just finished? Can I learn that slow sword dance from you?" Yin Lian asked in an eager and cheerful voice. She was not shy when it came to ferreting out new sword moves. She'd learned plenty from asking southern traders for their martial arts secrets. Yin Lian always looked for ways to improve the double sword technique passed down from her father.

"No, sweet one," Laotzu smiled kindly, "this is not a martial dance. It is not a dance at all. You cannot learn it."

Yin Lian pouted with disappointment, "Why not? It is so graceful. I love it. I am a very quick learner and I promise to practice very hard."

Laotzu patted her hand, "I know you would, sweet one, but this cannot be learned in the same way as your sword dancing. It is the flow of God's power, the Tao, floating, drifting, moving where it wills. I simply gave my mind and body over to the power of God. I let it take over, flow internally and float externally, in total harmony with the power of heaven, the Tao."

Yin Lian, Lo Yintz and KoYou all gazed at the sage with puzzled faces. Chong Zen nodded with an air of understanding, appearing to know what the sage now described. "Master, if I may," bowed Chong Zen, "I have tutored many young minds before, and perhaps I can explain for them."

Laotzu smiled and gave a shallow nod.

"From what the sage has taught, one must give up his ego, totally and completely, with no strings attached. One must let the mind rejoin with the body, and the body rejoin with the life energy – the Chi. Then one allows the Chi to go back to the state of Te, or that unit of the power of Tao within our body. Then one broadcasts out to match with the power of Tao, the ultimate force in the universe," recited Chong Zen, with his finger wagging high in the air. Even with his arm raised, his long scholar's sleeves still dragged on the ground.

"Bravo," clapped Laotzu. "Excellent report, scholar. I think you will have a long future here in West Peace. Just remember, it is one thing to recite the truth and another thing to feel and know it."

Chong Zen blushed again, as he sat down. How did this strange man seem to know everything? Did he already know about the prince's request for a report on the sage?

Persistent Yin Lian turned again to Laotzu, "Then why do you dance so slowly and gracefully?"

"Good question," Laotzu leaned forward toward the girl. "The power of Te is naturally looking for a way to rejoin the mother power, the Tao. If you had lost a parent, would you not try as hard as you could to find them?"

Yin Lian's eyes fell. She certainly knew the answer to that. She'd longed for her father more than anyone could know these last two years since he died. Did the sage already know about her father?

The sage's voice softened as if to soothe the wound he just opened in Yin Lian's heart, "As soon as you give yourself up completely, relaxing the body and paying great attention to feeling, you can feel the inner energy of the body moving gracefully toward the outside of yourself. At this point, you relax even more to allow the delicate, barely noticeable energy flow to push your physical body around any way it wants. To a bystander, it appears as a slow dance, or a moving prayer."

"I see," erupted KoYou. KoYou was excited by this idea, because while Laotzu was explaining this, KoYou followed the sage's coaching and tried to relax deeply. He thought he felt something move within his body – something subtle and barely noticeable. "So Yin Lian cannot learn it like she learns sword dancing because they are two totally different things."

"Why so?" Yin Lian fired back at KoYou. She did not like it when KoYou grasped a concept faster than she did, and resented any implication that she was not his equal when it came to the martial art of swordplay.

"Because, Yin Lian," KoYou explained, "You learn a sword dance by imitating a teacher's movement. So every movement of yours is just a copy of the sword teacher's move. Even if you do the dance on your own, it's just your memory telling your mind to move your body in the way you rehearsed before. What Master Laotzu said was to move from your own true and spontaneous feeling."

Laotzu smiled and nodded, obviously pleased that KoYou understood.

Chong Zen and Wei Lon also nodded at KoYou in agreement, but inside they both still pondered this matter of Laotzu's meditative dance.

Yin Lian Performs Her Double Sword Dance

What the honorable scholar and records-keeper couldn't see was that because he was still young, KoYou didn't bother to analyze what Laotzu taught. Instead, he immediately acted on the sage's directions to experience the effect Laotzu described. Because he acted spontaneously, the youth had a small experience of his own life energy. He could then understand that the life energy moves on its own terms, bypassing the mind and its thinking.

Conversely, Chong Zen and Wei Lon remained trapped in their analytical thinking, instead of feeling. They couldn't feel any energy at all. It would take years of practice for them to attain the level KoYou reached in just one morning.

Yin Lian would not give up her grudge that Laotzu refused to teach her his dance. "Well Master," she announced indignantly, "I am very smart and I have a good memory. My sword teacher showed me his most difficult moves only a few times and I remembered the entire sequence. If you would just let me follow you, I could learn your sword dance with just one try."

Rising to her defense, her friend Lo Yintz added, "She really could. She knows all kinds of dances, even the barbarian ones. She can do it just by watching them. Come on Yin Lian, show Master something." The stable girl grabbed Yin Lian's swords and laid them across her friend's lap.

Yin Lian feigned shyness, but soon stood up as the whole group applauded. She bowed proudly, determined to defend her reputation. Silently she paced out an open circle.

As the lithe young woman began to spin and dip, her two swords flashed in the glimmering sunshine. Twisting and jumping, her linen robe looked like a billowing white cloud as she gracefully and swiftly sliced through the crisp morning air. She performed a foreign dance requiring great strength and agility. She'd learned it from a dancing troupe that came with a diplomatic envoy last year. The troop performed it only once in a tribute to KoWu, yet Yin Lian's keen memory allowed her to practice and perfect each move.

While Yin Lian danced, Laotzu looked at KoYou. The young man sat fully absorbed in his fiancée's beautiful performance. He didn't know that earlier, Laotzu had secretly broadcast his Te power while speaking to the group. Only KoYou picked up the radiant energy that allowed him to feel what he did. KoYou could perceive the energy because the young man's own energy was so pure and far less contaminated than the others. The bombardment of Laotzu's energy allowed him to feel what he did. But the fact that he grasped the underlying concept so quickly gave Laotzu hope. Perhaps

KoWu's son was not as hardheaded as his father. "The boy has possibilities," Laotzu thought, returning his gaze to Yin Lian's elegant swordplay.

As she finished, everyone rose with approving smiles and applause. All of them bowed to her together, even Laotzu. Yin Lian broke into a proud smile, knowing that even the sage must admit she could learn whatever sword dance he could teach.

"Yin Lian," Laotzu said, "I believe that someday you will indeed learn my dance!"

In high spirits, the group dispersed as Laotzu retired to his guesthouse for a nap. The girls put away the swords, because it was time for Lo Yintz to return to her work at the stable.

Wei Lon and Chong Zen stayed and argued with each other over whether the Tao's energy originally came from the earth or the sky. KoYou stood next to them. A slow heavy feeling still covering his body, KoYou exclaimed: "It's the energy. I can still feel it! It's the power, I feel it!"

The two men grew silent, and watched KoYou as he walked back to the stable. They didn't know whether to envy the youth or to brush his remarks aside as the over-active imagination of an eager boy. After KoYou left, they decided to retire to the records room to review the carvings from Laotzu's previous talks.

Chapter Eleven

The Third Night with the Taoist Guest

On the third night, the palace sent no formal invitations. Those arriving at the palace did so on their own because of their own keen interest. No pomp or grand festivities greeted guests on this evening. The simplicity whittled off those who only came for prestige or simply a chance to be seen with the prince. It was a small and intimate gathering. Only a handful of servants lined the back wall, KoYou among them.

The prince arranged the affair this way on purpose. He wanted a chance to ask deeper questions, without a hundred pairs of eyes on him at once. In a smaller gathering, KoWu could think more clearly, engage the sage without interruption, and perhaps hear better what the master meant with his strange words.

Merely a dozen or so guests arrived at the hall, making the grand table look enormous and empty. Servants brought simpler fare, but in ample portions. Roast duck, vegetables and rice, two types of soup, fruit and sweets, followed by a hearty wine made in the nearby countryside. The meal seemed more like a big family dinner than a banquet.

KoWu motioned to Laotzu to come sit by his side instead of at his own faraway table in the center of the room. He turned to the sage beside him and began his questions while everyone ate. Tonight he spoke as casually as if he were talking with a brother during a family meal.

"Well, then, Master Laotzu. You've convinced me that I need to learn how to use this power of Tao so that I can broadcast good messages to all of my people. But how should I overcome the pollution of these so-called artificial systems to purify my mind, and to prepare for the power of Tao to enter my body?" asked the prince, selecting a plum from a platter of fruit in front of the two men.

Laotzu answered him with equal ease, reaching toward a small cluster of shelled nuts drenched in honey. "Understand the fact that when you first
19-1 *renounce holiness and give up wisdom, the people will benefit a hundred times*

over. Then secondly, 19-2 *stop touting 'kindness', throw away notions of 'morality,' and people will be filled with fidelity and love.* Third, 19-3 *give up cleverness, ignore the idea of profit, and there will be no more theft or robbery.*

"But keep in mind that 19-4 *these three only fix the surface; they are insufficient.* 19-5 *It is more important to help people embrace simplicity:* 19-6 *to hold one's true nature,* 19-7 *to restrain from being selfish and curtail desire.* As soon as more of your people dedicate themselves to a mentality of simplicity, your state will soon be ruled in harmony."

KoWu continued, "What should a person feel like after he connects his Te with the power of Tao?"

Laotzu replied, "He will 20-1 *give up learning and become worry-free.* He will suddenly think: 20-2 *Is there a difference between obey and command? Is there a difference between good and bad?* 20-3 *I fear what everyone else fears: so long this has been such a pointless idea. I wonder when it will stop.*"

Dai Dong leaned over from behind Laotzu and the prince and poured each a cup of a very fine wine. The palace saved this special wine for the prince's private enjoyment. After taking a small sip, the master continued his description, "I can tell you how I feel. 20-4 *Everyone else is indulging themselves, as if enjoying the sacrificial feast of the ox.* 20-5 *As if in spring some enjoy climbing the terrace at the park.* 20-6 *I alone seem unaffected and lost.* 20-6 *Like an innocent baby that hasn't yet learned to smile.* 20-7 *I alone have no place to go.*

"20-8 *Others have more than enough, but I alone am lacking.* 20-9 *I feel like a fool: as if I were confounded.* 20-10 *Everyone else appears bright, but I alone am dim.* 20-11 *Everyone else appears to be so smart, but I am the only one who is confused.*

"20-12 *I like to be as unpredictable as the immense ocean, as unstable as the gusty wind.* 20-13 *Everyone else acts capable, but I'm the only one who acts stubborn and foolish.* 20-14 *I am different but I am nourished by* the power of Tao, *the great mother.*"

Guests around the table looked at Laotzu in disbelief. How could such an accomplished master describe himself this way? Was it humility, or did he tell the truth? Did this power of Tao make one different from others? If so, why would one want to feel "dim" or "confounded," "stubborn," "lost" and "foolish?"

KoWu leaned on his elbow and asked, "Master, you seem to know everything about the ways of this world. Can we achieve this same ability, this same wisdom?"

Laotzu laughed a little, then replied, "It is very easy. After I let the power of Tao enter my body, then my internal power, 21-1 *the Great Te, follows nothing but* the power of *Tao, though Tao is elusive and subtle.* 21-2 *It seems elusive and subtle, and yet within it is an image.* 21-3 *It seems subtle and elusive, and yet within it is a form.* 21-4 *It appears vague and subtle, and yet within it is an essence.* 21-5 *This essence is very real, and therein lies a message.* 21-6 *From the very beginning until now its name has never been erased.* 21-7 *Thus I can see and perceive everything within creation.* 21-8 *How do I know everything within the creation? Because of this.*"

KoWu wondered how the sage made such lofty accomplishment sound so simple. Maybe life was simpler for a man who spent his life wandering the countryside on an ox.

But what about him? What about a ruler whose life was a series of problems to solve, decisions to make, enemies and allies to placate. The prince asked, "How should a person with the power of Tao deal with this complicated world?"

Laotzu answered, "First of all, a saint understands the Power of Tao: 22-1 *It yields and becomes whole;* 22-2 *bends and can yet become straight;* 22-3 *stays low and can be filled;* 22-4 *when old gains renewal.*

"Conversely, 22-5 *to be little* is a way to guarantee you will *always gain.* 22-6 *If reaching the state of too much,* you will *become confused.*

"22-7 *Therefore wise men* understand these things I tell you and *hold to the very One Power and are humble to the whole world.* 22-8 *He* who follows the power of Tao *does not promote himself: he shines.* 22-9 *He draws no attention to himself: he is given credit.* 22-10 *He need not boast: he receives recognition.* 22-11 *Since he doesn't brag,* he's never brought down. *He leads.* 22-12 *He need not quarrel, so no one can quarrel with him.*"

Laotzu took a moment to stretch and then rose from his place at the table and started to move around the room as he had the previous nights. This allowed his voice to carry farther, and made it much easier for the other guests to hear.

Laotzu finished his thought by quoting, "22-13 *The ancients say, 'To yield is to be preserved.' This is no empty saying.* 22-14 *If you are truly whole, all things will come to you.*"

"Master, what do you mean to be whole?" asked the prince, who likewise stood up and began to walk. They looked like two pacing generals discussing strategy in a tent, walking back and forth as if to help them think. The other guests sat as spectators, their eyes following the two around the room.

Laotzu further explained, "One who practices flowing his life energy, Chi, circulates it throughout his entire body, inside and out, and makes his body soft and lively. He then purifies his mind by reducing and blocking all artificial ideas, such as social ritual, man-made legal systems, man-made monetary systems, man-made fame, etc... He then guides his purified mind, which attaches and returns back to his life energy. This allows him to achieve a state of being that matches the stage when he was a newborn, when the power of Tao activated to form his life.

"When you are in the wonderful state of being born, with the message of softness, weakness, mercy and the need to be fed, this creates an energy field that allows the power of Tao, or the One Chi, to flow into your body. If the inflow of the One Chi is greater than the outflow, your body, mind, and life energy all turn into pure energy of the power of Tao, the original energy. One becomes wholeness."

Abudamancus called out across the room to the sage, "Master, although you speak so little, your words are powerful." His big voice thundered in the relatively empty palace hall.

Laotzu smiled. He, like the prince, grew fond of the big burly man from Dazos. He replied,"23-1 *To use few words is natural.* Talking to men is just like a storm moving over the earth. 23-2 *Look! A gusty wind will not last all morning. Showers can't last the whole day.* 23-3 *Who drives the wind and the showers? Heaven and earth!* 23-4 *Even heaven and earth cannot make things last forever.* 23-5 *How is it possible for man* if men just rely on empty talk?

"23-6 *Rather, men who exercise the* power of *Tao should be one with the Tao.* 23-7 *He who exercises the* power of *Te should be one with the power of Te.* 23-8 *He who exercises* the power of *loss should be with* stillness and feel the power of being lost.

"23-9 *He who is at one with the Tao,* the power of the *Tao will like to be with him.* 23-10 *He who is one with Te,* the power of *Te will always like to be with him.* 23-11 *He who is at one with the* power of *loss,* the power of *loss will like to be with him.*

"23-12 *If there is not enough faith* in Tao, one will never be able to witness the power of Tao, and will never believe the Tao and then *one will never have any faith.*"

KoWu rejoined, "If I try very hard to reach Tao, can I get it?"

"No. You are trying to 'get.' You are not letting Tao enter you. It is as if you try to stand on your toes and are not steady. 24-1 *One will fail to stand on only his toes.* It's as if you are trying to reach the power by yourself. You should empty yourself and let the power of Tao enter your body.

"24-2 *One can't walk if he tries to hop.* 24-3 *He who tries to make himself stand out will not be visible.* 24-4 *He who is self-righteous will not earn respect.* 24-5 *He who boasts of himself will get nothing.* 24-6 *He who brags will not lead.*

"According to followers of the Tao, '24-7 *Extra effort to reach Tao is like extra food and unnecessary luggage.*' No one likes leftover food, therefore 24-8 *the saint avoids self-effort.*"

KoWu shook his head. He was a strong and persevering man. To reach a goal without effort, and to set self-reliance aside was an unimaginable idea. He needed to know more. The prince continued with his seventh question for the night: "Master, you emphasize the importance of giving up ourselves to make room for the power of Tao. But what is the power of Tao?"

The teacher closed his eyes, as if in private communion with an unseen world. Without opening his eyes, he answered, "25-1 *Something mysteriously formed, born even before heaven and earth.* 25-2 *In the loneliness and the void, standing alone and unchanging, ever present and moving ceaselessly.* 25-3 *It is* a conscious being, *the mother of heaven and earth.*

"25-4 *I do not know its name. Let's just call it Tao.* 25-5 *For lack of a better word, let's call it the Great.* 25-6 *So great, let's call it the disappearing.* 25-7 *Disappearing into far away – let's call it the far away.* 25-8 *Having gone so far, eventually it returns – so let's also call it the return.*

"25-9 *Therefore,* the power of *Tao reaches to the greatest, so the heavens reach to the greatest; the earth reaches to the greatest, and men also can reach to the greatest.* 25-10 *In the universe, these are the four great powers, and man is one of them.*

"However, the way 24-1 *man* reaches out to the universe is by *following the* way the *earth* reaches out to the universe. And the way 25-12 *the earth* reaches out to the universe *follows the* way *heaven* reaches to the universe. 25-13 *And the* way *heaven* reaches to the universe is by *following the* power of *Tao.* 25-14 *And the* power of *Tao* reaches to the universe by *following the Law of Nature.*"

The southern monk Dao An rose and bowed to the prince apologetically. He realized that the night before, he'd neglected this courtesy when he asked Laotzu a question. Unfortunately, he'd let his enthusiastic curiosity get the better of him. He'd forgotten that he was but a stranger in this city, and a lowly monk at that. The palace only admitted him to the banquet because he carried the traveling seal of the Minglian Shan temple. This gave Dao An the status of a lesser diplomat.

Tonight, he made amends by observing proper humility toward the prince. He not only bowed, he kept his head down until the prince nodded his permission for Dao An to ask the sage his question. Dao An looked up and asked, "Master, while I practice the power of Tao, I feel the power is so heavy in my body, yet it is so easy to be distracted and think about things going on outside. Then I lose the feeling of Tao and Te. What should I do?"

Obviously, the monk had been practicing Laotzu's instructions from the night before. Laotzu nodded his approval and said, "For this I must draw you a picture."

As Laotzu walked over to the sand tray in the center of the room, the servant kneeling at the sand pit offered the teacher a long and smooth bamboo twig. Laotzu began to outline a figure in the sand while he explained: "26-1 *The* internal *heavy* feeling *is the root of the* external *light* feeling. 26-2 *The stillness is the master of action.*" (**figure 1**)

The guests all rose to their feet and walked around to the inside of the horseshoe tables so they could see what Laotzu traced.

Laotzu continued, "26-3 *Therefore the saint* holds on to his feeling of Tao's power as if he were *traveling all day,* and, being a careful traveler, he *does not*

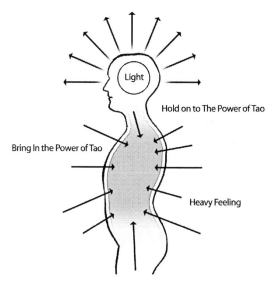

figure 1 *Heavy and Light*

lose track of his heavy luggage. **26-4** *And even though there are distractions of beautiful things to see, he remains unattached and calm,* still holding onto his feeling of Tao's power. **(figure 2)**

Finishing his drawings, Laotzu turned to the group adding,"**26-5** *Why should the lord of ten thousand chariots forget his status and treat himself lightly?* **26-6** *To* be distracted and *become light is to lose* one's feeling of Tao's power, *the root.* **26-7** *To be in action is to give up one's mastership* of the world."

Everyone remained standing by the sand even though Laotzu was finished drawing diagrams. Their backs and worn out knees appreciated the stretch.

KoWu, standing among them, offered his eighth question, "Master, after I hold onto the power of Tao and avoid distractions, how can I help others and save the world?"

"A saint helps people and the world in the same way that **27-1** *a good traveler leaves no wheel marks; a good speaker utters no mistakes;* and *a good counter needs no counting rods.*

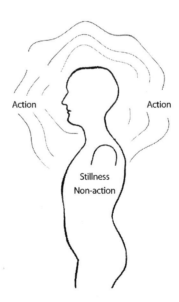

figure 2 *Stillness and Action*

"A good locksmith can *27-2 lock doors so well, even without a lock, no one can open it. 27-3 Good knot-makers use no cords or ropes, yet no one can loosen what they tie together. 27-4 Therefore the saint* exercises his power of Tao and *takes care of everyone and rejects none. 27-5 He* exercises the power of Tao and *takes care of all things and rejects nothing. 27-6 This is called 'following the wisdom'.*"

"The saint does things by broadcasting his power of Tao only, instead of taking action that requires cutting, attacking, addition, displacement, etc.... which, by the way, are very wasteful moves. By radiating the power of Te to tune everything, even the bad, the refuse, the used, can turn into good. It becomes useful and is renewed. There will be no need to discard things or, in this case, to abandon or give up on a hopeless person." Laotzu set down the bamboo twig. But everyone remained standing around him.

Since nobody else spoke, Chong Zen, the scholar from Nan Do asked, "Master, if I have a student who is thick and cannot understand, do I still have a liability to teach him?" He thought of the prince's son in the city he'd just fled. Chong Zen had been forced to spend day in and day out tutoring a boy who had no sense at all. His pupil never finished his lessons, and skulked out the door to ply the kitchen help for more sweets every time the scholar took his eyes away. Although as much as it pained him then to teach the pudgy, slow boy, it nevertheless made his heart sad to remember that executioners had probably killed the poor boy already.

Laotzu replied "*27-7 One who is good at* using the power of Tao in *helping others can be followed by those who do not know how. And those who do not know how* to use the power of Tao *to help others are the followers of the one who knows how.*" The master closed his eyes briefly. Suddenly he opened them and continued, "*27-8 If the leader is not appreciated by the followers, and the followers are not cared for by the leader, and he appears as a clever man, he is indeed lost. 27-9 This is a mysterious secret.*"

Chong Zen bowed and thanked the master. He wondered how this Laotzu had such a knack for answering both spoken and unspoken questions at once. It was as if Laotzu read the whole story from Chong Zen's very mind and gave an answer that encompassed the entire situation.

Could Laotzu have known that his former ruler, Prince Kah Chan, now murdered, had been the victim of his own cleverness? Prince Kah Chan thought that he could silently build his own army, and build secret alliances with neighboring territories without his king knowing. Year after year, Kah Chan plotted with great cleverness for the day he would surprise the king and take the throne of the whole kingdom by force and make Nan Do the new capital city. Prince Kah Chan did not know that the king had informers who posed as Kah Chan's own advisors. For years, the king knew of Kah Chan's plot. He allowed Kah Chan to believe that he was ignorant of the whole affair. Finally the king feared Kah Chan's power grew large enough so that Kah Chan would soon strike. He dispatched his own army to execute Kah Chan and his entire family, so that he could replace him with a loyal nephew. Kah Chan in his arrogance and ambition, never saw the king's counter-strike coming. It was luck that saved Chong Zen and those who fled, as they were warned by the king's own spy who'd posed as a monk in Kah Chan's palace for years.

At the same time, the perceptive Chong Zen could see a third meaning in what Laotzu said. The sage warned those who taught about the Tao not to do so from their own cleverness. It seemed as if the teaching itself was done through the wisdom of this mysterious power.

Chong Zen thought to himself, "Such a strange man this Laotzu! If I were younger, I would be his disciple and learn how to answer many questions at once with a simple handful of words."

While Chong Zen mulled over the sage's words, the prince realized he'd exhausted all but one of his questions for the night, and since the guests were already standing, he suggested they finish for the evening. He wanted a moment with the sage alone.

The guests seemed surprised that this evening's lesson ended so soon. Nonetheless, they made their gracious farewells.

When the room cleared, only KoWu and Laotzu remained.

KoWu stepped to the sage's side and said in a low voice, "Master, I saved my last question for when we would be alone. Last night you allowed me to feel this power of Tao. May I feel it again?"

"You will feel it again," answered Laotzu. "But when you feel it again, it will be as a result of your own efforts."

Laotzu bowed to the prince and retired to his cottage near the stable.

KoWu stood alone in the hall for quite some time, looking down at Laotzu's diagrams still in the sand. He spoke low to himself, "I hope that you are right, Teacher, I hope that you are right."

Chapter Twelve
A Scholar Seeks Employment

The day dawned with a gray overcast sky that hinted at rain but never surrendered any. Without the sun, the people of West Peace could feel the harsh chill of autumn as it warned of approaching winter. For the first time, heavy woolen robes covered the usual daytime attire, at least during the cool of the morning.

Chong Zen woke early. He stayed in the outer rooms of the palace along with the other prominent Nan Do officials who sought asylum in West Peace. A servant left a pail of water outside his door, and Chong Zen carried it into his room. He washed himself meticulously, and stroked oil through his hair before tying it back. His hairline, streaked with gray, was starting to recede, leaving his arched brows looking quite prominent. Chong Zen gave the appearance of intelligence in his narrow face and contemplative demeanor. The scholar's proud carriage evoked confidence in whatever he said. He was fortunate that way, if unfortunate in others.

If it weren't for the constant political upheavals during Chong Zen's time, he might have found a permanent home where he could produce writings and a following of his own. As it stood, just as he raised his reputation in one kingdom, he was forced to flee to the next.

He opened his trunk and ran his hands over the precious bamboo scrolls he'd brought with him from Nan Do. One scroll contained a small teaching from the new philosopher Confucius, who Chong Zen particularly admired. Under the scrolls were a silk hat and his finest black silk robe and a chain of gold with a pendant of amethyst carved into a dragon's head. He lifted the heavy silk robe from under the scrolls and smoothed it out over his bed.

Chong Zen saved this formal dress for just such an occasion. Today, he would appear before Prince KoWu in response to the ruler's invitation. Chong Zen knew that the prince would undoubtedly expect his commentary on the teachings of the visiting Master Laotzu.

But what could he say? Laotzu's teachings were almost beyond mere philosophy, but neither did they fall into the conventional spiritual beliefs of the day – ancestor worship, and the placating of good and evil spirits. The sage definitely had some sort of power, but it wasn't like the power of shamans who read omens and let spirit beings speak through their bodies. He bore no resemblance to the temple priests and their incantations and bloody sacrifices.

Luckily, Chong Zen knew he could engage the prince well enough if only because he brought news and new ideas from the interior. KoWu was obviously an intelligent man; more intelligent than other rulers Chong Zen had served in the past. Ambitious and obsessed with his title, the scholar admitted, but righteous and effective in an admirable sort of way.

What would he be hired to do, Chong Zen wondered? That boy yesterday was KoWu's son. He seemed made of good material, and quite bright, although a little impulsive perhaps. He would be a good charge for Chong Zen's tutoring.

Chong Zen couldn't understand why the prince made the boy a servant to Laotzu. That seemed highly irregular. Laotzu should be made to serve the prince's son, thought Chong Zen. "Well, customs often appear backwards in these border towns," he shrugged to himself.

The scholar put on his long robe. As he put the pendant around his neck, he debated whether to bring his scrolls or not. "No, better not," he thought. "Better to impress the prince with my own memory."

Chong Zen had a simple and light breakfast of rice and a small fish. He didn't want to be weighed down or dull-minded from food.

Later in the morning, Dai Dong came to his room to escort him to the prince's counsel chambers.

They walked silently together down the long corridors that wound to the other side of the palace. He could see that in this dry northern climate, the trees in the courtyard had to be watered and tended to keep their color. The stonework gave the palace a cold feel. With timber scarce in these lands, most buildings in the north were made from stone. The palace of Nan Do felt much warmer with its wood frame construction, painted walls and lush green gardens.

When they arrived at the counsel chambers, the prince dismissed two local businessmen who had come to him haggling over a property matter. He gave Chong Zen the honor of welcoming him personally. He invited Chong Zen to sit down. KoWu also invited his judicial and spiritual advisors, Po Fu and Fa Tingtz. They would hear and judge the scholar's words and advise whether the prince should offer him a permanent position.

The prince began by asking Chong Zen to recount why his party sought refuge in West Peace.

"Your majesty, as you know, the kingdom of Chou is different from your own. Our prince was not a son of the king, but rather a cousin only. The king violently deposed Prince Kah Chan in favor of a more politically important nephew."

"But surely he could have found another position for the nephew if the prince had done a good job," countered KoWu.

"The prince did a reasonably good job as a ruler; however he invested too much trust in certain advisors who were spies of the king, and told the king of Kah Chan's plans to kill him and move the capital city to Nan Do," reported Chong Zen.

"Interesting! And after watching all of this, what sort of advice would you give a prince about trusting advisors?" the prince fired back in a clever challenge.

"I would say that a prince should surround himself with many voices. Differing views will keep his mind broad and bring to light solutions that he may not have otherwise considered. However, there should always be advisors who speak from the same heart as that of the prince. That way, if he is ever in doubt he should then side with the advisors who share the same convictions as his own," replied Chong Zen.

"Prudent advice, scholar. Do you see any weakness in my choice of advisors?" asked KoWu.

Chong Zen began to perspire at the pointed questions. If he answered honestly would he risk offending the prince? If he gave only flattering answers would he be judged as useless or manipulative?

"I only question why you have so few monks," Chong Zen explained, "and why all but Fa Tingtz hold the exact same opinions on all matters. Most interior princes retain at least three or four spiritual advisors from each of the various temples or from several arcane arts. This gives them the ability to choose among them when a situation arises that begs for a ceremony or an explanation to the people."

"And what, do you judge, is the agreed opinion of my monks as opposed to Fa Tingtz?" The prince enjoyed cornering the scholar into speaking his true mind. How else would he judge whether this was an employee he could potentially trust?

"Well, your monks all hold to the doctrine of the local deities. All through our region, each state, and indeed each village, uses a priest or shaman to supplicate or receive messages from a variety of gods and ancestors. Often, they even make sacrifices of animals, incense, food and sometimes even human lives, to placate these gods. Most of the people believe in these old ways, and are very afraid of the magic that these monks and shamans wield," Chong Zen observed.

"However," he continued, "your advisor Fa Tingtz seems to hold the tenets of the ancient worship of Shang Ti. He counsels you that the supreme heavenly ruler will reward good actions and evil will likewise be punished. Undoubtedly he believes that when we die, we will join the heavenly palace and assume similar advisory and court roles to the ones that we held in life."

Confucius Likened LaoTzu to a Dragon

Fa Tingtz nodded, indicating Chong Zen was correct. KoWu seemed impressed that Chong Zen could make such an accurate evaluation after only a few days at the palace.

"Those are true observations. Fa Tingtz followed me here from my father's kingdom. The monks, on the other hand, are from local families. Because I was not raised in West Peace, many here see me as a foreigner. That is one reason why I married a local woman. To placate my critics and the temple priest, I agreed to give her the final authority over which monks would receive appointments at the palace. She is very devout and has pledged many vows to the temple. Although it ends up that the monks serve here as her consolation to the local priest, I have no trouble ignoring them," KoWu explained. "So how does this differ from the advisors to other rulers?"

"Well there are other ideas and other teachings that are making their way through the interior cities. For example, I had the privilege of meeting a new scholar named Confucius. He believes in some of the old teachings of heaven and the necessity of honoring our ancestors; however, he calls those living to hold themselves to specific virtues and a code of moral conduct. He urges people to adopt filial piety and family responsibilities. He blames us all for abandoning traditional ways and says that this caused the dissolution of the nation into warring states," offered the scholar.

"I have heard a little of the teachings of this Confucius," KoWu admitted. "But it is highly unlikely that he would travel here to share them with us."

"He wouldn't need to, Prince," Chong Zen assured, "For I can teach them to you. These are important teachings to know and are becoming quite popular with many rulers."

"Why?"

"Because they are specific and easily codified. They provide a way of life that the people can understand and follow," answered Chong Zen. "You yourself see that Laotzu's teachings rely on non-action. How can a ruler apply non-action? Confucius offers means for action on the part of the ruler and the people."

"Unlike this 'Tao' our guest Laotzu speaks of," KoWu added.

"Well, frankly, yes."

"Are you saying the teachings of Confucius are more powerful than those of Laotzu?" asked the prince.

"Not at all," replied the scholar. "Just that they are popular and easily understood and adopted. Laotzu speaks of mysteries that fall outside of conventional spiritual doctrines and are too large to be considered mere philosophies. Even Confucius acknowledged Laotzu's awesome power. He once composed the following poem in honor of Laotzu:

> *'Of birds I know they have wings to fly with,*
> *of fish they have fins to swim with, of wild*
> *beasts that they have feet to run with.*
> *For feet there are traps, for fins nets, for wings*
> *arrows, But who knows how dragons surmount*
> *wind and clouds into heaven?*
> *This day I have seen Lao Tzu and he is*
> *a dragon.'*

"If even Confucius speaks so highly of Laotzu, shouldn't we strive to understand and practice Laotzu's teachings instead?" asked the prince.

"One should always strive to broaden one's understanding of all worthy teachings. In one's personal life, the path of higher philosophy is an infinite one. However, in one's public life, practical answers are necessary. Confucius himself admitted the loftiness of Laotzu's Tao, but at the same time bemoaned the possibility of ever reaching it when he once said, 'If I learned the skill of Tao's power in the morning, it wouldn't bother me to die in the evening.'"

Chong Zen prided himself in offering his employers only practical advice that they could use and implement, backing it up with solid recitations.

"I don't know," mused KoWu. "Laotzu seems very clear that this power of Tao he speaks of is attainable by anyone. True, it is hard to understand, but in a strange way it seems simple as well. Perhaps it is so simple, it is like an unpolished gem in a bed of river stones. It is easily missed."

"But gems are only worth something if they are noticed and polished. If they remain in the riverbed, who will care?" Chong Zen replied.

The two men spoke at length. Servants brought in a noonday meal, and Fa Tingtz and Po Fu also had an opportunity to interview the man from Nan

Do. Chong Zen impressed them with his practical wisdom and extensive exposure to the leading teachers of the interior cities. All agreed that he would be an excellent addition to the palace staff, and Prince KoWu went further by assigning Chong Zen as a tutor for his son KoYou.

When the meeting was over, Chong Zen returned to his room in high spirits. When he got there, he found Dai Dong and a team of servants collecting his things.

"You are being moved sir," bowed Dai Dong. "Your new room will be in the family section, next to the quarters of the prince's son KoYou."

Finally, the scholar could exhale. Not only had he done well during the interview and secured employment with the prince, but this life as a refugee was finally over. The insecurity and unsettled nerves that followed him from Nan Do could now be put to rest.

Chapter Thirteen

The Fourth Night with the Taoist Guest

The fourth evening, several military generals joined the assembly. That afternoon, they had finally finished clearing the plains and burning the barbarian bodies. All of the enemy's discarded treasures were safely placed in the appropriate storehouses.

The presence of the generals gave the gathering a more businesslike demeanor as Laotzu entered the room. Instead of scholars and monks filling the cushions closest to the prince, war heroes and stern commanders now flanked him.

The other guests, who'd talked with each other and joked easily during dinner on the previous nights, ate silently tonight – intimidated by the icy soldiers.

As their leader, KoWu behaved like a general, staunchly in command. When he rose to begin the night's inquiries, he issued his question like an order: "Master, how can I apply the power of Tao and make my power of Te strong and able?"

Laotzu countered briskly and briefly, "Always hold on and stay in the power of Tao, aware of the principle of Tao, following the power of Tao. Meanwhile, allow the power of Tao to enter your body, to make your Te strength able."

"But how can I strengthen my Te?" the prince asked in a softer voice. He realized he'd better humble himself with the sage if he expected any answers.

Laotzu smiled and likewise softened his tone. "First, while 28-1 *always* staying *aware that there is the male-like force, yet* you must simultaneously *hold on to the* power of *female-like force as the stream* clings *to the world*. Be aware of the power of Tao and that it acts both in action and stillness. Feel both forces: the male force tending toward action, and the female force tending toward stillness." **(figure 3)**

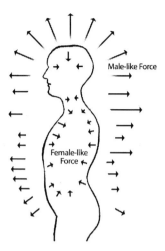

figure 3 *Male /Female Force*

While he explained this, Laotzu stooped down to pick up a bamboo twig from the servant kneeling next to the sand tray. The generals rose and one by one filed in a line around the inside edge of the table where they could assume positions around the sand pit. They clasped their hands behind their backs and gazed down at the sand seriously, as if judging strategies for their next battle.

Laotzu's nimble arm drew the outline of a man with arrows moving both out and in. He looked at the group to see if they could understand. Meanwhile he continued his answer to KoWu.

"Hold your mind and body together as if it were a stream clinging to the face of the world. After your mind and body become 28-2 *like the stream to the world, then the* power of *Te will not depart* from your mind *and* body. Then *one*'s life energy *becomes as if* it were the life energy of *an infant again.*

"Second step, while radiating or broadcasting your Te power, although you remain 28-3 *ever aware of the bright white, still hold onto the core of dark.* In this way, the power of Te works like a candle." *(figure 4)*

At this, Laotzu motioned for a servant to rake the sand smooth. Laotzu then took his twig and drew a candle in the sand.

"You must be aware of the radiation of bright white light, and rely on the core substance, the darkness. Hold onto dark substance and watch the white matter at work."

Bright White
(Mind and Te Power)

Core Substance of Dark
(Body and Te Power)

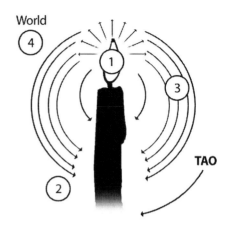

World

TAO

figure 4 *Candle*   **figure 5** *Candle Radiating*

He turned to the proud generals with the instruction: "Broadcast with an attitude of *being very humble towards the world.* 28-4 *Being very humble towards the world, the* power of *Te never changing,* one's power *returns to the state of the infinite.* If your mind and body maintain the state of being very humble, merciful, weak and low, then the 'white' power radiated and broadcasted, will return to your body and mind, or the 'dark' power, and the unchanged Te power will become infinite."

Laotzu now traced lines radiating out from the flame of his sand candle that flowed inward to once again fill the body of the candle. (**figure 5**)

"You should master the skill of recycling your broadcast power back to your mind and body, which stays low and humble," continued the sage, "While you remain 28-5 *aware of* the true meaning of *honor, still remain humble.* This third step refers to applying this process to real world matters, where honor and disgrace are man-made and artificial concepts. This fake energy of artificial thinking consumes the energy of Te broadcast by the saint.

"A saint chooses instead to stay aware of honor, while broadcasting his message through his Te power. At the same time, he will *hold onto the disgrace,* and uses disgrace as the fuel, so he won't consume his power of Te in a wasteful way. This way his Te power remains resourceful."

Laotzu could sense the generals' confusion, so he continued with more analogies:

"If you want to develop the power I speak of, 28-6 *rather be the low valley of the world. Being like the valley of the world, the original* power of *Te within becomes resourceful. And it,* the power of Te, *becomes* as resourceful as the original power of Tao. It's like useful products returning to *the state of the original uncarved block.* The power of Te can then radiate all over the world, as if 28-7 *the original uncarved material can be made into countless useful products* and distributed all over the world.

"28-8 *The saint uses it,* the power of Te, *to lead and rule.* 28-12 *Thus the greatest ruler rules* by doing little, *as if the best trimming cuts little.* The saint rules by broadcasting his message to the people through his power of Te, via the network of the power of Tao. There is no need to displace, install, or add anything. Nothing is wasted."

Laotzu gently set the bamboo twig down in the sand. He knew it would be a challenge to reach these military minds, so hard with determination and self-importance. Since they'd already missed the first three nights, it would be difficult for them to understand what he tried to teach them now.

KoWu did seem to understand at least part of what the sage said, and put forth another question. "Master, after I strengthen and learn to use my Te power and become resourceful as you describe, could I then make the world a better place and be an ideal ruler?"

The teacher put his hand on his belly and laughed. "Ha, Ha, Ha! 29-1 *Can anyone take over the world and improve it? I can see it is impossible.* 29-2 *God made the world, and no one should endeavor to improve it.* 29-3 *If anyone tries to change the world, one will ruin its wholeness.* 29-4 *If anyone tries to hold the world, one will fail and lose it.*"

The master continued as he paced the room, "Understand the fact that all things and people in this world follow the power of Tao. So instead of trying to change the world, the true saint only broadcasts his power of Te to follow the network of the Tao. He fine-tunes his message to make 29-5 *some things lead and other things follow behind.* 29-6 *Sometimes breathing gently, other times breathing hard,* accordingly. 29-7 *Sometimes* to strengthen something when it is *weak,* and *other times* to weaken things when they are too *strong.* 29-8 *Sometimes only trimming things a little, sometimes bringing down the whole thing* when it is necessary. 29-9 *Therefore the saint* just radiates his power of Te and *avoids* dealing with worldly matters by *overdone, wasteful obsessiveness.*"

One of the generals cleared his throat and raised his arm to speak. He looked gruff and concerned. If the prince took this strange teacher so seriously, the old soldier felt compelled to find out Laotzu's position on the military.

The general first bowed to the prince and began, "Master, if Prince KoWu practices this power of Tao to rule, and there is unrest or we are being attacked, should he use military force combined with the power of Tao? Or should I as his general use my military force to fight alongside him?"

Laotzu shook his head. "*30-1Whenever you assist a ruler with* the power of *Tao, do not depend on military force to conquer the world, for the consequences would return very rapidly.* Look at the facts: 30-2 *Thorn bushes spring up wherever the army has been; famine years follow after a great war.*"

Laotzu clearly shocked the general with his answer. Two of the other generals at the table began to whisper to each other, frowning. Laotzu, undaunted, faced them directly. "30-3 *If responding by force, just react and repel the offender.* 30-4 *Never depend on force to conquer.* 30-5 *After you achieve goals, never glory in them. After you achieve goals, never boast. After you achieve a goal, never be proud.*

"30-6 *Achieve goals, because there is no other alternative.* After all, isn't it better to 30-7 *achieve goals with no coercion* or strength? 30-8 *Anything being strong is followed by decay.* 30-9 *This is not how Tao's* power *works.* 30-10 *Whatever goes against the principle of Tao will meet with an early end.*"

The generals looked away from Laotzu and toward KoWu. They frowned in unison to their prince. Would he allow this sage to decry the prudence of a strong military? What nonsense did this guest promote? Their piercing eyes demanded the prince clarify this craziness.

KoWu realized he stood in a precarious situation. While he himself had experience in discussing abstract concepts with an open mind, his generals took everything very literally. They could not accept Laotzu's alternative view. It was up to KoWu to smooth the friction in the atmosphere. He thought if he could phrase his next question just so, it might force Laotzu to at least partially agree that the military is necessary.

To that end, the prince offered: "Master, my father the king trained me to be strong. He made sure that I had years of training with famous warriors to be a superior general. I only know how to lead my army and fight with the enemy. I respond when I am attacked. Isn't this only natural and since natural, following the power of Tao?"

But Laotzu wouldn't budge. He made no effort to placate the worried generals by accepting KoWu's proposition. "31-1 *Military forces are instruments of disaster; all creatures hate them.* 31-2 *Therefore those possessing the power of Tao never come close to them.*"

Before the gathering degenerated into a full-blown argument, providence intervened.

At that very moment, Pen Hei ran out of bamboo planks, and asked that the meeting pause so that he could gather more. Sensing the tension in the room, KoWu urged everyone to break for a walk in the palace gardens.

As the guests left the hall for their intermission, the scribe bundled the precious bamboo planks containing the notes from the evening and carried them to the record house for stringing and preservation. It was a long walk down to the records cellar, and this week, the cellar was a mess. The records keeper, Wei Lon, received another bundle of carvings that very afternoon – a commentary on war by the prince's second general, Hwang Yi.

Hwang Yi led the company charged with burning the barbarian horses and clearing the debris from the holocaust. Deeply affected by watching the terrible wind storm and its swift penalty of death, Hwang Yi was greatly moved by seeing the plains littered with so many of his enemy – soldiers all, just like him. With no other way to grieve, he wrote his reflections on the matter of war. He'd given them to the records keeper to set aside as part of the log of the week's events.

Bamboo Scroll

Pen Hei, bursting through the door in a rush, startled Wei Lon who'd dozed off over his work. The scribe thrust the bundle of inscribed planks from Laotzu's teaching at him, while at the same time barking orders for more bamboo. The poor flustered Wei Lon put the scribe's notes on the same table as Hwang Yi's commentary. After Pen Hei grabbed the new bundle of bamboo, and headed for the door, he demanded "Attend to the notes from the prince's guest right away, they must be your top priority while Master Laotzu is here!" The flummoxed records keeper set to work immediately, completely forgetting Hwang Yi's commentary. He mistakenly mixed Hwang Yi's notes together with the evening records from Laotzu's talk.

Hwang Yi elegantly wrote:

"31-3 *Gentlemen prefer to sit at the left,*

But during war prefer to sit at the right.

31-4 *Army weapons are instruments of fear; they are not a gentleman's*

choice. He uses them only when he has no choice.

31-5 *And he treats the entire action with a peaceful mind;*

Even victory brings no cause for rejoicing.

31-6 *For to rejoice in victory leads to delight in killing:*

For to delight in killing, you can never win the world.

31-7 *On celebrated occasions prefer the left,*

On mournful occasions prefer the right.

31-8 *The second general stands on the left,*

The chief general on the right.

31-9 *This indicates that war is conducted as if it were a funeral.*

31-10 *When many people are being slaughtered,*

They should be mourned with a sorrowful heart.

31-11 *A victory celebration must be observed as if it were a funeral.*"

Upon later readings at the prince's court, Hwang Yi's reflections made an odd counterpoint to Laotzu, who had gone to great lengths to oppose the use of military action or force. Laotzu stressed over and over that one must connect to the power of Tao, and apply the power of Tao to take care of matters – the so-called non-action power.

Yet in honor of the great victory and in honor of his second general, the prince ordered that Hwang Yi's commentary remain in the notes so they all could remember the massacre of their enemy with humility.

The inclusion might also smooth over the ruffled feathers of his other generals who developed a keen distrust of this foreign master. Unfortunately, Hwang Yi wasn't there that night. He would have been a moderating voice between Laotzu and the militant generals. Things might not have turned into controversy had Hwang Yi been able to intervene with his temperate views and eloquent poem.

*   *   *

Once Pen Hei returned with more bamboo, the guests meandered back to the hall. The fresh air had cooled the hot tempers of the generals, and KoWu decided that perhaps he could broach the topic of military force once more so that Laotzu could further defend his position.

KoWu opened the second portion of the evening talk by acknowledging, "Master Laotzu, you clearly have different views on war than that of my honored generals. But Master, if I rule by the power of Tao, instead of military force, how would it work?"

Laotzu tried to explain, "The power of 32-1 *Tao is forever undefined.* 32-2 *Even though it is minute*, it is the almighty power and *no one can ever dominate it.*

"32-3 *If kings and lords could possess it,* the power of Tao, *the ten thousand things would naturally follow.* And 32-4 *heaven and earth would come into harmony* and blessings would be granted *and sweet rain fall.* 32-5 *The people would* need no more direction and all would *get along well in harmony.*"

KoWu nodded but carried Laotzu's scenario one step further. He asked, "After the power of Tao prevails, we can agree the people might get along. But don't I still have to issue some rules, set some rank, grant titles, and tell some people what to do?"

Laotzu partially conceded, "Well, 32-6 *once the initial organization is established, there are many names;* but under the power of Tao *there will be no more need for names.*

"32-7 *The wise know restraint.* 32-8 *Knowing restraint prevents destruction.* Restraint means holding back from acting on your own and further complicating the natural order of the world. 32-9 *The* power of *Tao in the world behaves just like a stream flowing home to the rivers and oceans.* How can you improve on it? Better to restrain yourself from trying."

Thank goodness the topic had changed to a less controversial one. KoWu thought it best to continue on this new note. He asked, "Master, it seems to me that one must know how to apply the power of Tao to lead, to govern, and also know when to stop. How do I learn the restraint you say is so important?"

Laotzu tossed his flywhisk across his breast where it tapped against his own shoulder. "Following the power of Tao, you'll find that 33-1 *to know others leads to true wisdom.* Following the power of Tao, you'll also find that *to know the self leads to enlightenment.* Follow the power of Tao to 33-2 *overcome others and you possess true force;* following the power of Tao *to master the self develops true strength.*

"33-3 *He who* follows the power of Tao *knows he has enough* and *is truly rich.*"

KoWu leaned across the table and opened both his hands. He lifted his hands to all the luxury that surrounded them in the hall: the tapestries, the statues, the servants, and the banquet tables. "Master, it is hard to know when to stop since the whole world is driven by competition and possessions. Most people never have enough. It would be hard to stop and say 'it is enough' while all others continue to engulf more and more. What should I do?"

"Follow the power of Tao 33-4 *determined to execute* results, and you'll find the ability to *possess true will power.* In that power you will have everything you need. 33-5 *He who stays in* the *principle* of the power of Tao *endures.* 33-6 *Those who* follow the power of Tao and the power of Te *continue to prevail after the body dies* and *possess true eternal life.*"

One of the generals, now more at ease with the conversation, grew curious enough to ask, "Master, how can one stay with this power of Tao and succeed?"

Laotzu walked slowly toward the east side of the table where the general sat. He patiently answered, "You must know the way the power of Tao works: then you can stay with the Tao without losing it. 34-1 *The great Tao flows everywhere, reaching to the left and to the right.* 34-2 *The ten thousand things thriving on it; it nourishes everything with no reserve.* 34-3 *It accomplishes its purpose and makes no claim.* 34-4 *It raises the ten thousand things, and yet doesn't claim lordship.* 34-5 *It can be called very small.* 34-6 *While all the ten thousand things return to it, it still claims no lordship.* 34-7 *It can also be called very great.* 34-9 *It does not claim its greatness, and is therefore truly great.*

"You must realize that when you try to stay in the power of Tao, you must let the power of Tao enter your body and perform its great tasks. When what you want is accomplished, you must bear in mind that it is the power of Tao, not you, that did it."

Another commander sitting next to KoWu was less accommodating to the sage. He looked irritated and challenged, "Master, are you saying that if the ruler only practices the power of Tao everything will be fine?"

Laotzu replied, "Of course. You see the Tao ensures that everything will unfold with the ruler taking no action. All things and 35-1 *all men will come to him who possesses the great formless* power of Tao. 35-2 *Those who come, they all enjoy harmony, rest, happiness and peace.* The power of Tao will attract people just like 35-3 *passersby may stop for beautiful music and gourmet food.*

"I see this is hard for you to understand. That is because 35-4 *once you try to describe the Tao, it seems without substance or flavor.* 35-5 *It cannot be seen, it cannot be heard, and yet one can continue to tap it.* It is the source of power *and it cannot be exhausted.*"

The generals shook their heads and waved their hands at Laotzu in dismissal. Laotzu could not have made a worse impression on them. They quietly deliberated whether to walk out of the room.

KoWu didn't want the evening to end with the generals thinking Laotzu was an idiot, or that he himself was an idiot for admiring the sage. He had to think of a question that would hold the generals' interest for just a few more minutes until he could formally adjourn the gathering. He decided to press Laotzu by asking the question that he knew was on his generals' minds. He said, "Other states are rising and becoming strong. I have enemies, especially in the neighboring kingdom of Bou Yang. Master Laotzu, how can I deal with them and protect my state?"

Just as KoWu predicted the old soldiers sat back and nodded. At last the prince got to the point of the matter with the fancy-talking sage, they thought. Bou Yang was of great concern. Everyone knew Bou Yang's king, Lu Kuang, envied the lucrative trade West Peace enjoyed. If they dropped their military strength for one minute, Lu Kuang would soon be here beating down their gates.

But the generals would find no solace in Laotzu's answer, for he replied, "Do not mind what other states are doing. The power of Tao will take care of it all. Look at the power of Tao at work. 36-1 *To make* a state *shrink,* the power of Tao will *allow it first to expand. To make* a state *weak,* the power of Tao will *allow it first to be strong.* 36-2 *Before* a state *can be cast down,* the power of Tao *must first allow it to be raised.* 36-3 *Before seizing* the state, the power of Tao will *first give.*

"**36-4** *This is true observation* of how the power of Tao works: *Soft and weak will overcome hard and strong* and stay firm in the power of Tao. **36-5** *Just like fish cannot leave deep waters,* such *powerful weapons,* like the power of Tao, *cannot be visually displayed to others.*"

The old soldiers sat still as stones, frowning with their arms folded across their chests.

As he finished, Laotzu turned to generals and bowed. Lifting his head with a smile, he made apologies to the prince announcing that he would have to retire early since it was so late. The commanders glared from their table at Laotzu's back as the sage turned and left the room alone. Then they turned their stares toward the prince in disbelief that he would entertain a man with such ridiculous notions.

KoWu knew this had been an uncomfortable night for everyone. He told himself that he would give the generals new assignments for the next few nights to avoid repeating this evening's tension. He thanked the generals for their attendance and commended them for their excellent work at clearing the plains so swiftly. He bowed and made his way quickly to his chambers to avoid further discussion.

"Well, let's hope there's only one bad night out of nine," thought the prince. He'd best keep these evenings to the scholars, monks and nobility. His generals did better holding swords than holding their tempers, and Laotzu couldn't be budged in his position on war.

Chapter Fourteen

Laotzu's Marketplace Adventure

The next morning, KoYou arrived just in time to wash Laotzu's bowl from his simple breakfast of boiled grain and wild herbs. Soon afterwards, Dai Dong and a guardsman knocked on the door to the cottage.

"Excuse me, Master," Dai Dong bowed. "Prince KoWu and the queen request that you accompany them this morning so that they may show you the city."

"Oh? That would be fine. I haven't been out of these palace walls since I arrived. I've heard so much about the fine marketplaces of West Peace. It will be fun to take a look," Laotzu said. He looked over at KoYou with a raised eyebrow.

"Oh no, Teacher, I'll let you go by yourself today with my parents," said KoYou. "I already know enough about this town."

"You never know son," Laotzu winked. "It could be an adventure!"

"Thanks anyway," KoYou declined, rolling his eyes. Some adventure, he thought, shopping with his parents.

Later, Laotzu met the prince and Zhu Xiao Hua in the outer courtyard. A bevy of attendants accompanied them. Several guards would escort the touring party through the West Peace streets.

The palace gate opened onto the main road, which teemed with activity. Wagons and carts hauled cargo to and fro while camels and donkeys bellowed. Their masters added to the noise, hawking their day's wares.

The royal party made its way down the most prosperous avenue in town. They stopped to inspect samples brought out of tidy shops by well-dressed silk merchants, herb and spice traders. Several of the merchants offered the prince and Laotzu gifts of their finest goods, which KoWu waved aside. He didn't want to burden the shop-owners with demands of favors today, and Laotzu had no interest in the gifts.

Foremost on the queen's agenda was a stop at the largest of the local temples. Zhu Xiao Hua was the temple's most prominent patron, and her family had worshiped there for many generations. After her rescue from the barbarians, she visited even more often to pay her vows.

They could see the ornate roof from several blocks away. As they got closer, Laotzu saw that the temple's stonework was even finer than that of the palace. Painted with scenes of terrible demons and conquering heroes, the temple stood as a shrine to several local deities. Like so many other regions, the people here worshiped a series of local gods. The gods were created from old legend and myth; others were deified ancestors now said to watch over West Peace.

As they approached, a gnarled, thin man floated down the stairway to welcome them. He wore a high-collared robe of black, adorned with colorful embroidery and pearl beads. Although his face looked gaunt and his back bowed, the priest's mesmerizing eyes and chiseled profile betrayed that he must have been handsome in his youth.

"Your majesties," he bowed first to Zhu Xiao Hua and then to Prince KoWu. "I am honored by your visit." Several gold rings embossed with magical symbols and gems encircled his bony fingers. "Ah, Master Laotzu. I have heard much about you. I hope that you will pay your respects to our local gods today, it would be an honor to our faithful people."

Laotzu remained still and quiet. The obsequious priest waited for Laotzu to answer, but soon realized that he waited in vain. "Ah! Well, then do come in. We are praying for an easy winter."

They followed the priest's dark robes up the stairs and into the ornate temple. The slick floor gleamed with inset mosaics of marble and polished gems. The wooden beams, carved with fearsome dragons and smiling faces, peered down to intimidate worshipers. An altar dominated the temple hall, and to this altar the priest knelt. The massive table could barely be seen under piles of gold coins, silks, incense and valuable statues. In the center of the altar stood a solid gold image of a fearsome god who held fire in each palm. Smaller gods made of gold looked up to him offering flowers and gifts.

The priest's voice now echoed up to the rafters calling out prayers in an ancient tongue. He pled for favor from the gods for mild weather and enough rain during the upcoming winter. He begged for protection against the fearsome demons that haunted those who didn't pay respects to the gods. He fell prostrate before the altar as he mumbled incantations to the floor.

KoWu and Laotzu stood silently, but several of the guard and Queen Zhu Xiao Hua also knelt and prostrated themselves, mumbling the refrains of prayers they'd learned as children.

When the priest arose and turned to face them again, he looked genuinely moved. "The gods are troubled today. I don't know why. I hope we will not see drought this winter. There are spirits of the dead barbarians who threaten to snuff out the lives of new babies in revenge for their defeat. We must pray for the protection of the gods more than ever before."

"Oh dear," said the queen. She grabbed the priest's hand with her own. Letting go, she reached under her robes and pulled out a small silk purse and offered it to the priest.

"Your majesty," cooed the priest. "Nothing pleases the gods more than a ruler who honors them with their offerings." He made a great show of lifting the purse to heaven, and turned and laid it at the center of the altar in a place of honor before the golden fire god.

Laotzu could see KoWu biting his lip. The prince obviously indulged his devout yet gullible wife.

The temple, an important landmark in the city, garnered the support of a large majority of influential people. KoWu knew the priest was oily and his prognostications rubbish, but what could he do? If he opposed the priest openly, the people might rebel. The priest consistently referred to KoWu as "our foreign prince" in public. He wanted the people to remember that KoWu was not born in West Peace so that they would maintain an air of mistrust. KoWu despised him.

The priest returned to the group. "Master Laotzu," he inquired with exaggerated courtesy. "They say you worship a new god named Tao. What does your God do?"

"Gods will attract things that are like them. Your gods of gold attract gold. The Tao attracts that which is its own," Laotzu gave a small smile to the priest, but no bow, and turned to leave the temple. His enigmatic answer and wordless exit left the priest standing awkwardly with his mouth agape.

KoWu grinned at Laotzu's clever retort, and at the priest's embarrassment. He also nodded a small bow before joining Laotzu outside. The touring party followed Master Laotzu down the temple steps, leaving the embarrassed priest to stand alone.

Zhu Xiao Hua, so proud of her city temple, felt caught between the touring party and her priest. She stood at the top of the stairs not knowing which way to turn. She had no idea why Laotzu wouldn't worship here, or at least give the priest a small level of respect.

The priest pulled the queen aside once the rest of the touring party moved out of earshot. "Careful, your majesty," warned the priest. "I have reason to believe your visitor has evil powers and is a liar!"

"What?" asked the worried queen.

"People are saying he performs tricks and wonders and teaches this thing he calls Tao. I know for a fact that he took credit for the storm that killed the barbarians. But that very morning I had made a great offering and lit many candles to our gods. I gave them the gold you yourself left and said a special prayer for protection for our city against the barbarians. All of a sudden, a great flash of light exploded over the altar, and I knew our gods would answer our prayers and protect us. Our gods routed the barbarians, not this Tao he speaks of!"

"I'm worried," the queen confessed. "My husband and son are both caught in his spell. They can think of nothing but this Tao and talk of nothing but Master Laotzu all day."

"Be very careful my queen," advised the priest. "Guard your faith in our gods securely from this dangerous influence."

The queen again embraced the priest's jewel-laden hand with her own and thanked him for his warning. Her guard waited at the bottom of the steps to escort her to rejoin the touring party. "I'm no longer interested in touring with them," she announced. " Give them my regrets and say I'm tired. I will go home immediately."

As Zhu Xiao Hua returned to the palace, Laotzu, KoWu and the rest of the group walked along the lane beside the temple. The blind, the lame, and various diseased or elderly beggars sat along the edge of the road, hoping that temple worshippers might throw them money or food in penitence to the gods.

They moaned as the wealthy group passed, each looking more pitiful than the next. KoWu, embarrassed at the terrible state of the poor souls who had nowhere else to go, ordered a servant to return to the palace and bring a bag of grain for each of them. Laotzu merely gave each beggar a kind smile or a nod as he passed.

At the end of the temple lane, the prince, Laotzu and their companions turned down a more colorful street. Jugglers and stilt-walkers entertained the

The Busy Market Streets of West Peace

crowd, begging copper coins for their talent. Several tents boasted fortune-tellers or astrologers. Laotzu stopped in front of a man who said he could make fire spring from water and read the future in its flames. As the group gathered around the man's table, he brought a shallow pot of water and placed it on the center of the table. KoWu threw a silver coin into the basket next to the table and said, "tell the visiting sage Laotzu his future!"

The man hummed himself into a trance. Rocking back and forth, he waved his long sleeved arms back and forth over the shallow pot. In the blink of an eye, the surface of the water in the pot erupted in a flame. The flame turned blue and the man leaned over to peer into its secrets, muttering "Laotzu, Laotzu…" Suddenly, the blue flame jumped up and licked the man's face, singeing his eyebrows.

"Youch!" The man jumped up and his sleeve caught fire as well. He flailed and stamped as guards reached for a blanket to cover him and extinguish the flame. "I'm sorry, I'm sorry, it didn't work, it didn't work…." sobbed the poor fortune-teller covering his scorched face with his robe and scurrying into his tent.

The prince and the touring party left him to recover inside his tent. KoWu turned to Laotzu and said "How unfortunate, I've heard that man is pretty good at telling the future."

"Don't worry, he's not hurt. Actually, what he does is an easy trick," remarked Laotzu. "But the Tao is too big to see in a fortune-teller's flame. It is the origin of all power, and so a lesser power will lose potency in its presence. It is like lighting a candle on a hot and sunny day."

They continued down the winding, noisy alley. It had been only five days since Laotzu's arrival in West Peace and he had spent the entire time inside the palace walls. Nonetheless, he'd amazingly become quite a celebrity among the people in the marketplace. As they walked, they saw a storyteller recounting the tale of Laotzu and his pet tornado. He wove a tale of the tornado battling the barbarians to wide-eyed children whose mothers threw copper coins in the storyteller's basket.

Laotzu stopped in front of an old woman's cart. She sold herbal pills and elixirs meant to cure diseases and bad luck. She now crowed, "Buy your Power of Tao pills here! Made from a recipe from Laotzu's own mother! Two silvers a dozen. They will give you power of Tao, just like they worked for Laotzu!"

Laotzu looked at the old wrinkled herb woman, "May I try one?"

The cranky old woman barked, "No samples! These are very rare pills made from Laotzu's own family recipe. They give great power of Tao. The same power Laotzu used to make the storm!"

Laotzu replied, "I will give you a gold coin for one."

"You can have a hundred for a gold coin!" she replied. "Then you will have great power of Tao." She, like most villagers, had never really seen Laotzu's face, and had no idea who bargained with her now.

"I only need one," Laotzu answered. At Laotzu's cue, KoWu dropped a gold coin in to the woman's basket.

Laotzu chose one of the hand-rolled sticky brown pills arranged on a special bronze platter. He closed his eyes, popped the pill into his mouth and chewed it. "Hmmmm… mint…ginseng…and cow dung? That's a strange cure." He opened his eyes and told the herb woman quite seriously and sincerely, "These pills will not give you power of Tao, but they might greatly confuse the liver. My mother never showed me this recipe."

The whole touring party laughed and the old woman gasped. She realized that the sage Laotzu himself stood before her. She hurriedly put her platters of pills and vials of elixirs back into her cart and pushed it quickly down a back road and out of sight.

KoWu apologized. "Teacher, I'm sorry you see the worst of our city today. As I told you, this is a complicated border town. It is not easy to maintain order. Most of our merchants are honest people."

"Oh, don't worry," assured Laotzu. "I am enjoying this adventure immensely!"

KoWu should have saved his apology, since their small group soon came to a tent offering much worse than the old woman's pills. A stout man sat on a rug outside a crimson canopy. A draped woman stood at the curtain of the tent with her leg perched suggestively on the stout man's knee.

"Come in and learn the secret power of Tao!" the woman beckoned the prosperous group. "The Master Laotzu showed me how he creates the power through ancient bedroom arts."

The men in the group stifled laughter, as their faces turned red.

"When did he show you this?" asked Laotzu, stepping forward toward the woman who obviously did not recognize him.

"The sage does not spend all his time at the palace!" replied the sultry woman. "He comes to my tent after the palace banquets and shows me his real secret for making tornados."

"And you can teach this to others?" Laotzu inquired.

"What Laotzu transmitted to me, I can transmit to you for fifty silver coins" she replied.

One guard leaned over to another and whispered, "What she transmits you wouldn't want and your wife would be very angry about it!" The two men doubled over with laughter.

Laotzu turned around and scratched his head. He dropped his chin and put his hands on his hips, looking very sad.

KoWu turned to his guest and said, "Why does this woman's lies make you look so sad Master? Nobody believes her."

"Oh," said Laotzu turning to the woman so she too could hear his answer. "I am just sad because if I did make tornados in her tent last night, I must not have done a very good job. Otherwise I would have remembered the evening and she would remember my face this morning!"

Everyone roared with laughter at the sage's clever retort. The woman and her hawker realized they'd been duped by Laotzu himself, and quickly drew down their canopy. "No more customers today!" shouted the squat, pig-faced man. They could hear the woman shriek with anger inside her tent as the palace group continued their marketplace tour.

After they'd walked only a few yards past the harlot's tent, they saw an old man lying against the wall of a tumbledown storage shed. His torn clothes barely hid his red skin, ravaged with sores and boils from a severe wasting disease. Clearly the disease had spread to the man's mouth as well, for he could barely form the words to call "Help me, please!"

Laotzu stopped and looked down into the man's eyes.

"Oh great Master, help me please! My sickness makes it impossible for me to work or even to eat anymore."

"How did you know who I am?" Laotzu asked the poor sufferer.

"I heard a great master had come to our city, and I saw you here next to the Prince. When you looked at me, I knew you were the great master they speak of. Master, you can help me, please help," the poor man's voice withered as he stared up hopefully at the sage.

Laotzu closed his eyes and raised his palms upward. Slowly he lowered his left palm and aimed it into the old man's chest. The old man gasped and closed his eyes.

"I feel it pulling and tingling, like a great river of invisible water washing my skin," cried the old man. After only a moment or two, he opened his eyes and looked at his arms. He, as well as the touring party, could see the welts and boils shrink while the redness subsided into a healthy amber tone. The man's mouth soon became clear of sores, his lips moist and pink. He exclaimed clearly and strongly, "Master I thank you. You used your power to heal me!" He fell prostrate at Laotzu's feet.

KoWu and the guards stood speechless. They'd never witnessed such a miraculous healing.

Laotzu looked down at the old man. "No need to bow, friend. I did not heal you. Your sincerity was so great when you asked for help that it reached the vast and subtle net that is the power of Tao. The Tao is mercy and tenderness and when you touched it with your sincerity, the power of Tao used my body to remove the illness from you."

"I can't understand such things," cried the healed man. "But I know that I was weak and helpless for so long, and had no other hope. When you looked at me, I gave up every other idea than to reach your ears with my plea. Thank you."

Laotzu reached down and patted the man's shoulder. KoWu bent down and pressed a silver coin into the man's palm. No one in the group had words to express their wonder.

Later, when KoWu, Laotzu and their companions were farther down the road, KoWu turned to Laotzu and asked, "Master, we saw many people begging today. Many of them were even sicker and more pitiful than the man you just healed. If you have such great power, why did you not heal them all?"

Laotzu pursed his lips and squinted. He struggled for the right explanation. "It is like I told that man. It was his own sincerity as he asked for help that reached the net of the power of Tao."

"What do you mean, 'net'," KoWu asked.

"The power of Tao is like a net or like a vast spider's web that penetrates through all things in the entire universe. The Tao, like a spider, can feel when anything touches its web. Like a spider, it responds instantly when it senses a connection with its network. But the Tao, of course, is not a spider, but rather a conscious being with the nature of tenderness, mercy, compassion and care. So when someone touches the network of the Tao with true inner sincerity, the power of Tao will respond according to its nature," explained Laotzu.

"So those other beggars and sick ones were not sincere?" KoWu asked.

"That's correct. They may truly be sick and helpless and sad, but something within them is not sincere or blocks their true and humble cry for help. That is why I could not respond. They did not call to me and ask my help. If I try to help them without that connection to the power of Tao, it either would not work or I would act outside the flow of the Tao."

"What does that mean, Master? How can you act outside the flow of the Tao if you help someone?"

"The Tao has its own ways, plans and reasons, and to access and stay in the power of Tao, one must flow with the power of Tao. To act from your own ideas of good and bad, right and wrong, can put you outside of the flow of the power of Tao, or interfere with the flow of Tao. That is what I try to teach you when I tell you about non-action," the sage explained. "But now you trick me into answering more questions. You should save these questions for tonight!"

KoWu bowed apologetically to the sage.

On the party ambled, past carts and wagons full of fruits, vegetables, medicines and lucky charms, until they came to the end of town. At the end of the road loomed a rather large, windowless building with two huge, bare-chested men guarding the door. The well-muscled guards looked very formidable.

"What's this?" asked Laotzu.

"Oh," said the captain of the civil guard. "This is Zhi Tzi's training academy for the martial arts. It is very exclusive, and the master is famous in these parts."

"Really," replied Laotzu. "What do they teach?"

One of the bare-chested men stepped forward and shouted, "Our master Zhi Tzi teaches many dangerous skills. He now teaches us Laotzu's Flying Tornado Form. It is the very practice Laotzu used to get his terrible martial arts power that killed all the barbarians."

"Can I learn this Laotzu's Flying Tornado Form?" asked the unrecognized sage. It seemed that Laotzu had a knack for maintaining his anonymity today.

"Only the best fighters can learn it. You may be too weak," replied the bare-chested man, leaning forward and wrinkling his upper lip to intimidate Laotzu.

KoWu stepped between the bully and the sage. "Get your master and we'll talk," ordered the prince.

The muscleman did recognize the prince, of course, and bowed apologetically as he went inside to fetch his master. When Zhi Tzi came to the door he bowed to the prince and invited the group inside to watch the training.

They soon found themselves in the dark school's arena. Several strong men, covered in perspiration, worked in a large pit of sand lit by a circle of torches. They swung long slings around in circles. A heavy stone weighing twenty pounds or more rested in the pocket of each sling. Each man would spin the sling around five or six times until his arms collapsed from the weight of the stone, or until he stumbled from dizziness.

The school's master leaned over to the prince, ignoring the old man beside him. "Your Majesty, welcome! This is the special Laotzu Flying Tornado Training. I learned it from the famous Laotzu when I met him in Bright Plain. He took me in as his student and taught me his secrets. It is the same training he uses to develop his power of Tao," the vain con man Zhi Tzi confided.

"Oh really?" KoWu played dumb. KoWu would keep quiet like Laotzu did before with the herb woman and the prostitute and see how far Zhi Tzi would take his lies.

"Oh yes!" added Zhi Tzi. "And what's more I think your son KoYou would be good at this. He has much talent with the sword. You see, by spinning around the heavy stone, my disciples build great strength for the Tornado Form. When they finish with rock training, they spin with their sword, which is much lighter by comparison. They then find that they are fast and unbeatable."

Zhi Tzi stepped forward and yelled for a disciple to toss him his sword. Catching the hilt of a thin blade in mid-air, the master leapt into the center of the torch-lit pit. All of his students bowed and made room as their teacher spun in maddening circles, making his sword dance and whirl with menacing fury.

"He's pretty good!" whispered Laotzu to the prince. "It almost does look like a tornado." KoWu chuckled. Both KoWu and Laotzu enjoyed the unfolding joke on the arrogant self-proclaimed master. "Shhhh...." Laotzu elbowed the prince. "Let me say something now!"

The sage stepped forward into the pit. "Very good, disciple!" said Laotzu applauding.

"What? Who are you!" puffed the master, now out of breath from his rigorous performance.

"Why Zhi Tzi, I'm your master, Laotzu!" the sage pretended to be affronted.

"Oh...oh.... Master!" Zhi Tzi bowed. "Ha...ha...I didn't recognize you since I was so honored by the prince's visit. I... I...." Realizing he'd been caught in his fraudulent game, the con man stood speechless.

"Oh, that's okay," said Laotzu. "You've worked very hard and trained your students well."

The poor swordsman had no idea why Laotzu played along with his story about being his disciple. Perhaps the master pitied him enough to help him save face in this most embarrassing moment. Whatever was going on, Zhi Tzi knew he was now at the old man's mercy.

"Unfortunately I don't believe I had time to teach you everything I know, Zhi Tzi," Laotzu apologized. "There is one rock exercise you never learned!"

"Oh? My honorable master, will you teach me?" Zhi Tzi bowed, his face now red as he worried that his high-paying students and the prince himself might discover the emptiness of his teaching.

"Pick up one of those stones, disciple!" ordered Laotzu, mocking the stern tone of a martial arts master.

Zhi Tzi bowed and went to pick up one of the huge stones out of its sling. He carried it to the master. "Yes, Master Laotzu. Here it is."

"Are you holding it tight?" demanded Laotzu loudly.

"As tight as I can, right here against my chest," answered Zhi Tzi.

Laotzu gently touched Zhi Tzi's shoulder. All of a sudden, the twenty-pound rock that Zhi Tzi cradled grew heavier. His knees began to shake and buckle as the stone bore down on him. He collapsed to the floor with the rock, now feeling as if it weighed a thousand pounds or more, crushing his chest. "Please Master, stop! It's...too... heavy!...uhhhh"

Laotzu dropped his hand, and the stone became light once more. Zhi Tzi's face paled with fright as he rolled over onto his stomach, letting the stone fall into the sand. He panted and collapsed face down in the pit, prostrate in front of Laotzu.

"Be sure to teach your disciples that one, Zhi Tzi," said Laotzu. "They will need it for the Tornado Form."

Zhi Tzi could barely lift his head to watch the prince and Laotzu turn and leave his famous school.

Out on the street, the prince and sage laughed together at the trap Zhi Tzi made for himself. KoWu asked Laotzu "What did you do to him?"

Laotzu replied, "I simply broadcast the message of 'heavy' to his body.

The signal was much finer than that of his own mind and penetrated quite easily. He could not resist the force of 'heavy' pushing his body down."

"Once again, Master, I must apologize for our city. It seems we saw nothing but charlatans and hucksters today. Now they even dare to use your own name and the name of the power of Tao to peddle their wares," said KoWu.

Laotzu didn't seem offended. Instead he replied, "What you have seen today is just the beginning. In the future it will be even worse. There will always be those who use the name of Tao to sell their arts. But what will be worse will be the scores of scholars who misinterpret my words. They will claim to teach the Tao, but without any true knowledge or experience of its power, they will not really understand it.

"They will even found schools, temples, and write great documents to perpetuate their misunderstanding. Unfortunately, because of their confusion, the true teaching and practice of the power of Tao will be lost to many. Well-intentioned seekers will waste precious years of their lives in empty practices and meaningless studies."

KoWu looked straight into the sage's fathomless eyes as Laotzu warned him, "You have been given a rare opportunity to hear, see and feel the truth of the power of Tao. I've given you many of its secrets: secrets that many generations will seek but never find. You know the difference between what is real and what is merely just talk. Hold onto that knowledge, and practice with a sincere heart."

KoWu reflected on Laotzu's words as they made their way back to the palace down the winding market alleys. As the rooftops of the palace came into view, Laotzu turned to thank KoWu. "What an interesting adventure we've had today! But I think when we get back to the palace, I'll rest until we meet this evening."

Turning the corner toward the palace, they spied the same old herb woman again with her same rickety cart. She'd relocated to a new corner and now called, "Buy Laotzu's famous Power of Tao Liver Pills here! Laotzu himself tried one today and said they have the power to heal the liver!"

Laotzu and KoWu lifted an eyebrow at each other and shook their heads.

Chapter Fifteen
The Fifth Night with the Taoist Guest

After bathing and resting from their busy day at the market, his highness and Laotzu met the guests in the palace hall for the fifth night's banquet. Once again Pen Hei the scribe and his aides set up their special worktable, and once again the servants prepared a feast beyond description. But this night, many cushions remained empty, since all of the generals refused to come.

The previous night's arguments on the virtues of war left the generals in such an uproar that they decided tonight would be a fine night to call a special meeting of all the guard to discuss plans for winter patrols on the border. They would boycott that foolish Laotzu. Let the sage spin his fancy words to the scholars and the townspeople. Men would retire to men's business.

The prince, instead of being outraged, hid his quiet relief at their absence. He sent word to the generals that although he was disappointed that they would not be joining the banquet, he thought their plan seemed like a prudent idea and expected a report in the morning.

Back at the palace hall, a core group of guests found places close to the sage's table. On cushions nearest either side of Laotzu sat Abudamancus, Chong Zen, Dao An and Fa Tingtz. The prince remained at the center of the great horseshoe table. The room gradually filled with notable townspeople. Many came for the first time, just to see the legendary master who had caused such a stir in the markets that day.

Once the guests finished their main meal, KoWu rose to welcome them while servants brought sweets and wine. KoWu began the evening, posing a question that probed at the heart of the previous evening's disagreements:

"Master, last night you urged that rulers refrain from conventional action and refrain from military force. Instead, you advised that a ruler should use the power of Tao to rule. My first question to you is this: If kings apply the power of Tao to rule, but still decide or feel impelled to take action to rule, would you agree to let them combine the two?"

Laotzu shook his head and set down his cup to answer. "37-1 *The* power of *Tao prevails* and broadcasts everywhere, yet it does so *without action.*"

"37-2 *If kings and lords firmly possess it, the ten thousand things would* also follow the power of Tao and things would *take care of themselves.* 37-3 *If the ten thousand things start to take care of themselves, kings may still try to act upon them.* Rulers can't seem to leave well enough alone! Maybe they are afraid they would lose their jobs if there were no problems in the world." The guests shared a muffled chuckle. Laotzu followed, "You think you are so talented, KoWu, that the Tao needs your help?" Even the prince laughed when the sage's humor focused on him.

"If I were ruler over the ten thousand things," Laotzu continued, "37-4 *I would place them under the nameless tool*, the power of Tao. *With the nameless tool, they would return to desirelessness.* 37-5 *Achieve without desire; with no action. Without the desire to act there is tranquility, and thereby the world would be at peace.*"

At this, Laotzu paused to push himself gracefully to his feet and wandered about the hall tapping the inside of his palm with his flywhisk.

"The Tao is a void, a self-existing, almighty and eternal conscious being. But when the power of the void is in motion, and the power of Tao put into action, it simultaneously and equally goes in two directions. One direction flows toward the center, and one flows toward the boundary: inward and outward with equal speed and force. Meanwhile, there is the third force, which is in between the two equal powers of Yin and Yang. This third force flows to harmonize and support the two forces accordingly.

"This Yang and Yin inter-reaction, supported by the third force, called the One Chi, or the original Chi, creates and gives form to everything: God, devil, spirit, ghost, space, time, universe, gases, materials of all sorts, plants, animals and human beings. All of the above are saturated and all bathe in the power of Tao. The power of Tao is the ultimate net of heaven. It is huge, invisible, yet inescapable, because each and all are made with the power of Tao. As soon as the power of Tao is in action, the power of the nourishing Yang and the power of the disassembling Yin, form and create everything, visible and invisible. They are kept in harmony by the third power, the Chi, which circulates within, through and around everything." The listeners remained still and quiet now. They wanted to understand Laotzu's words. Nobody so much as raised a cup to his lips.

The sage went on, "Since the power of Tao is used to create everything, a tiny identical piece of the power of Tao is trapped inside the human body.

However, it is quickly downgraded as it starts to decay into a less powerful force. Though less powerful, it is still made of the substance of Tao, the original conscious being. Although it struggles to return to its original state, since the downgrade action is already in process, it turns into the power of what we call the Te.

"Te continues to support the activities of consciousness as it further declines into the void. This human consciousness turns into knowledge that becomes pollution and a burden for the power of Te. This is because men use their consciousness, which comes into contact with the limitations of space and time, to make up a story – a partial truth. This blocks the path that the Te can use to connect and communicate with the power of Tao."

Laotzu looked from eye to eye, trying to see if anybody understood. Much to his surprise, it was KoWu himself who still followed along more closely than the others. Such tenacity and understanding was rare among the rulers he'd seen.

KoWu asked. "You mention we are all born with an identical piece of Tao in us. You say that that is our virtue, but you also indicate it is not a social virtue. I understand that the power of Tao is trapped inside each of us and in each of the ten thousand things. But how can we make this Te power become the Great Te power you speak of if we don't practice social virtue?"

Laotzu answered, "Yes, it's true. I have said that 38-1 *one who possesses the* power of *Great Te doesn't follow the social virtue; he therefore possesses the true* power of *Te.* Does that puzzle you? Some people can realize that social conscience, and so-called goodness, kindness, justice, righteousness, and ritual are all merely man-made rules, not the way the eternal Tao flows. These wise ones try to shut down their sense of that which is false, and dedicate their consciousness to the feeling of the original Te. When they succeed, they allow the Te to change back again and become restored and thus connected back to the power of Tao. These men possess Great Te. 38-2 *One who possesses low* or no power of Great *Te follows the social virtue firmly; he therefore has no* true power of *Te.*"

"Master, I'm still confused," KoWu admitted.

"You see, the man obsessed with social virtue surrounds his consciousness with all of the man-made social rules and rituals that clog up and contaminate his Te power. How can he have any Te power?" Laotzu continued. "38-3 *Men who possess Great Te* power *follow the non-action principle, and need not perform action for virtue's sake.*"

"I still don't understand how a person using the power of Tao can do better than a person who is performing from a sense of virtue," KoWu shook his head.

Laotzu walked to the side of the prince and leaned over his shoulder. "He does better because he lets his Te power broadcast a good message to bless and help people, achieving more than any social virtue could. He does not need to behave and act for 'virtue's sake.' **38-4** *Men who possess low Te* power *must try hard to act and win the result of being virtuous.*

"By the same token, a man will behave different socially if he possesses the power of Te, such **38-5** *men who truly possesses kindness exercise it* through non-action power *and need not perform kindness.*

"On the other hand, **38-6** *men who are truly just exercise justice and take a lot of action to achieve it.* Because justice is merely an artificial concept made up by men."

"Well, Master, it so happens that my new spiritual advisor from Nan Do," The prince gestured toward Chong Zen, "informs me that the highly esteemed master, Confucius, places a high value on proper social conduct and order. He is having much influence in the interior cities. It seems easier for rulers to adopt what he says rather than what you teach. Why can't we rely on social order, defined roles and ritual to keep peace among ourselves?"

Laotzu laughed at the mention of Confucius. "I had this same discussion with my good friend Confucius not long ago. I will tell you what I told him. Try and follow my logic. **38-7** *If a man with a high level of social dignity performs his social task and no one responds, he will roll up his sleeve to repel anyone who disagrees with him.* You see, **38-8** *when people fail to connect with* the power of *Tao, they count only on their own Te* power. **38-9** *When people fail to connect to their own Te* power, *they count on being kind* and hope everyone will follow the rule of being kind to each other. And **38-10** *when kindness is lost, there is justice.* People can only count on the hope that everyone believes in the same idea of justice. **38-11** *When justice is lost, people can only count on social ritual to get along.* **38-12** *Now,* if people depend on *social ritual* to maintain relationships, it *is a lack of faith and loyalty, the origin of the chaotic.*

"After I told him this, I then scolded Confucius for feeding his scholars and followers from only the lower branches of truth. He should know better! But he argued with me that his teachings would help rulers to build peaceful, productive kingdoms instead of the warring, selfish states we suffer under today. That, he said, was his vision. Then I laughed at him, for when he said it was his vision, he proved my point. So I told him, '**38-13** *People claiming to* *have vision only show a flowery embellishment of Tao. It is the beginning of igno-rance.* **38-14** *Therefore a great man stays in the thick faith* – counting on sincerity, dedication to his power of Te, following the power of Tao – *and not on the thin cleverness* of artificial ideas. He rather counts on the true result; *he stays on the result and not on the glory.* **38-15** *Therefore he rejects the latter and takes the former.* This means he rejects artificially constructed ritual and embraces the true original energy."

Chong Zen could contain himself no longer, for he held great respect for the teachings of the popular master, Confucius. "So are you saying Confucius is wrong?" the scholar rose to ask, his voice indignant.

"No, not at all," Laotzu assured him. "His teachings can and will have a great positive effect, much like he envisions. I am just saying there is an even higher way."

The scholar sat down again, calmer now that the sage gave Confucius a measure of respect.

"You must remember that he and I are great friends, and he loves to argue with me. You should hear what he says about my teachings to his followers! Ha!"

Fa Tingtz, who sat next to Chong Zen interjected, "So Master, you only speak of the leaders themselves. Would it be best then for all of us to connect to the power of Tao?"

Laotzu shrugged "Of course! The power of Tao is the absolute, the very original, the only One Power of the universe. It would do well for anyone to restore his connection to the One Power.

"See the fact that **39-1** *these things, from ancient times, all arise from the only One Power*, the power of Tao. **39-2** *Heaven is formed by the only One Power, and is* whole and *clear.* **39-3** *The earth is also formed by the only One Power*, Tao, *and is* whole and *stable.* **39-4** *The gods are all powered by the only One Power*, Tao *and* become whole and *spiritually functional.* **39-5** *The rivers receive the only One Power,* Tao, *and become* whole and *full.* **39-6** *The ten thousand things, created by the only One Power*, Tao, *become* whole and *alive.* Therefore, **39-7** *in order for kings and lords to be* whole, *and followed by their countrymen, they must* also *possess the only One Power*, Tao."

"**39-8** *All these are powered by the only One Power* of Tao. Otherwise, **39-9** *heaven may fall apart and lose its clarity.* **39-10** *The earth may split and lose its stability.* **39-11** *The gods may cease to function spiritually and be invalidated.* **39-12** *The rivers may run dry and lose their fullness.* **39-13** *The ten thousand things may die out.* **39-14** *The kings and lords may lose their leadership and the countries fall.*"

Fa Tingtz nodded, thanking Laotzu for the answer.

"Master Laotzu," the caravan leader Abudamancus rose from his seat next. With a big smile he shook his finger in the air. "It seems that you are saying that everything is already run by the power of Tao. If that is so, then it would make sense to connect to it. After all, I know the value of good relationships with whatever power is in charge!"

The guests' shoulders shook with laughter as the big foreigner poked fun at his own high connections that gave him such influence wherever he traveled.

"Tell me then, how can I receive this only One Power? It might come in handy in kingdoms where I'm less popular," the giant Abudamancus asked playfully.

Laotzu also laughed. But then the sage took advantage of the opportunity to challenge Abudamancus' notions. "The most important thing to do, first, is connect to the power of Tao, then to hold on to it, by being humble and letting the power of Tao run its course. 39-15 *Therefore the high rank is rooted in the low rank.*

"You must understand that everything, and everyone, are all made of the One Power of Tao, regardless whether they are noble or humble, rich or poor. So you must treat everyone equally with sincerity. Understand that 39-16 *the high uses the low as its foundation.*

"39-17 *Therefore*, all Chinese *princes and lords consider themselves 'orphaned,' 'widowed,' and 'worthless,'* They all achieve the highest social ranks, but soon find that they are all alone. They feel lonely and humble. 39-18 *Do they not use low rank as their root? Don't they?*

"On the other hand, 39-19 *if everyone is socially low and humble, then there aren't any socially low and humble around.* By then, 39-20 *no one wants to behave 'nobly' and tinkle like jade or put on humility and clatter like stone chimes.* The artificial ranks and titles prove meaningless."

Abudamancus bowed in appreciation. He knew when his own quick wit met its match. Laotzu effortlessly turned a playful question designed to amuse the party into a lesson encouraging his own humility.

But as lighthearted and gregarious as Abudamancus was, the monk Dao An was conversely serious and reserved. Dao An rose apologetically and inquired softly, "Master, if I try so very hard to practice and connect to the Tao, can I feel the power of Tao at work?"

Laotzu shook his flywhisk back and forth in warning, "No. As soon as you 'try' hard to act, your mind shuts out the power of Tao and you feel nothing of the power of Tao."

"If I shouldn't 'try', what, then, is the proper way to receive the power of Tao?" the monk pressed.

"To start," the sage obliged, "one must understand clearly the way the power of Tao works. First, 40-1 *the* power of *Tao* always *moves toward the direction of returning*: returning to the purest origin, the One.

"Secondly, understand the principle that 40-2 *the* power of *Tao acts with the function of weakening*. Weakening means refining, taking away from, and being rid of contaminants. This is necessary because 40-3 *everything under heaven is created having forms*, by the action of the two forces of Tao: Yin and Yang.

"And yet all *forms* are *created from the* power of the *formless*. The formless represents the origin of the power – pure and everlasting. Therefore the saint always returns back to the original state by connecting to the power of Tao; following the direction of the Tao, riding on the function of the weakening force of the Tao, letting the power of Tao enter his entire body, mind and spirit –- the Te. This transforms his entire body, mind and spirit into the pure force of Tao."

Chong Zen watched Dao An question the sage. The monk undoubtedly grasped a good deal of the sage's teaching, he thought. Undoubtedly, his Minglian Shan training was better than whatever background the local monks possessed. Dao An certainly held his own in this intimidating group. The palace monks, on the other hand, simply huddled together looking threatened; cowed by Laotzu's wisdom. Dao An was a monk that might be good to have as an ally, he thought. With his own position in the palace secure, why not help another unfortunate refugee from Nan Do enjoy similar security? He'd speak to the prince about it in the morning.

When Laotzu and Dao An were finished, Chong Zen decided to make a clever observation of his own.

Chong Zen rose and began with delicate courtesy. "Master, you talk about the power of Tao. It is so powerful, wonderful, and so sophisticated and high level, it seems terribly hard to reach. It is so incomprehensible, I'm afraid people in their ignorance might think it is laughable. Are you ever ridiculed for your teaching?"

Laotzu turned and squinted at the scholar. "Of course. But I find that 41-1 *the top wise men hear of the* power of *Tao and practice it diligently. Average intellects hear of the* power of *Tao and think about it once in awhile. Lower average people hear of the* power of *Tao and laugh out loud.* 41-2 *If there is no big laughter, then it is not referred to as the true* power of *Tao."*

KoWu considered Chong Zen's question. It was true. Embracing Laotzu's teachings could open him up for ridicule. Both his wife and his generals silently criticized him for even considering Laotzu's philosophies. While KoWu could appreciate the master's brilliance and his power, others around him could not. If KoWu practiced as Laotzu taught, things could go rough for him with other people.

The prince was no stranger to ridicule, for he always had his critics. But he felt the need to ask, "Master, indeed the power of Tao is so vague and mysterious, people may laugh at me when I try to practice it. I don't mind ridicule for doing what I know is right. However, is there a way, a guideline that I can use to tell if I am on the right track and on the way to the true power of Tao? The answer may help me avoid much frustration."

Laotzu, again encouraged by KoWu's tenacity, explained, "To approach the power of Tao, one must be aware that the Tao is very subtle and mysterious. 41-3 *Just like it is said: 'The bright path of Tao seems dim.'* As you practice, remember that 41-4 *going forward on the curved road of Tao sometimes appears like retreat.* To work on one's power, the Te, 41-5 *the easy way of Tao seems rough.* 41-6 *The highest* power of *Te always seems like a low valley.*

"After practicing hard and working on your power of Te, when you examine your power of Te you discover that 41-7 *great purity* of the power of Te *seems soiled.* 41-8 *A wealth of* the power of *Te always seems inadequate.* And the more you practice and advance in your power of Te, you start to feel that 41-9 *the strength of the* power of *Te seems weak.* 41-10 *Real* power of Te *seems unreal.* Given all this, don't worry about how others judge your practice. They won't understand. And even beware of yourself if you aren't a little confused!"

"I only ask these questions because you keep insisting that you are leaving," KoWu reminded the guest. "If I practice as you say, I will have no master to help me know if I am on the path of success or on the path of failure. Since you'll be gone, tell me, how should I feel after achieving the Te power?" KoWu drummed his fingers a bit nervously on the table in front of him.

Laotzu answered, "After achieving the power of Te, it's as if: 41-11 *The great square has no corners;* 41-12 *A great work takes a long time to complete;* 41-13 *The highest notes make little sound;* 41-14 *The greatest image has no shape.* 41-15 *The* power of *Tao is hidden and nameless.* 41-16 *Only the* power of *Tao nourishes and brings everything to completion."*

"That's what I mean," cried KoWu. "How do you expect me to figure this out when you're gone if your answers make so little sense? And no, that is not one of my nine questions!" KoWu's frustration began to show.

Like a loyal servant, Chong Zen stepped in to diffuse the tension lest his employer embarrass himself by possibly losing his temper. Clearing his throat, Chong Zen jumped in to ask a relatively harmless question. "Master, I have studied the philosophy of *I Ching*, the Classic of Changes. Does this have anything to do with the power of Tao you talk about?"

Laotzu gave the prince a chance to compose himself. He'd gladly chat with the scholar awhile. The sage calmly answered Chong Zen, "If you are familiar with the *I Ching*, then you will know it discusses various powers and their numeric equivalents. But fundamentally, 42-1 *The power of Tao created the wholeness, the one. And the one flows into two* separate, opposite yet complemented, equal powers. And between the two equal yet opposite powers, there lies the third kind of power, the Chi. *The two powers generate the third power, the three.* Yin power, Yang power and Chi make three powers. 42-2 *And the third kind of power at work begot the ten thousand things."*

Chong Zen continued, "Master, how do the Yin and Yang power work?"

"42-3 *The ten thousand things all carry Yin power and embrace Yang power,"* Laotzu replied. (figure 6)

"Then Master, how does the third power work?" continued the scholar.

"42-4 *Yin and Yang power achieve harmony by combining their two powers through the third: the Chi."*

Laotzu walked over to the shallow tray of sand as a servant handed him a long piece of bamboo. The sage repeated everything he'd just said to Chong Zen, but this time, he drew a picture to illustrate each point. (figure 7) In the time it took for the guests to gather around the sand diagrams, the prince successfully regained his good humor and joined the group. He caught Chong Zen's eye and nodded an inconspicuous "thank-you" to the wise scholar for giving him time to cool off.

While he drew, Laotzu motioned for the servant to smooth the surface again in between each picture so that he could continue with the next.

The scribe Pen Hei alone remained in his seat, thankful for the chance to catch up with his carvings.

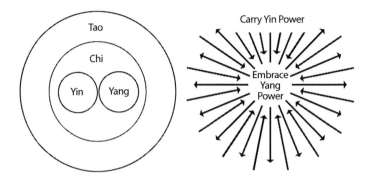

figure 6 *Laotzu Descibes Yin and Yang Power*

Servants also took the opportunity to catch up with their work, clearing away the dinner debris and serving trays from the long tables while the guests studied Laotzu's tracings.

When he finished drawing, Laotzu set down the bamboo twig, signaling the guests to return to their seats.

Prince KoWu continued his questions asking, "Master, could you explain more about the opposite powers of Yin and Yang, how they actually work in our life?"

Laotzu looked happy that the prince rejoined the conversation. He wanted to answer the prince as clearly as he could. "Look, every coin has its opposite side. For example, **42-5** *men dislike being 'orphaned,' 'widowed,' or 'worthless.' But this is how kings and lords regard themselves* because they are high above everyone and are alone. **42-6** *Therefore, things in reduction lead to gain: adding on to it may cause decrease.* It's as if the Yang power must turn into the Yin power, and the Yin power must become Yang power.

"**42-7** *What others teach, I also teach: 'A violent man cannot die peacefully.'* The violence is Yang. People forget about the opposite Yin side of violence: death.

"**42-8** *This will be the root of my teaching.* People must understand that everything has its upside and downside."

"Okay Master, I understand that there are two sides to everything. But that still doesn't explain how this power of non-action is supposed to work. So I am forced to ask the same question I started with this evening, and the same question my generals had last night: Master, how can one possibly apply the non-action power to world matters?" asked KoWu.

Laotzu smiled, not seeming to mind this recurring question. Since it was a key concept, he offered yet another description. "It is easy, just apply the power of Tao and broadcast it to the world, for the power of Tao is the most refined power. It is invisible and as such, 43-1 *the most refined* power *travels freely, even through the most dense* object."

Surprisingly, of KoWu's palace monks, Hon Su Tz, chose to speak. This was the first time one of the monks had the courage to do so. As a group, they didn't have the intelligence, much less the courage to confront or question the sage. They simply listened every evening and then ran back to the temple priest with a full report.

Earlier that day, the temple priest informed the monks that Laotzu had greatly embarrassed him that morning by insulting him in front of the royal family. He asked the monks if they would do the gods a favor and watch for any inconsistencies in the sage's remarks.

Hon Su Tz thought he cornered the sage in an indefensible position, so he leaned forward to ask: "Honorable Master, how can one broadcast his thinking? Isn't this the sort of wishful thinking that children imagine?"

What foolish answer could follow, thought Hon Su Tz.

Laotzu closed his eyes and nodded a few times as if to admire the skeptical monk's question. "Very good question."

Instead of answering right away, Laotzu slowly began to swirl his fly-whisk in the air in an ever-widening circle. Suddenly, everyone in the room felt a buzzing sensation in their sinews and brains. They looked at each other, furtively, to see if the others felt the same sensation. The awe in the room grew as Laotzu's arm continued circling and circling.

Hon Su Tz eyes widened in panic. "What is this?" he thought. He looked at the other palace monks to see their equally shocked faces.

"You see," the sage continued, "I do not have to actually touch each of you, but you all feel the energy of Tao. Wishful thinking or artificial thinking can only reach the inside of your skull and can travel no farther. You need more power to transmit outside of your body. It is this power that can penetrate anything, soft or hard.

"The only way to obtain this kind of power is to reduce your routine thoughts, which are polluted by man-made ideas. A head full of ideas are only thoughts. They neither carry power to travel nor offer any impact force to the outside world. Reducing artificial thought will enable you to let your true self, the power of Te – which is a piece of the power of Tao trapped inside you since you came into this life – connect back to the whole network of Tao.

"It is not enough just to connect your Te back to Tao. You must also practice the power of weakness. This means to condition yourself to be humble, to be empty, to be low, to allow the subtle, invisible, yet ever almighty powerful Tao particle to flow into your body, to charge up your entire body as 'Tao body.'

"You can use the inflow of the power of Tao, combined and tuned by your Te power, to broadcast outward."

While Laotzu continued talking, Hon Su Tz furtively slipped out the back door. Once out of eyesight, he ran through the palace courtyard and out into the street straight to the temple, still vibrating from the master's powerful display. The priest heard Hon Su Tz' frantic knocking, and unbolted the door to let him in.

The priest looked shocked that the monk waited outside. "You're sup-

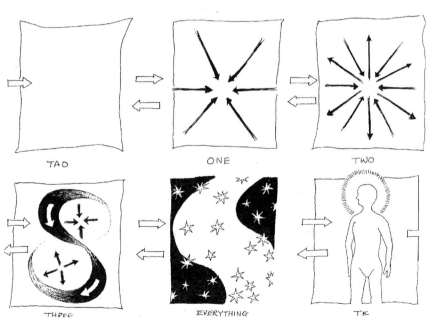

figure 7

Laotzu Broadcasts the Power of Tao

posed to be at the banquet!" he barked.

"Master," bowed Hon Su Tz, "let me in. The sage has frightening powers!"

The priest grabbed Hon Su Tz' sleeve and tugged him inside, where he sat Hon Su Tz down and gave the poor monk some hot herbal soup to settle his nerves.

The monk explained how he'd challenged Laotzu's notion of broadcasting the power of his god Tao through his thoughts. He recounted Laotzu's demonstration of the broadcast power to all of those attending the banquet. He tried to describe for the priest the buzzing in the marrow of his bones and the tingling fog in his head and the sense of ominous presence in the palace hall when Laotzu circled his flywhisk around and around.

"Hmmm..." the priest rubbed his angled chin. "This is more difficult. He may be a sorcerer after all." His silk slippers began to tap the floor nervously. "Well we can't have him luring the prince or, heaven forbid, the queen into thinking this Tao power is more worthy of their worship than our local gods. That could prove disastrous for all of us, not to mention the temple."

"But Master, everyone is asking this sage difficult questions. He answers them easily, and never loses his calm. He speaks in riddles, but all who hear him seem entranced."

"Is he wearing any special charms or necklaces?" asked the priest.

"No," answered Hon Su Tz. "And he performs no incantation that I can see."

"Does he have any disciples with him?"

"No. But KoYou, the prince's son, follows him everywhere he goes on most days."

The gnarled priest sighed. "That's bad news. I don't care about that foreign prince, but his son is much loved by all the people. If KoYou adopts it, this Tao worship could become very fashionable."

"But what can we do?" asked the monk, still frightened and overwhelmed by Laotzu's display of power.

"Oh I have plans for that sage," the priest replied. "I have plans. If he wants to play games with spiritual power, we will show him our powers."

*   *   *

Meanwhile back at the palace, none of the guests noticed Hon Su Tz missing. They were too mesmerized by Laotzu's vast abilities.

KoWu's enthusiasm fired up again. He had to find the way to use this power!

"What do you mean 'broadcast'?" asked the prince. "Do we want to push it out as hard as we can?"

Laotzu smiled, "No, not at all. The power of Tao enters and charges up your body. However, the nature of the power of Tao likes to downgrade to Te or lower, and it always seeks to return back to its pure wholeness, so you must hold on to the power of Tao and keep your body charged up. At the same time, if you want to broadcast a message, you must keep your mind in tune with your power of Te and let the power of Tao go."

"Let it go?" asked Dao An.

"Yes," confirmed Laotzu. "Just let the power of Tao return to its omnipresent state.

43-2 *The invisible* power *can penetrate even through objects without space.* If you learn how to connect your power of Te to the almighty power of Tao, you can just broadcast your message and get the job done without any action. **43-3** *This is how I know the effectiveness of non-action* power. Indeed, **43-4** *delivering messages without words and effecting results without action are understood by very few."*

Next, a portly man, with a heavy crimson robe fastened with clasps of gold rose from his mat and bowed first to the prince, and then to Laotzu and finally to the whole assembly of guests. A new face to the series of banquets, Den Fah never spent much time pondering philosophies or spiritual matters. Den Fah served as financial advisor to KoWu, and also represented one of the wealthiest merchant clans in West Peace. His family's wealth was rivaled only by that of Yin Lian's mother.

Den Fah bowed and addressed Laotzu. "Master, if I have been blessed in this life, how can I apply the power of Tao to protect what I have – power, wealth, fame, and life itself?"

Laotzu looked at Den Fah briefly with a nod. He answered the nobleman with his own question.

"Consider this: **44-1** *Fame or self: Which is more important?"*

"Self," answered Den Fah.

"**44-2** *Self or wealth: Which is worth more?"*

"Again, self," replied the stately advisor.

"**44-3** *Gain or loss: Which is more harmful?"*

"Loss, of course," answered Den Fah.

"Are you sure of that?" the sage replied. "Our life is made of Te power, which follows the rule of the power of Tao. The Tao moves from zero, or nothing, into one. When you take a wife for yourself, you are like a one who has added a zero. By adding a wife you are now a ten. When you have children, you add another zero for each one, and now you are a hundred or a thousand. When you have a house and servants, you add even more zeroes until it adds up to tens of thousands. But! If you lose the first one, the Te, all you have left is many zeroes."

"Good analogy," applauded Den Fah. "I never thought about it in quite that way." The other advisors looked to each other and nodded in appreciation of Laotzu's clever wit.

The sage continued, "44-4 *Therefore, desire for many things results in suffering.* For you risk losing your power of Te in your chase for artificial satisfactions. Also, 44-5 *whoever stores up much has much to lose.* It is sad when a man accumulates wealth but cannot hold onto his very power of Te. 44-6 *Those who know contentment will not be disgraced,* because they won't get carried away with outward pursuits and forget about their power of Te. 44-7 *He who knows restraint will not suffer harm.* He restrains his outward efforts in an even greater effort to develop his power of Te. *He will endure.* Why? Because he holds on to the 'one' and lets the zeroes flow. He doesn't chase the zero and forget the one, for if he loses the one, he knows he will lose every zero."

KoWu nodded to Den Fah, thanking him for the question and for his presence at the banquet.

Then the prince turned to Laotzu. "Master, once again we've come to the end of our evening," the prince sighed, "And I have only one question left to me. I know you continue to advise me to use the power of non-action. Yet when I rule, all eyes are on me. People judge every word I speak and every decision I make. Even other kingdoms await my edicts because they affect how trade will prosper on the entire continent. How can I be with the power of Tao and meanwhile lead the world?"

The teacher resumed his seat on his cushion for his final answer. "One who possesses the power of Tao and applies the power of Tao to do things may give the appearance that 45-1 *great achievement seems flawed.* This is because he lets the power of Tao turn everything into harmony – not too much, not too little – *so its usefulness does not wear out.*"

"By the same token, to the one receiving the power of Tao, the 45-2 *great fullness* of that power *seems empty,* yet the power of Tao *can never be used up.*"

"Because a saint uses the power of Tao to broadcast a message to execute and achieve a task, he requires no physical action. Whatever he does, he follows the guidance of the power of Tao, not any man-made idea. Therefore, whatever he does is always the right thing to do – no matter if it does not coincide with our human artificial notions or win the approval of others. That's why an event that leads toward the greatest good may not seem right to observers who do not understand the Tao. To them, 45-3 *Great straightness seems bent.*"

"Because the saint applied non-action and broadcast the power of Tao, the action appeared to be invisible. It looks to others as if the one responsible was incapable of doing the right thing, or was extremely clumsy. In this way, 45-4 *great skillfulness seems awkward.*

"And since a ruler with the power of Tao need not speak a word to get his message across, he appears as if his tongue is tied. In this way, 45-5 *great eloquence seems dumb.*

"But, when practicing non-action, the power of Tao works 45-6 *just like movement overcoming cold and stillness overcoming heat.* When one possesses the power of Tao, he can broadcast the power of Tao. Even if 45-7 *one* remains *in stillness and tranquility* he can set things in order and find that he indeed *leads the whole world.*"

As Laotzu finished, he motioned for the servants to bring him a cup of water. He closed his eyes as he relished the cool drink, then placed the empty cup in front of him. He folded his hands on the table and bowed his head to the group – his signal that he was finished with the evening's teaching.

Several of the guests came to bow and say good-bye to the seated master. Prince KoWu left with Den Fah to walk him to the gate. His son KoYou stood by Laotzu's table until the sage was ready to go, and accompanied the master back to the stable cottage.

The palace monks, still pale from Laotzu's frightening display of power, left without bowing to anyone. They'd been deeply disturbed by the evening affair. Out in the courtyard, they conferred privately on what would happen to them if the prince followed this sage too far. Their only comfort was that the sage planned to leave soon. They agreed with the temple priest about the threat posed by KoWu's interest in this new "Tao" worship.

Failing in their mission to embarrass the sage, they walked through town as a group to join Hon Su Tz at the temple. They would appeal to the priest to see if he had any plans to steer the royal household's loyalty away from this "Tao" and back to the old religion and the local gods. Perhaps the priest could offer a way to discredit these strange new teachings.

When they arrived at the temple, they found the priest already waiting at the door. "You're finally here! Well let's have it. Was there more of what Hon Su Tz described? Did our little master do more tricks with his flywhisk?"

"Sir," they bowed. One of them stepped forward. "I think that it's time we talked about protecting our beliefs from this foreign influence."

"I so agree," nodded the priest. "The queen herself expressed concern to me this morning that she fears her husband and son have fallen under a strange enchantment with this sorcerer Laotzu. I've taken her concern as a mandate to do anything we can to restore proper clarity of mind to the royal household."

"It will be hard to debate him, for his words are flawless," one of the palace monks offered.

"Oh we won't use words," said the priest. "We will use the only language this so-called sage can't refute. If it's tricks he wants, we'll give him tricks that will send him packing back where he came from on that wretched ox!"

Chapter Sixteen

A Monk Questions His Own Worth

The next morning was blessedly quiet as the visiting monk, Dao An, walked alone among the palace gardens. He looked for a secluded spot to place his small statue of the virtuous goddess who protected all monks of his southern temple, so he could pray to her.

Every morning, since he was a small boy at Minglian Shan, he'd made prayers and offerings to the goddess. This ritual ensured that he could count on the goddess' powers of protection when he needed it either for himself or for others. He had other holy relics in his pouch as well: talismans and powders necessary to summon both light and darker forces to perform the magic and blessings expected of a monk. But for now, he set his pouch aside and swept clear a place in the courtyard to kneel.

Just as Dao An had settled into meditation, young KoYou skipped out from the stable and loped along the path right past Dao An's impromptu altar. Noticing the kneeling monk, KoYou slowed down to investigate.

"What are you doing?" asked the curious young prince. He'd never seen any of the palace monks pray outside in the open courtyard without an audience.

Dao An rose and bowed to the boy. "I pray to the goddess every morning for protection. She is the guardian of my temple."

"Where are you from? I never heard of a temple with a female guardian in our city," said KoYou.

"I come from Minglian Shan. It is a very famous temple near the city of Nan Do," replied the monk.

"My father heard that there's been alot of trouble in Nan Do, and that the Nan Do Prince was killed."

"That's sadly true," Dao An nodded. "And that's why I find myself in your courtyard this morning. When trouble came to our region, many of our monks were forced to scatter, fearing we would be targets for the execution-ers as well. Our temple had been very loyal to the Nan Do Prince."

"Oh," said KoYou. "We've never had that kind of trouble here. It's a very stable city. Our only threat is from barbarians and the city of Bou Yang. I'm afraid, though, that you'll have a hard time finding a place here."

"Why is that?" asked Dao An.

"My father rarely takes on a new monk, and then only monks who have come from our own temple," answered KoYou.

Dao An had heard long ago that the prince of West Peace, KoWu, was a fair and intelligent man. Yet KoWu also had a reputation for employing rela-tively few monks in his service. Dao An thought maybe it was because most of the best monks preferred the larger interior cities. West Peace, as a border town, was less desirable to most scholars and monks because of its remote location and the danger of barbarian raiders. Maybe KoWu didn't have enough well-trained monks to select from.

Dao An mistakenly thought his temple training would set him apart and that he would be eagerly accepted by KoWu. Minglian Shan's order special-ized in spiritual worship. Many monks worshipped nature, the sky, land, water, animals, trees, deceased ancestors, leaders, wise men and local gods. They, like Dao An, knew special rituals to invoke or placate such spirits. But Minglian Shan monks were highly sought throughout the region for their special prayers and rituals. Many thought it was because of the grace and compassion of their patroness goddess.

"My father might make one exception," said KoYou.

"Do you think so?" asked Dao An.

"I know he would. That is, if Master Laotzu wanted to stay at the palace, or anybody who could teach about the power of the Tao he speaks of," said KoYou, as he started to walk away down the path again, leaving Dao An behind. "Do you know about the Tao too?" KoYou called over his shoulder.

Dao An looked crestfallen as he watched the boy go. At that time, any understanding or practice of the mysterious Tao that Laotzu taught about was quite rare. Rumors and legends spoke of men with incomparable power like Laotzu's, but the people had no name for them. These saints' passed down their secrets from master to disciple, mouth to ear, generation to gen-eration, and rarely did this secret society share their knowledge with the established temples.

Dao An had heard of such powerful masters, and knew that they practiced a higher spiritual discipline than he had learned. He had even heard of the name Laotzu and the sage's unusual ability to interact with the human spirit and the force of nature.

After he arrived in West Peace, it astonished Dao An to watch Laotzu arrive just a few days later. Dao An jumped at the rare opportunity to meet with such a legendary spiritual master. As a foreign monk bearing the traveling seal of his temple, the palace would admit him to Laotzu's talks as a diplomatic courtesy. Maybe, Dao An thought, by attending the banquet honoring Laotzu, he could find a quiet moment to approach Prince KoWu about a position, and perhaps impress him with a ritual prayer of blessing.

What the monk hadn't counted on was the small army of Nan Do's elite like Chong Zen who had also migrated to West Peace seeking positions. The day after Laotzu arrived, so did the party from Nan Do – replete with scholars and military strategists, who would all make their offers of service to the prince. Both the long line of applicants, and the awesome spiritual powers of Laotzu, completely overshadowed Dao An and his ordinary temple training.

Nevertheless, while exploring the streets of the city, Dao An kept his eyes and ears open. He learned that the local temple priest could perform astonishing magic tricks. The priest also held a formidable influence over the queen. This being the case, the palace employed no monks without the queen's consent – meaning the local priest's approval.

Dao An learned that all monks at the palace served as pawns of the town priest. They were his eyes and ears at the palace. For this privilege, each palace monk regularly delivered a third of his salary to the local temple in supplication to the local gods. KoWu had but one spiritual advisor, Fa Tingtz, who remained independent of the corrupt local priest. Fa Tingtz, apparently, came with KoWu from the capital city when KoWu first received his title.

Dao An noticed that the shrewd local priest steered clear of the evening gatherings with Laotzu. Laotzu's ability blazed like the bright sun, while the petty monks and magicians in the palace sputtered like shooting stars in a lonely night sky. The local priest saw that his only hope was to discredit Laotzu from a distance. His loyal weasels, posing as holy monks inside the palace, would bring the priest any pertinent information he needed from the nightly banquets.

Dao An shook his head, reminding himself, "No kingdom is free of strife inside its walls."

Although Dao An worried that Laotzu's powers would make his own skills look inadequate, he enjoyed watching the palace monks fret and worry even more. They questioned the security of their positions now that Laotzu brought true teaching to Prince KoWu. The monks feared they might lose their luxurious accommodations, soft silk robes, and their positions of undeserved honor. Dao An could see them squirm during every night's teaching.

As for Laotzu himself, he was so transcendent, thought Dao An. He seemed to care nothing for the ordinary world or for material gain. Laotzu needed no fame, honor or title. One could see that this master possessed a power that surpassed the value of all worldly things. With this power Laotzu could have anything he wanted, and yet he seemed to need nothing. He chose simple food, a plain guesthouse near the stable, and traveled without luxury.

As Dao An knelt down in the garden and placed his goddess statue on a smooth stone, he spied Prince KoWu heading out of the palace with armed guards on the way to the Han Ku gate.

"General, according to reports, a foreign trader attacked one of our gate's guards. Now a gang of caravan thugs surround him, demanding his apology," one of the guards told the prince as they passed.

Although he walked at an earnest pace, KoWu nodded to Dao An as he passed. The monk rose and bowed. Dao An offered politely to come with KoWu and say a prayer of blessing to restore peace to the Han Ku gate. He offered a spell of protection for the prince and his armed guard to keep them safe while they settled the affair.

KoWu sniffed, "I have enough 'monks' in my service." As he mounted a horse that the stable man Lo Han led to him, the prince turned a cold shoulder to Dao An. He and his guard started to ride off, when the prince had an afterthought and raised his hand to stop. He turned his steed around and guided the tall black horse back to where Dao An stood.

"Why do all monks say loud prayers that never work?" the prince glared down from his mount in a challenge to the monk. "And why doesn't Laotzu need loud prayers and yet he can still command the sky? Could you tell me that, Dao An?"

The prince surprised Dao An by knowing his name. But Dao An could no more answer the prince's current question than command the sky itself.

"Yes..." the monk could only agree. All temples trained their monks to pronounce their ritual language in strong words, whether praying, blessing, asking the help of spirits or ghosts, or to beg for a god's mercy. No matter how loud, the calls rarely received an answer. The prince ironically echoed Dao An's own doubts.

"Your majesty," Dao An searched his mind for a good answer during the long silence while the prince waited. This surely was no way to win an appointment, worried Dao An, rummaging for a reply. "I...I...think every monk should do his best to say a strong prayer to ask for the gods' mercies. We are all trained to do this in the best way. I myself was the best and most devout of the monks in my temple and...."

"Well," interrupted the prince, "In this city, I'm facing real barbarians and real trouble. All types of merchants from the west, south and east all come to cause strife and steal a profit from my town. I need an advisor on my staff who can really pray, to really ask God to bless me and my family and my city. I don't need any more 'ritual' monks."

"Yes, your majesty," Dao An bowed, knowing he didn't have the status or the cleverness to answer the prince any further. What a babbling idiot he'd been. He figured then and there that he'd lost all prospects of employment at this palace and wondered if his remaining gold would take him as far as the next town.

But surprisingly, the prince didn't ride off immediately. "I tell you what," said KoWu to the humbled monk. "This afternoon you will come to me. I will ask you questions. If you can answer me, or even help me understand this mysterious Tao that Laotzu speaks of, perhaps I will decide I need another monk. But don't hand me any rituals. I want truth, not rituals." At that, the prince turned and galloped away with the guards.

After the prince left, Dao An stood and looked down at the goddess statue that smiled so graciously and beguilingly. Had she failed to protect him and allowed him to make a fool of himself in front of the prince? Or had she been the one to give him a second chance to prove himself to KoWu this afternoon?

How could he know? These sorts of questions eroded his faith daily. He saw clearly that all the prayer and blessings and magic tricks the temple trained him to perform were just that: performance. It was a job. Whether he or other monks had sincere devotion inside was secondary to most rulers. They, too, merely wanted a performance.

But here lived a prince who wanted more, who wrestled with the same doubts as his own, and who sought deeper answers. What a privilege it would be to serve him. But poor Dao An didn't know where he'd get the answers KoWu sought.

He looked toward the stable, "Perhaps I need the help of one who does know the true answer." Dao An quickly gathered his goddess back into his satchel and made his way through the courtyard toward the stable cottage.

When Dao An peeked inside the old wooden door, he saw Laotzu reclining in the straw and pillows with his arms behind his head. His eyes were closed, as if napping. Dao An, not knowing whether to wake him or not, stood quietly in the corner and waited patiently. Suddenly, the sleeping sage spoke without opening his eyes.

"Every monk thinks about the same problem. It's been that way for a long time. But in the end, it is only a job."

Laotzu surprised Dao An by speaking directly to him even while he seemed to sleep.

The sage continued, "A monk is a monk. It is a monk's duty to perform the gestures of ceremony, to offer comforting words of blessing or say loud prayers. Why do you come to me?"

"Master," apologized Dao An, "forgive me for intruding on your rest."

"I am not resting," Laotzu sat up. "I was just meditating. Tell me, Dao An, why do you care about that advisor post?"

"Master, I need a job. I have been raised as a monk, and this is all I know." Dao An's voice quavered. He trembled with shock that the teacher already knew why he came.

"Ha ha!" Laotzu laughed. "Okay, so you need a job to be a monk. Then why do you look so worried?"

"Master, Prince KoWu wants to question me later today and test my ability in spiritual matters. I know he already has too many ritual monks on his staff. Because you are here he will be looking for deep truths from me. He wants to see strong power, such as the power you display. I need your help," Dao An fell to one knee and bowed his head to the master on the hay bed.

"Calm down inside, Dao An," Laotzu smiled. "You are too nervous." He leaned over to the side of his bed and picked up his trademark flywhisk. Waving it back and forth slowly, he asked, "What makes you think KoWu's questions will be too hard?"

"Master, this morning he asked me why monks' loud prayers do not work. After you displayed your awesome force, he wants monks who can use the power of Tao. That's why I need your help."

"Hmm," Laotzu sat up on his pallet. "Sit down and relax." He pointed his flywhisk at the mat next to the bed. Dao An sat as he was told. "I already knew you would come to me. There are so many monks doing spiritual work, but it never has any lasting effect. You know why?" Laotzu asked.

"No. That very question haunts me," replied Dao An.

"I actually gave you the answer to that question the very first night, but you didn't hear it," Laotzu shook his whisk at the monk in a playful scold. "I told KoWu that the named made up the ten thousand things. Do you know what I meant by that?"

Dao An shook his head.

Laotzu continued, "We humans use artificial words to give names to everything we know, so we can communicate with them and about them. We forget that what we name is the real thing, and the word itself is not the real thing. Over time, we get lost in words and forget what is real."

"But how does that answer the question of why monks' prayers go unanswered, and their quest for enlightenment unfulfilled?" asked a confused Dao An.

"This is very simple," replied Laotzu rising off his bed and stepping over to the fire pit. "Here, spread some ashes over the hearth, and I'll draw you a picture."

Dao An took an old cup and scooped some loose ash, sprinkling it in an even layer across the wide hearth.

"This is how we are made. It is our spiritual anatomy. Your prayers go unanswered and you will never reach the Tao on your present course. Why? Because you pray in the wrong direction."

Laotzu grabbed a twig from the kindling pile and began to trace the figure of a man into the ashes and then drew concentric circles radiating out from the man's center(**figures 8a and 8b**). Dao An leaned over on his elbows as the teacher revealed a most interesting lesson.

"Most religious people, like priests and monks, and even evil sorcerers and magicians, all pray to powers outside of themselves for help. But to do that, they use words and artificial concepts. Sometimes, because of great sincerity, talent or practice, they are successful, and sometimes they aren't. They

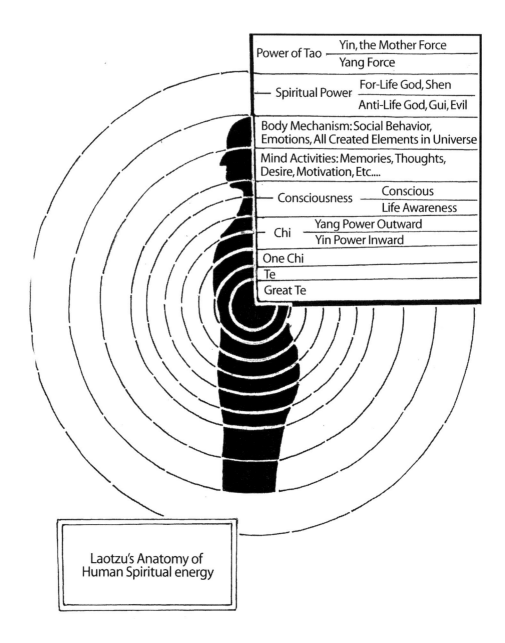

Power of Tao	Yin, the Mother Force
	Yang Force
Spiritual Power	For-Life God, Shen
	Anti-Life God, Gui, Evil
Body Mechanism: Social Behavior, Emotions, All Created Elements in Universe	
Mind Activities: Memories, Thoughts, Desire, Motivation, Etc....	
Consciousness	Conscious
	Life Awareness
Chi	Yang Power Outward
	Yin Power Inward
One Chi	
Te	
Great Te	

Laotzu's Anatomy of
Human Spiritual energy

figure 8a

	Laotzu's Anatomy of Human Spiritual Energy
1	Within the very center, the core of human spiritual energy, is the Great Te (Sen Te). It is the very origin of Te. It is almost identical to the power of Tao.
2	After birth, the Great Te power quickly transforms, or degrades, into the power of Te, the core energy of human life force.
3	While the body forms, the One Chi turns into pure life force, the Chi. The Chi directs forces to perform life functions. The Yang Chi is the life force that moves outward, and the Yin Chi is the life force that pulls inward to accumulate and amass.
4	The Chi's activities generate activities of consciousness. Underneath there is a foundation of life awareness or feeling. Above this foundation is conscience.
5	While coming into contact with the outside world, as the body grows, the back and forth of communication triggers mind activity. This includes desire, memory, thinking processes and thoughts.
6	Mind and body finally build a tight co-relationship with the outside world. After growing up, the entire mind and body fuse with a body mechanism, emotions, social behaviors. These correspond to the material universe made of the same grade of energy - slow, sluggish, heavy, just like the plants, animals, earth, sky, etc....
7	Above and outside the human life force, there are spiritual forces moving in different directions. One force moves in the direction of life, called the power for life or Shen, and the other power of anti-life spirits, or Gui. (note: Laotzu regarded God as a two-edged sword: one edge for life, flowing in the direction which nourishes and creates life, while the other is responsible for tearing down life and recycling the life force. From our human-level viewpoint, the "for-life" God force is a good God, and the opposite force is a bad God, or Devil.)

figure 8b

8	Next there is the absolute origin of everything and eternality: the conscious being of the absolute. There is no Yin and no Yang while it is in stillness. When it is in action, it will move toward the center first to become the mother power. After this, power will move outward to become the Yang power. These interact forever.
9	The power described in (7) and (8) has no relevance to time or space. The Tao is a conscious being - a huge network - very fine, yet dense and omnipresent. As a whole, nothing can escape it.
10	As a human being, the decayed energy of the Te, the mind, cannot comprehend or feel the power of Great Te, or God or Tao. One must put his mind back into his body, and his body back into his life energy, Chi and his Chi reined back into One Chi. This will convert back into the power of the Great Te which will allow him to connect back to the power of God or spiritual power. Then he may travel freely in the unlimited space of Tao, the mother power, forever.

may reach the level of what we label as good or evil spirits, or even command ghosts. But certainly men will never reach the original One Power, the Tao, going outward with artificial words or concepts. Dao An, tell me, don't all your rituals depend on words, a talisman, or statues?" asked Laotzu.

"Yes," answered Dao An, now leaning closer toward the drawing, beginning to understand.

"So tell me, even if you possessed utmost sincerity, how could you, a mere human, use such things and manage to penetrate the outermost layer of spiritual power to reach the Tao? You are not able to do it. Indeed, no human can.

"No, Dao An, the way to the Tao is to head backward. You must turn away from the artificial world of mental concepts and words and go within yourself to the center where your core energy, the Great Te resides. If you are able, with a pure mind, to reconnect to your original life energy, then you will be able to connect with the power of Tao. No words or rituals are necessary. They are only obstacles."

Dao An nodded. He began to see what Laotzu meant.

"You see, the spiritual power is invisible force," continued the master. "But it is the real thing. If you want to communicate with the real thing, you have to use the real thing. If you want to communicate with the artificial thing, then you use the artificial thing."

Laotzu set down the twig, and folded his hands on his lap. "When we think with words and names, we are exercising artificial energy. It is not real force. When we speak aloud, it is just putting this artificial energy in motion.

"The spiritual force is the real thing. This force penetrates everywhere, and if we would like to contact the spiritual forces, we need to speak the words the spiritual forces recognize, then we can communicate and even manipulate those forces."

Dao An nodded. For the first time, somebody could answer his burning questions in a way that made sense. Laotzu saw the light in Dao An's eyes when the monk asked, "Master, but how can I learn how to speak in god or ghost language since they do not understand our language?"

"Ha, Ha..." The monk's question obviously amused Laotzu. "Of course anyone can learn how to speak with good or evil spirits with the language they understand."

"How long does it take to learn? Can I learn it?" asked Dao An hopefully.

"Of course you can. But it isn't like learning a southern tongue or a northern dialect. It's simpler than that. You do not have to 'learn' it. You already know how to do it."

"Me? I know how to speak the spiritual language?" Dao An looked puzzled.

Laotzu nodded and smiled. "The only question is whether you would like to do it or not."

While Dao An scratched his head in bewilderment, Laotzu continued, "If you are willing to speak with your utmost sincerity, without any fake wording, just absolute, pure feeling, you then can instantly communicate with the spiritual world."

"Utmost sincerity? What does that really mean?"

"When you were a newborn, you thought of nothing. You had implicit trust and faith in your feeling. You, as a newborn, would simply feel. You didn't think, you didn't wonder, you didn't doubt. You went for feeling, not for words when you needed to communicate. That, my friend, is utmost sincerity." Laotzu paused and stared at Dao An.

The monk closed his eyes and tried to simply feel, to communicate from feeling. "Master, this is very hard to do," Dao An shook his head, discouraged.

"Very hard to do indeed, if you allow it to be difficult," Laotzu smiled. "As I said, it is possible only if you are sincerely willing to do it. You are unwilling because your artificial thinking clogs up your network. It blocks your gut feeling. Remember, do not go for what your eye sees and your mind thinks; go for your belly where you can feel."

Dao An tried again. He felt his belly when he closed his eyes.

"We allow too many fake things to enter our memory. This clogs up our communication channel with our true feeling. Grown-ups learn how to hide their true feeling, and so that true feeling retards and even dies," coached Laotzu as Dao An continued to meditate on his feeling.

Laotzu continued, "Inside true feeling, you can feel your true life energy, the Chi, at work. It flows all over your body when your mind – the I (pronounced "ee") – pays great attention to it. As soon as your mind is distracted by the outside artificial world, your feeling of life energy disappears. You need to continue this effort to feel your true life energy, and dedicate yourself to it until that energy reaches your awareness level. At that point, you can almost 'see' your own body, inside out."

Dao An tried as Laotzu talked. He felt a strong and sure feeling of his belly – soothing and warm, sensitive and comfortable. "Master, what should I do after I feel the warmth in my stomach?"

"Pay extreme attention to one spot." Laotzu got up and walked over to place his finger on Dao An's lower stomach area. "Only on this spot, inside your belly. Nail your focused mind to it. Allow not even the slightest drift. Try very hard not to 'overdo' it."

Laotzu guided Dao An's work through the whole process, step by step. Dao An tried his best to concentrate, but he had a hard time focusing on just one spot. His mind always drifted around; distracted from the spot, no matter how hard he tried.

"Master, why do I have such difficulty staying on one spot with my mind?"

"Take it easy," Laotzu coached. "Try to focus on one spot. The key issue is not to try too hard. Quite the opposite – you should try very hard to not even try."

"Yes, Master." Dao An closed his eyes, struggling to pin his concentration on the one particular spot where Laotzu still held his finger. "I'm trying to not try too hard now."

Laotzu smiled, and with the monk's eyes still closed, Laotzu raised his free hand above his own head and flowed energy through his index finger into Dao An's stomach.

"I got it!" Dao An cried out. "I got it. My mind can focus on it now. I see white light, like a bright star in the dark clear night."

"Okay," Laotzu nodded. He dropped his arms and walked back to the bed to recline on his pillow. "Keep going, continue to focus your mind power on your stomach."

In only a moment or two, Dao An saw the tiny bright light in his stomach, where Laotzu pointed before, grow in size and radiate a soothing white light. "This is amazing. I meditated all my life, and learned a thousand chants, but I never experienced anything like this. It is beautiful,." he said, enthralled, relaxed, and enjoying the new wonder of this sensation. After a few moments, he asked, "Master, why couldn't I see the light without your help?"

Dao An kept his eyes shut tight to remain focused on the light even as Laotzu answered, "Our mind is the only tool we have to initiate our connection with the spiritual power in this world. But if we contaminate our mind, pollute it, we will never get there.

"The quality of your mind is very important. If your mind is not clear, then it will soil your life energy and spiritual power. It will make all of your meditation get worse. Just as if you used a dirty hand to handle clean food: if you eat the food, you might not get any benefit from the food and in fact, might get very sick. But you didn't get sick from the food itself, rather from the unclean substance contaminating your hand.

"Our mind power is very clean when we are born," the teacher went on to explain. "But it picks up artificial ideas and wrongful interpretations while we grow up. These artificial ideas contaminate our mind. With an unclean mind, when you use your mental power to concentrate and push your life energy, you will definitely pollute your life energy."

"Master, how can I clean my mind? Isn't it a very difficult and complicated process?" asked the concerned Dao An.

"Not at all. Actually, it is opposite to what people think it is. People think it is very hard to clean a polluted mind, when it is actually very easy," Laotzu smiled.

Dao An finally opened his eyes and looked at Laotzu. He waited for the answer on how to easily clean his mind, but Laotzu now closed his eyes as if falling asleep.

"Maybe he's just meditating again," thought the monk. Dao An waited for awhile and then crept closer to the sage but couldn't tell whether Laotzu really slept or just reclined on the pillows breathing smoothly. Dao An wondered whether to rouse him by repeating his question about how to clean the mind, but decided against disturbing the sage.

Yet Dao An knew this was a critical question. If he could use a clean mind to push his life energy, the Chi, he could grow his life energy, making it strong, as Laotzu described night after night. Then, perhaps, he would acquire the very powers and spiritual wisdom of Laotzu himself. Then he could go anywhere and be invited, not hired, as a chief spiritual advisor to any prince in the region, any king he chose.

While Dao An wondered about this, he heard Laotzu start talking to himself, "…and then I will be so successful, and then, except if I could know how to have a clean mind and…" Laotzu stopped talking as abruptly as he began and drifted back into his meditative sleep once more.

The monk's jaw dropped as he realized Laotzu could read his mind. He didn't even speak but Laotzu could hear his thoughts. He was simultaneously awestruck and horrified to know that the sage could pick up his thinking so exactly. Yet when he looked down at Laotzu, he could see that the sage rested comfortably like a baby on its mother's breast, satisfied after a milk feeding.

Dao An, not knowing quite what to do, knelt down and whispered quietly "Master, could you…." Laotzu also spoke simultaneously "..could you just tell me how to calm my mind…. yes, you said it is easy…" When Dao An stopped thinking, Laotzu stopped talking.

"Master, you are a god, I am nothing." The monk now prostrated himself with his head to the floor. "I know I am just a fake monk. All the masters and monks I've known in this world have no real power. We only know how to use words to pray and use rituals to bless. We never receive real power or hear the real teaching you can give. You have the true lineage and the true discipline. Master, I beg you, please teach me." The sleeping Laotzu seemed not to hear him.

Dao An realized in his heart that the spiritual life he'd led up to that point was woefully incomplete. All his brothers at the temple merely played roles – learning the proper gestures during ceremonial rituals, shouting the appropriate words while performing prayers for hire. They all knew how to recite ritual blessings and act like a speaker for gods or devils, and especially how to socialize properly with the rich and powerful patrons whose support they relied on. They would use these skills to help a ruler deal with his subjects, the poor, the demanding, and those needing answers.

So many years he'd followed the Minglian Shan abbot, his master, to be groomed as a monk. With the power he possessed, he would be known as a spiritual person who would go between the spiritual world, both good and evil, and the people: A diplomat between the heavens and earth.

As a monk, his greatest service to his employer would be to provide the ruler with an ironclad excuse in front of meddlesome subjects. He could answer questions in a way that would lift any blame off of a king and place it squarely on the shoulders of a jealous god. Conversely, if a harvest turned out good, he could attribute the gain to the king's own fervent prayers during the previous spring that brought the necessary wind and rain. Either way, both a good or bad outcome always called for more offerings to the temple to placate the gods.

Now Dao An looked down at a man who played no such roles. This Laotzu, whose eyes remained gently shut, held the real power of heaven in his hands.

"Master, I beg you. I know I was wrong in the past. Even my sincere devotion was tainted by ambitions and selfishness. I know I am not a monk. I am just a 'monk-like' monk. Not real at all. I need your help. If you would teach me – accept me as your student, not even a disciple. If you would need someone just to follow you and serve you, I am willing to take any humble position. Please teach me!"

Laotzu turned his body to lie on the other side, still not opening his eyes.

"Ha, ha, ha!" A loud guffaw from behind startled Dao An making him jump. Chong Zen, who'd been listening at the door, hugged himself and laughed. "You are here. I looked all over for you. I just ran into Lo Han the stableman, and he said he saw you walk over here. So here I find you!"

"Shhh...' Dao An signaled Chong Zen to be quiet. "Master Laotzu is asleep. No, I mean he is at meditation....or both."

"Well, well," Chong Zen found it very amusing when he came in to find Dao An kneeling down in front of Laotzu and begging Laotzu to teach him or even take him as a servant. He even heard Dao An's confession that he just acted like a monk and that he needed help.

Scholars like Chong Zen often scoffed at monks for their clever acts that played on people's superstitions. At least here stood a monk that acknowledged his empty performances and recognized a true teacher, thought the scholar.

"If Master Laotzu is asleep or meditating, then why do you bother him by saying all this nonsense?" Chong Zen asked with a wry grin.

"I...I..." muttered Dao An, embarrassed. "I was talking with the master and he just fell asleep. I just continued to talk without knowing that he was sleeping."

"I see, well then if Master Laotzu is asleep, we should both get out of here then. Let's walk in the courtyard so we won't disturb his nap."

"But...." Dao An looked down at Laotzu. He knew the master could hear their conversation, and he wanted badly to continue his plea to learn how to cleanse his mind, but with Chong Zen there it was too awkward.

Hesitatingly, Dao An followed Chong Zen out of the stone hut and through the stable into the courtyard.

Dao An had heard of Chong Zen even before their meeting in West Peace. Chong Zen was a well-known and respected scholar in Nan Do. Now that KoWu invited him to be an advisor, he would certainly win the prince's trust. He was seasoned and sensible. Although he knew a word or two could turn a prince's mind, he was always discreet and never abused his position. The scholar handled palace politics with grace and finesse. His keen intuition told him that the Nan Do Prince Kah Chan would loose his power and his life someday, and that intuition saved his own neck.

Chong Zen could accurately appraise a person after just one meeting and a few words. Because of this, he navigated through tricky situations with ease. Dao An envied his abilities. As a monk, his own skills with people were far less sophisticated.

Yet although Chong Zen had a silver tongue and an excellent mind, he had no spiritual power. His memory, sharp thinking and timing might give the appearance that he knew people as well as Laotzu did, or that he could predict future events, but it was merely mental acumen.

"Can I be any service to you sir?" Dao An bowed with his sleeves touching, for now, unlike their first meeting, Chong Zen was a superior to be courted and obeyed.

"You mentioned to me last week that you would like to get a job as a spiritual advisor to KoWu. You asked for my help. It so happens that I had a talk with the prince about the matter and he said...." Chong Zen paused and looked down.

"Tell me please, what did Prince KoWu say?" Dao An asked.

"Oh, I just remembered. Didn't I see you kneeling down and begging Laotzu for a job too? Or were you begging him to teach you so you could advance your prospects with the prince?" Chong Zen couldn't resist the chance to press Dao An into an uncomfortable position. The monk would learn, whether or not Prince KoWu employed him, that this scholar was too wise to be played with casually.

Dao An, now red-faced, hastened, "No, no, it wasn't anything to do with the job specifically. But perhaps it was in a larger sense."

"Well, what did the great master say? Can he help you?"

"No, Master said nothing. Please, tell me what Prince KoWu said about me obtaining a position?"

Chong Zen chuckled to himself. "Master Laotzu wouldn't help you and fell asleep. So you still need my help after all."

Dao An couldn't reply. He simply bowed his head silently toward the scholar. Today seemed to find him in one embarrassing situation after another.

"I mentioned to KoWu that we indeed need more spiritual monks on the advisory staff. Because this is a border town, the prince doesn't know that rulers in interior cities have many different spiritual advisors and that this works to their advantage. As it stands, too many of his monks speak in unison on behalf of the town priest. No monk except Fa Tingtz can give any differing opinion. This hamstrings the prince greatly. I suggested that you had good training and that the Minglian Shan monks in Nan Do were famous for their spiritual power and prognostication. I even persuaded him to make new appointments on his own, without the traditional consent of the queen."

"And then?" pressed the monk.

"And then the prince said…" Chong Zen began to walk slowly. Dao An followed anxiously behind. "He said he'd agree to hire more spiritual monks as advisors, but…."

"But what, sir?"

"But he wants a real monk." Chong Zen stopped and looked back at the stable. "He insists he needs someone as wise and capable as Laotzu."

The southerners both walked through the courtyard silently as their slippers bit into crisp autumn leaves that fell from the decorative fruit trees. Dao An wondered how anybody could meet the prince's criteria. A "real" monk: Dao An wondered if the prince knew there was no such thing. But at least Chong Zen's report explained why KoWu remembered Dao An's name this morning, and why he'd been invited to see the prince this afternoon.

Chong Zen stared straight ahead as he walked. Without turning, he confided to Dao An in a low voice so no one else could hear: "I am a scholar. We scholars believe in right and wrong, good and bad. We use our minds to learn, to remember, and to study a wide range of knowledge so that we can solve problems. I know how to advise KoWu in many of his decisions, but I know little of these spiritual matters. Neither do I believe in most of it, frankly." Chong Zen confessed, "But sometimes people will only listen to a monk, and a frightening ceremony is often the only means to rule the people. Perhaps, between you and I, each using our gifts and working together, we could help the prince and outsmart the other monks and their mercenary priest."

"Sir, if you would help me with this appointment, I would certainly be grateful."

"Of course I will. I've already opened the first door by convincing KoWu he needs more monks."

"In my heart, I will always remember your help. Whatever you advise, I will take seriously," Dao An pledged. "But scholar, the prince has asked to interview me this very afternoon and ask me about Laotzu's spiritual power and my own. He asks very deep and difficult questions."

"Excellent!" clapped Chong Zen. "You must be well prepared and do your very best to win his trust."

"Yes sir," Dao An bowed deeply. "I will do my very best."

"We may be good friends here at the palace for a long time, Dao An."

At that, Chong Zen left the garden. Dao An stood and stared at the court-yard gate watching the scholar go, wondering what had just happened.

Alone under the morning sun, he felt lost. One minute he'd been prostrate before Laotzu confessing the false pretenses of his profession, and the next moment he found himself hatching alliances with the scholar. Oh how bewildering his own mind and heart could be. Aimlessly, he wandered back toward the stone hut.

As he walked through the stable, Dao An thought how clever and dangerous scholars were. Even good-hearted ones like Chong Zen had tongues like oiled knives that could slip and pierce through the most steadfast resolve. He would certainly hold much influence and be a great asset to KoWu. With Chong Zen's learning, his knowledge of the law, his social eloquence, he could make a good thing sound illegitimate and a terrible thing sound sacred. With their twisted words, scholars could launch wars against a country for a holy cause. In their own way, they were far more powerful than monks.

"You should be a scholar then," a kind voice came from behind. Surprised, Dao An turned around to see Laotzu standing behind him in the stable.

"Master, you are awake now." Dao An swallowed his surprise, and wondered how the sage appeared out of nowhere.

"I was awake. I never slept. I heard your conversation. Very impressive." Laotzu still spoke kindly, and smiled so childlike.

"Master," Dao An knelt down in front of Laotzu and wept, "Wise man, I am so lost. Please help me."

Laotzu gently touched his shoulder, "Please get up. Let's go inside." Dao An got up and followed Laotzu slowly back to the guesthouse.

Pouring a cup of hot herbal soup for the beleaguered monk, Laotzu told him, "You spent many years to be a monk and tried very hard to be a spiritual man. Now you look at Chong Zen, a successful scholar who now has great influence over KoWu. You wonder if you should try to be more like that scholar and throw your lot in with his." Laotzu spoke what was on Dao An's mind, but then challenged him, "Why don't you just let it go?"

"Let it go?" puzzled Dao An, holding the cup of broth without bothering to drink.

"Yes. Let it all go. Your body, your mind, your ego, your dreams of honor and success. Isn't it painful to make up this life for yourself and find that when you make something up, that something is nothing?" Laotzu stood still holding the stone pot.

Dao An, humiliated and confused by the twists and turns of the day, set down his cup and slumped against the wall.

"Just let it go," the sage continued. "Be yourself. Be honest. Be real, like a newborn. Let the power of Tao take over and run everything for you."

"But then won't I lose control?" asked Dao An looking up at the master, his eyes welling with moisture.

"Control is just an illusion. No one can control anything," Laotzu assured him. "We only can follow the flow of the power of Tao. We can control nothing."

The monk closed his eyes and grimaced. Laotzu tidied up the small kitchen area around the fire pit and gave him time to digest his words.

After awhile, the sage began again. "There is no such thing as 'control' or 'own' or 'possess.' These are just false sense. Whoever thinks he or she is in charge is really just a servant meant to serve. Look at me. I am so happy that I don't have to own anything, or owe anything. I am burdened by nothing, liable to no one. Why should I worry?

"Look around. There are so many smart people to invent ways to make life better for me. So many aggressive people look for success and work their rear-ends off to achieve what is good. Meanwhile, I benefit from their effort. I'm surrounded by people who work hard day in and day out for their very livelihood, and I am surviving right alongside them. But all I do is nothing and the power of Tao takes care of everything. If I do nothing but flow with the power, then I worry about nothing. Worry is counterproductive. I take whatever comes. I am just a humble and ordinary person. I let go and surrender to my true self.

"I give up everything inside and out. I let the power of Tao enter my body, because it is not my body. I am so humble and laid low because I am nothing. Yes, I let the power of Tao run my life. I have no body – 'Wu Shen.' I have no self –'Wu You.' The power of Tao owns me. I only flow with what is going on with no concern and no worry. I don't have to know anything in this world, but I know everything. I don't care, and I pay no attention to it. I don't own anything. I let it go. I eat when I am hungry. I sleep when I need to. I am not smart because I find no use for my own intelligence. I am not successful, because I do not know what it means. I receive no honor and no title, because I do not need it. You can live like this too, Dao An. Just let it go. Let the true you, the Te, merge with the power of Tao."

Dao An remained silent. What question could he ask?

Laotzu went on, "The use of words and intelligence just builds a thicker barrier around your true self. People chase endless artificial goals and end up losing everything. Give up yourself, forego the words, names, titles, and practice the power of emptiness. Let the original absolute power of the Tao enter your body. You are a part of the Tao. You have inexhaustible power. Why should you look for titles? Jobs? Being 'spiritual'?"

He and the monk stared at each other for a long time. Laotzu, realizing that he'd finished his task with Dao An, stretched and sat down on his straw pallet. Lying back, he closed his eyes in repose and this time truly did fall fast asleep.

Dao An looked up to see the teacher sleeping. Tears streaming down his face, the monk kneeled in front of the sage's bed in thanks. Inside himself, Dao An saw a glimmer of the truth. He knew now exactly what he had to do.

*   *   *

In the palace counsel chambers, KoWu sat on a cushion at his worktable. One by one, advisors filed in, forming a line to await an audience with the prince. Each came to report a bit of news from their sector of the city or make a special request of funds from the treasury. A guard stopped Dao An at the doorway. The prince looked up and seeing the monk, motioned for the guard to let him pass and join the line. After several other petitioners finished their appeals to KoWu, Dao An found himself face to face with the prince of West Peace. He dropped to his knees.

"Well, monk, do you have any more answers for me today? You seemed out of answers this morning," the prince goaded him. "What special spiritual powers do you have that will make you a good advisor? How are you any different from the dozens of monks that feed off our treasury and whisper behind my back? Will your prayers be answered? Can you summon this power of Tao like our guest Laotzu? Do tell."

The prince folded his arms across his chest. He had an innate dislike and distrust of most monks. Fa Tingtz was the only one he confided in or whose words he'd listen to. He would follow Chong Zen's advise and seek more spiritual advisors, agreeing that a wider variety of opinions could only help dilute the leverage of the odious temple priest. But KoWu certainly wouldn't make things easy for them. Any new monks would be carefully selected and closely watched.

"Your majesty," Dao An began, "I can offer you nothing that you expect from a monk. I have spent time with Master Laotzu and he has confirmed for me what you and I both know: The spiritual power offered by my training and by my brother monks is inferior at best, and artifice at worst. We have no idea why our prayers sometimes work and why they don't."

The advisors and guards who heard Dao An's confession gasped. They couldn't believe the blunt and self-deprecating words from this would-be advisor.

"Furthermore, your majesty, I do not have the power of Tao. But I do know the way to find it. I have listened closely to the sage these past nights, and will continue to burn every word he teaches into my very soul. I even spent the morning with him today looking for answers or power that I could show you," explained Dao An.

"And what did you find, you strange and honest monk?" asked KoWu, now intrigued by the monk's candid report.

"I found the important keys to practice so that I may someday have the power of Tao own me and work through me as it does through the sage. I also found the will to forsake all other allegiances but to this Tao he speaks of. It may take time to reach the heights of this sage, but I have at least found his way. And this is all I have to offer your majesty if you choose to take it. It is no longer any concern of mine where and how I live," Dao An bowed his head.

Prince KoWu leapt to his feet. "Hear, hear! Let us all appreciate the refreshing sincerity and honesty of this monk. Dao An, can you teach me what you have learned from Laotzu, even when Laotzu is gone?"

"I can recite for you every word, and draw you the diagrams he showed me in the ashes of his humble cottage. I can show you how he showed me to meditate and how to live. I cannot promise you success, but I can promise you that I, too, will practice unwaveringly until I join Laotzu in his level of knowledge." Dao An remained kneeling.

Prince KoWu looked over at Fa Tingtz who was equally amazed at Dao An's candor and devotion. Fa Tingtz shrugged his shoulders at the prince as if to indicate "Why not?"

"Then, Dao An, I give you my appointment as spiritual advisor to the city of West Peace. You will serve under Fa Tingtz and will come at my command and render all assistance and teaching necessary for my own and my family's practice of spiritual meditation and study." Prince KoWu nodded to the assistant scribe who carved the pronouncement into the day's notes.

Dao An rose and bowed, both to the prince and then to Fa Tingtz. Fa Tingtz stood up and put his hand on Dao An's elbow. He led Dao An out of the counsel chambers and down the corridor to the advisors' quarters.

Chapter Seventeen

The Sixth Night with the Taoist Guest

On the sixth night of Laotzu's stay, the master came to the palace hall quite early and took his seat and shut his eyes. He spent the later half of the afternoon and early evening meditating in this position while the servants quietly set the tables and prepared the cushions for the other guests. He sat so still that the servants almost forgot he was there.

As the time for the banquet grew near, the palace monks arrived first – all of them except Fa Tingtz and Dao An.

The monks had spent the day conferring with the temple priest on how to handle this visiting sage who threatened their livelihood with his powerful words and demonstrations. The priest chanted several empowering spells over the monks and armed them with the temple's most potent relics. Each monk memorized a special spell to chant silently during the gathering with Laotzu. Although they didn't use such spells often, ancient carvings buried in the temple vaults specified each word and hand gesture. Each spell would summon one of several troublesome demons that served the local gods. If invoked at the evening's banquet, the demons would vex Laotzu by causing him to stutter, itch or lose his concentration.

To practice each spell, the priest took the monks out to the back alley behind the temple. There, several vagrants foraged the trash for food. Some of them were old or mad, or stricken with boils from an unfortunate illness. With no family to care for them, these sad souls ended up homeless and alone to fend for themselves in the shadows of the temple. The priest stood with each monk in turn as they surreptitiously practiced their chosen spell on one of the poor misfortunates.

Surely enough, when one monk chanted his evil incantation and rubbed a stone beetle, a disheveled old woman leaning against a post began to babble incoherently and scream, her mind twisted by torturous visions.

Later, another monk hid behind a corner and rubbed a scorpion talisman while reciting a horrible curse. The priest nodded when a one-legged man sitting on the ground started scratching and swatting as if a swarm of invisible stinging insects bit him.

Each monk had a turn to practice his black art and convince the priest that he could perform his spell accurately.

The monks, amazed at the power of the magic, were even more amazed at the priest himself. After they cast an evil spell and its victim suffered from the awful consequence, the priest merely made one of several hand gestures and the victim was instantly relieved of the curse. If their spells and sacred relics invoked such demons, what magic did the priest have to command them back into submission, they wondered?

Sending them off to the evening gathering, the priest gave them final encouraging words. The situation warranted such mischief, assured the priest, for the end result could only be good if such spells forced Prince KoWu to recognize the superior power of the local gods and his own monks. Evil power wielded for a good result was always pardonable, according to the priest, and that cheeky sage might show a bit more respect to the local temple after they taught him a lesson.

That night, the six monks arrived and took strategic positions scattered around the room, instead of huddling together as they had in nights past. This would protect them against any countering spell the sage might cast, since Laotzu would have to aim in six different directions, they reasoned. This way, too, he wouldn't know exactly where any given spell came from, and thus would have a hard time neutralizing the curses with any special magic he might have.

The other guests came in and immediately grew silent seeing the master in his meditation. They also looked puzzled that the monks, including Hon Su Tz, sat apart from each other around the room.

Dao An and Fa Tingtz looked at each other with concern when they arrived. They knew enough of spiritual matters to know that the other six monks were up to no good. Dao An spied one fingering a small black onyx figurine of a scorpion under the table where nobody else could see him. They wanted to warn Laotzu, but the sage was still deep in meditation. Fa Tingtz and Dao An could only choose seats closest to him and hope that they might shield him from the negative curses the other monks no doubt aimed at the sage, or at least be prepared to run to Laotzu's aid.

KoYou arrived at Chong Zen's side, no longer dressed as a servant. Tonight he wore the full attire of a prince's son. Earlier that day, Dai Dong brought him the news that his father wished for him to study under Chong Zen as his new tutor. When KoYou finished attending to Laotzu for the day, KoWu ordered, he was to report to Chong Zen immediately. Chong Zen felt it was important for the boy to attend the night's teaching as a full participant, not just standing in the back by the servants as he had on previous nights.

KoYou was elated that he could at last be part of the sage's real teaching to the adults. Standing in back with the servants made it hard to hear, and he couldn't see the diagrams Laotzu drew in the sand. Perhaps now that he sat at the table, he'd even be allowed to ask a question or two.

Chong Zen asked the boy to sit next to him, so that he could explain to KoYou any difficult concepts that Laotzu might convey. After all, the scholar thought, most of Laotzu's talk flew far above the heads of experienced men. The boy would undoubtedly need Chong Zen's help to understand the sage.

The prince arrived last. He'd had a busy day. The earlier trouble at the Han Ku Gate required additional meetings with the civil guard in addition to his regular business.

The meal offered a celebration of autumn. Fall game and vegetables stewed in a savory broth complemented flat cakes of herbs and grain. Some clever cook had meticulously stacked the last of the perishable fruits into the shape of a colorful pyramid on a large silver platter. A special wine made from rare mountain herbs and berries finished the meal. The light fruity wine offered a promise that spring would someday come again.

The devious monks ate little. Silently, they each ate and drank only enough to seem inconspicuous.

Laotzu opened his eyes from his meditation and looked as refreshed and calm as if he'd enjoyed a relaxing night's sleep. He practically beamed as he saw the luscious food, and helped himself to plenty. His smile infected the entire room as the other guests, except the sullen monks, began to laugh, relax and enjoy each other's company.

Finally, when the guests had eaten their fill, the prince signaled for quiet and began the night's teachings with his first question.

"Master, last night you showed us your ability to broadcast the power of

Tao. You also mentioned that this power is the most original power that can penetrate anything. If it is so powerful, and if a leader learns how to broadcast the power of Tao – and if he further learns to exercise the non-action power you talk about to lead and rule – could he theoretically take over the whole world?"

Laotzu narrowed his eyes at KoWu. Such ambitious talk did not become the prince. The sage answered, "46-1 *When the* power of *Tao is offered* in its omnipresence to *the world, the warhorses haul manure for farming.* 46-2 *When there is no* power of *Tao* broadcast *in the world, warhorses are bred outside the city borders.* 46-3 *There is no greater sin than not knowing when to stop, no greater curse than wanting more.* 46-4 *Therefore the person who knows contentment will always have enough.*"

KoWu continued, "Master, you travel all over the world. I rarely travel beyond my city, for it isn't safe for me to do so, and my leadership would be missed. If I try to learn the power of Tao, do I need to travel as you do to learn more about its application?"

"When you receive and apply the power of Tao properly," responded Laotzu, "especially in your daily life, there is no need to travel. You see, the saint, although perhaps 47-1 *never going outdoors, yet he* finds he *knows everything under heaven.* Although 47-2 *never looking outside of the window, he can see the Tao of heaven.*

"On the other side of the coin, in the case of 47-3 *he who tries to act, the farther he searches, the less he knows.*

"Armed with the power of Tao, 47-4 *a saint takes no action to investigate, yet knows everything.* 47-5 *He doesn't need to appear everywhere but he is well known.* 47-6 *He doesn't take action, and yet he accomplishes.*"

By now, each of the palace monks mumbled quietly to himself. Dao An could see their mouths moving. Each of them had their hands under the table, either making foul intentioned gestures or holding some baneful object.

Dao An was no stranger to the dark side of the spiritual arts. He'd been trained in some. But at Minglian Shan, the abbot saved destructive arts for punishing traitors and routing murderers or black sorcerers. To use them against this holy sage reeked of evil. How could he serve in the same palace with such vermin?

Yet as Dao An watched, he also saw that the sage appeared to be just as peaceful and radiant as the moment he'd awoke from meditation. Whatever spells the evil monks used appeared impotent against Laotzu.

KoWu, ignorant of the hidden attack against his guest, continued with his questions. "Master, besides practicing the power of Tao, do I also have to study daily affairs and conventional knowledge to increase my wisdom?"

Laotzu shook his head. "No, 48-1 *in the pursuit of studying world affairs, every day your knowledge accumulates.* 48-2 *In the pursuit of the* power of Tao, *every day you abandon* artificial knowledge. 48-3 *You abandon more, you reduce* artificial knowledge, until your power of Tao takes over; then *you no longer need action, you reach non-action.*

"If you act from your own knowledge, then you are bound by the limits of your own capabilities and understanding. However, when performing the power of 48-4 *non-action, there is nothing that cannot be done.* 48-5 *Rule the world by non-action power,* it is true ruling. 48-6 *Rule the world by full action, it is not true ruling.*"

"Master, there are so many people in this city, and some simply won't follow my orders. How should I regulate them to keep them in line?" KoWu complained to the sage.

Laotzu gestured with a flat hand as if to encourage patience. "49-1 *A saint need not be concerned about others. He just lets other people alone, lets their minds do whatever they like.*

"49-2 *Those who are good I treat as good. Those who are not good I also treat as good.* 49-3 *It is* more accurate to say that I broadcast my power of *Te with* the message of *good faith* to them all. 49-4 *I have faith in people who are trustworthy. I also have faith in people who are not trustworthy.* 49-5 *It is* more accurate to say that I broadcast my power of *Te with* the message of *trust* to them all. 49-6 *The saint rules the world by* broadcasting his power of Te through *the heart* with a message *of simplicity and sincerity.* 49-7 *He treats everyone with a childlike mind.*"

While the prince asked his questions, Dao An and Fa Tingtz watched the other palace monks like hawks. Clearly, they tried to cast spells of some kind, but nothing seemed to affect the sage in any negative way they could see. They looked at each other, their eyes sharing both curiosity and concern. Laotzu looked over at each of them and offered a calming smile.

All of a sudden, each of the palace monks froze stiff in their place. Dao An and Fa Tingtz looked at each of them and saw that the monks' hands were all frozen solid under the tables. The monks strained to pull their arms up, but couldn't. Their fingers felt like blocks of ice, no longer able to make the baneful gestures that invoked their talismanic evils. They couldn't say anything, because their mouths wouldn't move. The paralysis left the monks scared out of their wits, but unable to run. Only Dao An and Fa Tingtz paid any attention to the monks, and were the only guests to notice the monks' predicament.

At the head of the table, KoWu grew serious. "Master, as the leader of a critically important city, I have many enemies in neighboring states. Some even wish me dead. How should I protect myself against death threats?"

Laotzu answered, 50-1 *"Stay out* of ordinary life and stay in the power of Tao, *live. Stay in* the ordinary life, and stay out of the power of Tao, *die.* 50-2 *In our life, three out of ten may live after birth, three out of ten may die after birth, and the chance to encounter death in his life while one lived after birth is also three out of ten.* 50-3 *Why so? Because he only tries very hard to live,* but never tries to stay in the power of Tao.

"50-4 *He who truly knows how to live* by the power of Tao *can walk on land without fear of encountering a rhinoceros or tiger, and need not be equipped with armor and weapons when encountering an army.* 50-5 *For* the broadcast power of Tao shields him. With such a shield, *rhinoceroses find no place to thrust their horn, tigers find no place to claw, and weapons find nowhere to place sharp edges.* 50-6 *Why* is this *so? Because he* is shielded with the broadcast power of Tao and *never enters the death zone."*

At this, the sage turned his eyes to each of the palace monks with a kind, forgiving and almost sad smile. The monks each sat stock still, not so much as venturing a blush. Four of them had already given up trying to move, while the other two strained against their own limbs to no avail.

But as Dao An watched the monks, he finally understood what the sage meant. Laotzu's current answer to the prince was right. The power of Tao, since it was the original power, could not be manipulated or harmed through the use of good or evil powers. As the origin of those powers, it would be as if one's own left hand tried to attack his right hand. It just simply wouldn't work. And since the Tao was the omnipresent and most subtle power, no other power could separate from it, much less penetrate it. Anyone wise enough to merge with this power would similarly become impenetrable.

Dao An smiled to himself. At last he'd found a real master. The power of Tao Laotzu spoke of was truly real. It was real enough to neutralize all evil intentions against Laotzu without the sage himself doing anything at all. He relaxed as he realized the sage would be fine regardless of the other monks' spells.

KoWu seemed more animated than usual this evening. He dominated the floor firing one question after another. "Master, every night you speak of Tao and Te. You say that Te arises from Tao, and we use Te to connect to Tao, but yet they aren't the same. What is the difference between the power of Tao and the power of Te?"

51-1 *"All things are created from the* power *of Tao,"* replied Laotzu. *"They are nourished* by the power of Te. 51-2 *They are formed into matter. They are shaped by opposite powers.*

51-3 *Thus the ten thousand things all follow the* power *of Tao and possess the* power *of Te.*

51-4 *Everything, therefore, is not forced or demanded. All are in the way of the nature of things – following the Tao, possessing the Te.* 51-5 *Therefore, all things are created from the power of Tao.* 51-6 *They are nourished, developed, cared for, sheltered, comforted, grown and protected by the* power *of Te.* 51-7 *Creating them without claiming ownership, acting without demanding credit, guiding without taking authority – this is original* power *of Te."*

The prince's son, KoYou, leaned on his elbows mesmerized by the sage's every word. In his adoration, he blurted out, "Master, how can you seem to know everything in this whole world?"

Laotzu laughed at his young friend's innocent compliment. "It is very easy, boy. 52-1 *Since the original* power *of the universe is the mother of all things,* it is actually a conscious being as a whole. So, *knowing the mother* power – the whole thing – comes first. It is like the root. The saint does this by practicing so that his Te can connect to let the power of Tao enter his body and spirit. This way, *one also knows the son's* power – the branches. 52-2 *Knowing the son's* power, the saint succeeds because he is *still also remaining firmly connected with the mother* power." Then Laotzu looked over at Dao An and Fa Tingtz, "If one practices his Te power in this way, *through one's whole life he will encounter no danger."*

Fa Tingtz, like Dao An, was greatly impressed by the sage's invulnerability to the palace monks' spells. Laotzu apparently "encountered no danger," just as he described. Fa Tingtz couldn't help but ask, "Master, how do you achieve this powerful ability?"

The sage replied, 52-3 *"Shut your knowledge, close the door of your cleverness,* and let the power of Tao prevail, *and life is ever full.* If you instead 52-4 *open your knowledge, be busy with all your knowledge,* your situation *and* your *life is beyond hope of salvaging."*

Fa Tingtz followed with a second question, "Master, how can we know we are in the power of Tao?"

The sage had no difficulty keeping up with the fast pace of this evening's questions. He slid right from one topic to another with ease. He continued his explanations to Fa Tingtz and said, "52-5 *One who understands* the power of *the very small possesses insight;* 52-6 *One who observes* the power of *yielding to force also possesses strength.* Using the light of the power of Tao to see, 52-7 *employ one's inner light and return to insight* into even the smallest thing. In this way, you can see through everything while 52-8 *bringing no harm to self. Thus is knowing the constant* power of Tao."

"Master, I hope you will forgive my impatience," KoWu continued, "but I want to reach your level of ability as soon as possible. I want to be the type of ruler you describe. If I increase my regular meditations, and study the wide variety of ancient writings kept in our palace vault, will I reach the power of Tao more quickly?"

"Not necessarily. Keep in mind that 53-1 *if I have clear sense, I will practice the great* power of *Tao and my only fear will be straying from it.* 53-2 *Staying in the great* power of *Tao is easy, but people love to make shortcuts* — they jump out of practicing the power of Tao."

"But perhaps I'm farther along than I think Master," mused the prince. "Den Fah's questions last night got me thinking: since I am successful, have a fancy palace and live a good life, doesn't that prove I possess the power of Tao? Doesn't the power of Tao bless me in order for me to enjoy such success?"

Laotzu frowned at KoWu's arrogance. "53-3 *The court is kept in splendor yet the farm fields are full of weeds and the granaries are empty.* And there are some so-called successful 53-4 *people who wear fine clothes, carry sharp swords* at their sides, *and enjoy their fill of good food and drink. They have a surplus of possessions,* more than they can use. What thieves! 53-5 *This is certainly not the work of* practicing the power of *Tao!"*

This took Prince KoWu aback, as he hadn't expected the scolding. Dumbstruck, he couldn't think of what to ask next.

Laotzu, on the other hand, looked decidedly unrepentant for any discomfort his harsh remarks caused the prince.

To help KoWu save face, Chong Zen leaned over to remind the prince that he was a leader in world affairs. "Your majesty," Chong Zen whispered. "Wouldn't it be prudent to consult the sage on matters of diplomacy?"

Truly, China at that time had many states both large and small. All had different cultures, dialects, and customs, but all had one thing in common: every state wanted to grow larger and more prosperous. Because of this, all states had to defend themselves. To have his finger on the pulse of each state, to foretell potential skirmishes, to thwart possible attacks, was key to KoWu's survival as a leader.

KoWu nodded his thanks to Chong Zen and changed the topic. "This world has many states that all boast different ways of life. They are always ready to confront each other to protect or expand their power. How can one keep abreast of the whole world with his power of Te?" the prince asked.

Laotzu nodded, "There are three steps to achieve this ability. First, you must stay firm in practicing the power of Te. You must be like 54-1 *a good builder* who *builds a foundation that cannot be uprooted. One who knows how to grasp* does so *firmly so that what is grasped does not slip away.* The power of 54-2 *Te* is one that *can even be passed down and honored from generation to generation.*

"Second, you may then 54-3 *apply* the power of Tao *to your self, and the* power of *Te will be real.* Likewise, 54-4 *apply* the power of Tao *to the family, and the* power of *Te will abound.* 54-5 *Apply* the power of Tao *to the village, and the* power of *Te will reach beyond.* 54-6 *Apply* the power of Tao *to the nation, and* the power of *Te will be abundant.* 54-7 *Apply* the power of Tao *to the world, and the* power of *Te will be omnipresent.*

The sage continued, "Third, you can 54-8 *therefore apply the* power of *Te to the whole body to look at the body; apply the* power of *Te to the whole family to look at the family; apply the* power of *Te to the whole village to look at the village; apply the* power of *Te to the entire nation to look at the nation; apply the* power of *Te to the whole world to look at the world.*

"54-9 *How do I know the world? By looking with the* power of *Te!"*

Silence filled the room. Clearly everyone was sated with wisdom for the night, so Laotzu said no more. Prince KoWu rose again, this time to suggest that everyone retire so as to bring their best minds to the next night's forum.

The monks found that as soon as Laotzu finished, they could move again. Nevertheless, they sat where they were, tense and nervous, anxious to leave.

Once the evening session formally adjourned, they were the first to rise and leave the hall. Together, relieved and bewildered, they walked quickly through the courtyard toward the palace gate. They didn't see Dao An and Fa Tingtz following silently behind them.

"What happened?" hissed Hon Su Tz as he led the way through the outer court.

"I don't know! None of our spells worked," cried the monk with the scorpion.

"I couldn't move my arms or my fingers! I felt as if I were made of rock!" exclaimed another.

"Shhhhh…." said another. "We'll figure it out when we get back to the temple."

The ill-fated magicians hurried until they got to the main palace gate. They hoped to leave and make their way to the temple, unobserved, through the quiet city streets. However, as soon as the monks left the palace gates, complete pandemonium ensued.

Screams cut through the stillness of the dark night as Dao An and Fa Tingtz saw Hon Su Tz start ranting and raving like a lunatic. The monk with the scorpion started slapping and itching his skin shouting, "Get them off! Get them off!" Another tore at his hair while laughing hysterically. Another one started to gag and spit.

Whatever mischievous spells they'd sought to place on Laotzu attacked them instead once they left the safety of the palace walls. The flailing, shrieking monks whirled and stumbled as fast as they could down the city thoroughfare. When they finally made it to the temple, they scrambled up the stairs of the temple where they banged on the door. The priest flung the door open and the tormented monks soon disappeared inside.

Dao An and Fa Tingtz had never seen such a sight in their lives! They looked at each other not knowing whether to laugh or fall to the ground in sheer awestruck terror. Instead they bowed their heads humbly as Fa Tingtz whispered to Dao An, "Brother, let this be a lesson to us both." They returned to the palace without a word.

Chapter Eighteen

The Sage Engenders Discussions

When KoWu woke, his wife stood in his chambers, already dressed. She stood with her back to him at first, but then turned around as he roused.

"Dear, come sit by me," KoWu offered. His wife looked away again. Clearly she was upset. "What's wrong?" he asked.

Zhu Xiao Hua began to pace slowly back and forth with her arms folded across her chest. She didn't speak, but her eyes darted at KoWu each time she turned.

"You are angry, wife," KoWu said as he pushed aside his bed covering. "Are the girls causing trouble again?"

"The girls?" she bristled. "And what would you know of your daughters? You have no time these days for them. Only for Laotzu!"

"Oh, I see," nodded KoWu. "And what would you have me do? Leave our guest to host his own banquet? Set aside my duties for a day and weave flower crowns?"

"You don't care about your daughters, and you don't care about your son!"

"KoYou? What has he done?"

"It's not what he's done. It is the fact that you cannot see that he is under that strange man's spell. You can't see because you are under his spell too."

"What strange man? Laotzu?"

"Oh!" the queen stomped her foot in frustration. While always the picture of calmness and propriety in public, behind closed doors she wasn't afraid to speak her mind or show a bit of temper.

"The sage is quite harmless and teaches strong wisdom," the prince said calmly. "I think KoYou is quite fond of him."

"He sees you fawning over him night after night and believing this Tao talk, and so he worships him too. Is that so hard to understand?" The queen spoke faster as her anger built. "I find Laotzu rude, addled and worse, a bringer of evil to our house."

"Evil?" said KoWu. "It was his power of Tao that saved this city from the barbarians?"

"So he says," the queen argued. "How arrogant! I have seen this city saved many times from danger. It is our own gods who protect us, not some foreign Tao god. You did not grow up here so you easily stray from our beliefs and embrace those of a foreigner."

"Oh, so you would join my critics' voices and call me a foreigner too, then?" KoWu's face flushed with rage. "Let me remind you that it was I who brought peace inside this town, and it was I who brought you into this palace."

"But you refuse to pay homage to our local ways, and you refuse to worship at the local temple and make offerings to our local gods. You dally with dangerous notions from every master who wanders down the road, even crazy ones riding on an ox!"

"When have I ever failed to provide gold for a temple feast? When have I not appeared at a temple ceremony? When have I not given you all that you ask to keep your local customs? When have I imposed any of my traditions on you?" KoWu challenged.

"You do only what you must, but in your heart you never accepted our ways," Zhu Xiao Hua cried. "You don't go to our monks for wisdom, but keep your own countryman Fa Tingtz glued to your elbow."

KoWu shook his head. "I have provided you with a good life. I have always been gentle and kind to you. We have shared many joys together over the years."

"And that's why it is so sad to see you pulled away from me," the queen now broke into tears. "You and KoYou, all you think about now are Laotzu and his Tao. I see your eyes and I watch you talk. You are changing from the man I knew."

"I am the same," he insisted.

KoWu stopped and thought. Perhaps he lied to his wife, and perhaps he had changed. All that he learned from Laotzu did make him look at the world and people around him in a new light.

"Well consider our son!" the queen said. "You are from another city, but he was born here. He will rule here for the rest of his life. Would you have him doubt the religion of his ancestors, and fall away from the temple traditions? If he does it will go hard on him, not only with the people of this town, but from the gods themselves. Our city could be destroyed!"

KoWu had no way to comfort her now. If he assured her that the city would not be destroyed, she would accuse him of not believing in her gods.

Instead KoWu replied soberly, "Young people should be exposed to new ideas, and new ways of thinking. Besides, Laotzu has done nothing to discredit the temple or tear KoYou away."

"He behaved very rudely to the priest on our visit," said the queen.

"He made somewhat of a curt remark, true, but perhaps the sage wanted only to teach the priest an important truth," KoWu defended.

"It was insulting. And he is worse than rude, he has powerful witchcraft!" said Zhu Xiao Hua.

"Witchcraft? Wife, he is teaching about the power of Tao. It is a totally different thing." KoWu knew he couldn't explain the Tao to his wife and how the original energy differed from witchcraft. Her narrow views and blind devotion to her beliefs formed an impenetrable wall.

"It's witchcraft! Pure and simple. I know you think I'm stupid. But I know a few things. It is witchcraft. That's why he didn't get harmed by those spells...."

"Spells? What spells?" KoWu asked.

"Never mind," the queen looked away. She'd revealed more than she should have and she knew it.

"Woman, are you telling me that those palace monks tried to place spells on our guest?"

"They only try to protect you! They serve you with undying loyalty and do not wish to see our palace destroyed by foreign powers and lies from this Laotzu's lips," said the queen.

"Ha, ha, ha," KoWu burst into guffaws. "And whatever spells they used didn't work on Laotzu, hey? Ba, ha ha...."

"So you laugh!" shrieked the queen. "All that it means is that your sage has great evil power that he could turn to use on you someday."

"My dear, I'm afraid that you are greatly confused. That you could call the sage evil, while those monks used spells to try and cause harm..."

"They did harm for good reason," she cried. "I only wish they'd succeeded. You mark my words, husband, bad things will come of this sage's visit. Bad things...." She turned away, her face now streaked with tears, and stormed out of the room.

KoWu watched her go. This wasn't their first argument, and it wouldn't be their last. He respected his wife's courage to speak her mind, no matter how implacable it was on spiritual matters. He bristled, however, at the thought that her friendship with that oily priest brought his influence into their private lives.

This argument would end like the others, thought KoWu. Zhu Xiao Hua would take a large sum of money from the palace treasury and give it to the temple, as if to dare KoWu's rebuke. KoWu, as usual, would say nothing, and after a day or two of silence between them, the whole row would blow over.

*　　　*　　　*

"Come on!" urged KoYou. He waited at Yin Lian's door leading two horses from the palace stables. "It's a beautiful day, and we can go riding outside the walls together."

"But don't you have lessons with your new tutor, Chong Zen? Don't you have to serve Master Laotzu?" asked the pleasantly surprised young woman.

"No. Chong Zen and Pen Hei are spending the day with Laotzu to go over Pen Hei's notes. They want to be certain that the scribe is using the correct characters," the boy explained. "I have the day off for once, and we can go riding before the cold weather comes."

"Okay," replied Yin Lian. "But I must get my other clothes."

"I'll wait."

When she finally emerged from the stately home, she wore linen robes split up the middle like large pantaloons. Over these she wore a plain but stunning woolen cape tied around her waist by a leather strap. She carried a silk bundle holding her double swords, just in case they met danger or in case KoYou wanted to teach her some new moves.

She straddled the brown horse that stood beside KoYou's favorite black stallion. She noticed that Lo Yintz had tied green ribbons in both horses' manes as her special way to say hello to both Yin Lian and KoYou.

Since all remained quiet on the plains after Laotzu's stormy arrival, the gatekeeper smiled and nodded his permission for them to ride out into the countryside. The crisp autumn breeze ruffled their hair and robes as Yin Lian followed KoYou's horse down the south road and through the farm fields toward the riverbank. Their young and agile bodies moved in perfect synchrony with the horses, as they darted back and forth around scrub brush and rocks. They both knew this land like their own palms, and guided the horses effortlessly through the well-worn landscape.

Eventually, they came to the river's edge, and slowed the horses to a walk. They rode single file along the riverbank, until they reached a secluded outcropping of rock with overhanging trees. Without speaking they simultaneously dismounted and tied the animals to a tree with enough lead to allow them to drink.

KoYou climbed up the rock face easily and stood on top waving his sword like a conquering hero. Yin Lian laughed and then pretended to be a helpless maiden besieged by bandits. KoYou jumped to her rescue with flair and daring, cutting the imaginary bandits to ribbons.

They both collapsed into peals of laughter. When they could finally catch their breath, they got up and walked together toward the river. A large flat rock, only half shaded from the warm sun, served as a sprawling table where they could lean back on their elbows and watch the river. They sat together to enjoy a rare moment of shared solitude. Fingers of light filtered through the drying tree leaves and played patterns over their robes.

"Yin Lian, you have known me for longer than anyone else besides my own family," KoYou started.

"And I'll probably end up knowing you even longer than they," she retorted, alluding to their planned marriage.

"Do you think I would make a good king?" KoYou looked at her.

"Of course you will," she answered.

"No, really. Seriously think about it. You know how I really feel inside, how I yearn to travel and learn more about the things that Master Laotzu teaches. You know how I hate killing and hate how my father has to bark orders all day and all night. Do you think I will ever grow to enjoy it?"

"I know that you will always do what is in your heart, and because of that you will always do well," Yin Lian assured him.

"That sounds good and is easy to say," KoYou replied as he looked away and started picking up pebbles to toss into the stream. "But what if my heart told me to walk away from becoming king and took me down a completely different road."

"Then whatever road you traveled, you would still do well because you followed your heart," Yin Lian answered. She wondered why KoYou's eyes looked so far away.

"Do you believe in destiny?" he asked her.

"Well, kind of. I understand what the word implies. But I guess I still think we have choices to make," said Yin Lian.

"Well I believe in destiny. But the trouble is, destiny can be very confusing," mused KoYou.

"What do you mean?"

"Look at my life right now. I shouldn't even be alive. The barbarians should have killed me when I was six, like they killed my father. But here I am. And then, not only did I cheat death, but I was soon adopted by a prince, and stand to inherit his palace and rule West Peace. Is that destiny?" asked KoYou.

"I don't know, probably." Yin Lian stayed on the rock while KoYou stood up so that he could throw his pebbles with his full arm.

"So perhaps destiny wants me to be a king then."

"I don't think destiny is the kind of thing you can figure out in your head," said Yin Lian. "I think destiny just happens."

"But then," KoYou didn't really hear her reply. He seemed lost in his own thoughts. "Then this strange monk comes to the city and a great windstorm vanquishes the entire barbarian army. This master speaks of such truth and holds such amazing power. Everything in my chest bursts to be near him, to learn what he teaches, to become like him. Is that destiny? If I hadn't been the prince's son and living in West Peace's palace today, I wouldn't have met Laotzu."

"True," said Yin Lian. "We are fortunate to talk with him face to face. No other young people in the city even get that chance."

"So then what is my destiny? To be a king or to follow Laotzu?"

"Maybe you can do both," replied Yin Lian.

"I don't know. That is what my father thinks he can do. That is why he wants to push Laotzu to stay and not travel west. But if Laotzu stays, my mother will be very upset. He frightens her. I heard my parents arguing this morning. She doesn't want me to follow Laotzu's teachings because she is afraid I will abandon faith in our local gods."

"Your mother is a very devout woman. She is only afraid because she cares about you so much," Yin Lian comforted him.

"But it makes everything so confusing. If I follow my heart I might break the hearts of others." His stone landed with a loud splash in the river, refusing to skip.

"What? Are you thinking of following Laotzu then?" Yin Lian exclaimed.

"I don't know. Maybe," KoYou confided, glad they were alone. Such talk from a prince's son would be quite scandalous if other ears could hear.

"Think of it, Yin Lian. If I stay here, I know what life will hold for the rest of my days. Every year is a stretch of squabbles to settle, barbarians to feud with, palace gossip, diplomatic banquets. These matters are exciting for a while, but year after year, it's like an endless circle that goes nowhere. Sure, you and I would always have each other and it would be very enjoyable. We would have suitably bright and handsome children. We would raise them to do what we do. We would all live in the same palace until the end of our days, and our children would continue the endless, aimless circle."

"You make it sound like a terrible chore," Yin Lian replied.

"Don't you think about such things?" he asked.

"Well, yes. You might not believe me, but I do. It is harder to be a queen, you know. A queen must always smile and always be polite. I would never be allowed to do my sword dances in public, nor would I enjoy rides in the country with you like right now. I would be stuck in the palace supervising servants and choosing curtains and planning menus. But I don't worry about all that, even though that is not my nature. I guess I figured as long as I have you by my side, it would always be an adventure," Yin Lian looked at him.

Inside, Yin Lian felt a hole open inside her heart. Would he really leave with Laotzu? She knew if he left, a very dreary life awaited her. Betrothed to a prince's son, she wouldn't be allowed to marry anyone else. And she wouldn't want to anyway. She would probably spend the rest of her days caring for her aging mother, and then caring for the family business after her mother died.

"So should we both keep plodding along then, doing what everybody expects us to do? Is that our destiny?" asked KoYou.

"What will you choose?" she countered. She tried to hide her fears as best she could.

"I don't know. How could anyone make such decisions?" KoYou threw the whole handful of pebbles into the stream and sat back down on the rock next to Yin Lian. He placed a hand on her shoulder and kissed her cheek.

They sat in silence while Yin Lian quietly contemplated decisions of her own. What would she do if KoYou left? What about her own desire to learn more about the Tao and its power?

Suddenly, Yin Lian spoke. "When the other trader spits!"

"What?" KoYou asked.

"Oh, it's just something my father used to say."

"Tell me," he urged.

"Well, every time my father went to market to bargain over a large order of silk, my mother would ask him 'Wong Xu, what is your purchase price today?' My father would wink back at her and say 'I'll know when the other trader spits!'"

She continued, "You see, my father always told us that when you drive a bargain as low as it can go, the other trader will try to bluff you into paying more. My father knew when he reached the lowest price, because the other trader would pretend it was too low and spit or kick the wheel of his cart. That would be the price my father would stick to. He would never plan in advance."

"So why do you think of that now?" KoWu asked.

"Well, whenever I don't know what to choose, I remember what my father said. I don't make any plans until I know for sure. Something will happen at the last minute that will let me know the right choice to make. Like 'when the other trader spits.'"

"Oh, I see," KoYou nodded. Then he looked at the side of her face as she stared at the river. How could he be so lucky as to know a girl like Yin Lian?

If there was such a thing as destiny, he thought, Yin Lian was proof that it must be very kind at times.

Chapter Nineteen

The Seventh Night with the Taoist Guest

When KoYou returned to the palace, KoWu instructed him to send a special invitation to Yin Lian and her widowed mother, Wong Yuen, to join the royal family and their guest Laotzu at the evening banquet. KoWu had no idea that the young man had just spent the better part of the day with his fiancée. Nevertheless, KoYou gladly ran back to Yin Lian's house to fulfill his father's order.

Wong Yuen was no stranger to the palace. As a wealthy silk dowager, she often counseled the prince on investments in prize tapestries. She was proud of her daughter's engagement and always did her best to flatter her daughter's future in-laws. She hadn't come to the earlier banquets, and KoWu realized that she might have assumed she wouldn't be welcome as an unescorted woman to a formal assembly.

KoWu saw his responsibility to rectify the oversight and make sure Wong Yuen could come to at least one of the banquets. If she were left out because KoWu hadn't thought to provide her an escort, the city gossip would report it as a snub. KoYou escorting the mother and daughter would ease any awkwardness the widow felt, and also give her a special position at the evening affair.

Many considered Wong Yuen an old battleaxe. KoWu, on the other hand, admired Wong Yuen. She'd done a commendable job continuing her husband's business after his death. Her daughter would make a fine wife for his son, and having her family's wealth tied to his own only strengthened his power.

When the time came, the two ladies arrived in their finest attire. Yin Lian, whom KoYou had last seen in riding clothes, wore a cream silk gown with several silk sashes tied around her long waist. Several chains of gold and pearls glistened around her neck. She rarely wore such formal accessories, as they weren't suited to sword dancing, nor to her personality. But KoYou could certainly appreciate that his favorite swordswoman could truly be feminine and beautiful on a night like this.

KoYou always treated Wong Yuen with the same courtesy he would show his own mother. He extended his elbow for Wong Yuen's hand as he escorted her and Yin Lian to the main hall.

Guests milled around the corridors as servants offered refreshment. When dinner was ready, Dai Dong ushered the guests into the main hall, where their eyes took in yet another sumptuous feast. They sat down to roast lamb and vegetables, several varieties of dried fish, and sweet compotes of autumn fruits. The rice filled the room with the aroma of saffron that Abudamancus had brought to the kitchen as a gift for KoWu's wife.

KoWu's wife, however, once again sent her apologies to KoWu and the group for her absence. She gave the excuse that her youngest daughter was sick and needed her by her side. The real truth was that Zhu Xiao Hua could not face her husband so soon after an argument. She feared that Laotzu's presence would upset her even more. Yet Zhu Xiao Hua had to send an excuse for Wong Yuen's sake. Fortunately, her absence gave Wong Yuen the privilege of being the most honored woman at the table that evening. That would be a consolation for Wong Yuen.

Wong Yuen enjoyed the role and sat at the head of the table next to KoYou and KoWu. She gave directions to the head servant to clear the serving trays when the last guest finished his meal, and told Dai Dong when and what wine should be served. The capable woman could take charge of any affair, and looked forward to having more influence at the palace after KoYou and Yin Lian married.

After the meal, Laotzu went into a brief meditation. When the din of conversation died down, the sage slowly opened his eyes and surveyed his audience. He smiled and nodded at Yin Lian and then, taking in the grand lady, gave a small wink to her mother Wong Yuen.

The widow blushed that the teacher flirted with her like that, and gently shook a scolding finger at him. But inside she smiled. No man had given her as much as a second glance in this dusty border town since her husband died. A wink like that was worth more than gold. Now she knew why her daughter referred to him as "Uncle Laotzu." He was charming!

KoWu wasted no time and began the evening's session in earnest:

"Master, if the power of Te is so useful, so wonderful, and so powerful, I surely want to develop my power of Te as much as possible. If I try my best to eat properly, live a good life, and exercise hard to become strong, can I increase my power of Te?"

Laotzu waved his hand to indicate KoWu was on the wrong track. "You must follow the way Tao works. You are talking about artificial physical strength, not the integrity of the power of Te. 55-1 *He who is filled with the* power of *Te is* so because he meditates *like an infant.*

"Look at this: 55-2 *poisonous insects will not sting a newborn baby; ferocious beasts will not pounce upon him* and *birds of prey will not attack him* because he radiates very rich power of Te.

"55-3 *A newborn's bones are weak, his muscles soft, but his grip is firm.* 55-4 *He has no experience of the union of man and woman, but his sexual energy is whole. It is because his life energy is full and strong.* 55-5 *He could cry all day without becoming hoarse. It is because he is in perfect harmony* with the power of Te. 55-6 *Knowing harmony* with the power of Te *is called the constancy. Knowing constancy is called wisdom.*"

The servant women blushed at the mention of the baby's sexual energy, and the union of man and woman. Wong Yuen didn't bat an eye. She'd heard much coarser talk from men in the silk trading world. Some very bold talk often flew her way when she drove a hard bargain.

Laotzu continued, "Most people aren't content to be like the newborn, working toward the ability to be in harmony with their power of Te. They don't realize that 55-7 *trying to improve one's well-being by living in a gross life leads to disaster.* 55-8 *Trying to exhaust your life energy causes strain. Striving to be big and strong is followed only by exhaustion and age.* 55-9 *This is not the way the* power of *Tao works. Whatever is contrary to how the* power of *Tao works will not last long.*"

KoWu offered his second question for the evening. "Master, how should I practice to increase my power of Tao in daily life?"

Laotzu responded, "56-1 *Those who really know* the power of Tao *do not talk* about the Tao, instead they practice the power of Tao. *Those who talk* about the power of Tao and don't practice the power of Tao *do not know the truth* of the power of Tao.

"To practice the power of Tao, you must first feel the power of Tao. And to feel the power of Tao, you must feel your own power of Te. To feel your own power of Te, you must 56-2 *shut* the inflow of *knowledge,* and *close* your contact with your *smart senses* to eventually feel the power of Tao.

"And in daily life, one must follow the power of Tao and *act dull rather than be sharp.* 56-3 *Free from one's problems, store the brightness* — the brightness obtained from practicing the power of Tao.

"Yet you should also 56-4 *be at home with the down to earth. This is the state in which you are united with the power of Tao.* As soon as you reach this state, you are therefore 56-5 *unconcerned with friends and enemies, with gain and harm, with honor and disgrace.* 56-6 *This therefore is the most preferred achievement in the world.*"

"Master, I have tried very hard in every possible measure to be a good ruler, yet there are many goals I haven't been able to achieve. No matter how skilled my soldiers are, we can't win every battle. No matter how many well-constructed laws I set forth, there is still trouble in our streets. Despite wise counsel and careful action, why can't I achieve my goals?" asked the prince.

"Most people would try to 57-1 *rule a nation with normal justice and wage war with unusual tactics.* There is nothing wrong with this," Laotzu explained. "Anybody would try every commonsense way to be a good ruler. But if you want to be the true leader of the world, you must 57-2 *practice* the power of Tao and exert the power of *non-action to govern the world.* Then you can really rule the world.

"57-3 *How do I know this is so? Because of the following mistakes:* When a ruler tries harder, 57-4 *the more taboos for people there are, the poorer are the people.* 57-5 *When men have more sharpened weapons, there is more chaos in the country.* 57-6 *The more men rely on cleverness and ingenuity, the more novelties abound.* 57-7 *When rules and regulations grow, there are more thieves and robbers.*

"57-8 *Therefore the saint says: 'I apply the power of non-action and the people are orderly.* 57-9 *I am* broadcasting the message of being *in stillness and the people become honest. I am* broadcasting the message of being *at peace and the people prosper.* 57-10 *I broadcast the message of having no desires and the people return to lives of simplicity and goodness.'*"

"Master, could you talk more about the right way to apply the power of Tao to rule?" the prince implored.

"Certainly," Laotzu agreed. "We all know that 58-1 *with less government the people are simple. When the government is intrusive, the people are sneaky.*

"But the fact is that without applying the power of Tao to rule, counting only on human knowledge to rule, 58-2 *happiness is rooted in misery, and that misery hides underneath happiness. Who knows where this will end?*

"58-3 *And as soon as there appears to be no honesty, honesty becomes abnormal,* 58-4 *and goodness can turn into evil. For a long time, people don't know whom to follow.* 58-5 *Therefore the saint's* method is to apply the power of Tao to rule and follow the message from Tao to rule. Because he does this, all of the resulting *policies are straight but not stiff, sharp but not cutting,* **58-6** *straightforward but not losing control, shining but not unbearably blinding."*

"Master, you emphasize the importance of following the power of Tao and applying the power of Te to rule. In this way, how long can one expect to rule?" KoWu asked.

"**59-1** *In dealing with people, and* in the pursuit of *connecting to* the power of *heaven, nothing is better than 'Se,' storing up the power* of Te. **59-2** *Only by practicing charging up and storing the power* of Te *can one be well prepared.* **59-3** *Well prepared ahead of time, one must heavily charge and store up his* power of Te. **59-4** *Armed with heavily charged up and stored up* power of *Te, one overcomes anything. If one can overcome anything, the potential is unlimited.* **59-5** *With unlimited potential, one can easily rule the state. With this as the foundation of the state, it will last long,"* said the sage.

"I use the word 'Se' meaning 'thrift.' I say it to mean that you must be diligent in bringing in the power bit by bit until you save a large volume of power. You must also be 'Se', or thrifty, when you expend it. Do not spend your power needlessly or unwisely," warned the master.

"Practice storing up Te power, **59-6** *as if planting deep roots; stand firm, everlasting, and long-visualizing,* then you may rule for a long time."

At this point, a golden bell chimed. All eyes turned toward Dai Dong who announced the arrival of a special gift.

Abudamancus, the gregarious caravan leader, stood tall and ordered his own servants to bring in several large jars of wine from his native country, Dazos, by the Red Sea. Men with burgundy turbans and wide burgundy sashes around their white linen pantaloons carried several large jars on poles into the palace hall. The jars offered a precious treat for Prince KoWu and his guests. The wine was of Dazos' best quality, both sweet and smooth.

After one sip, KoWu was so delighted that he heartily encouraged all of his guests to enjoy the gift as servants brought in cups for everyone. The assembly rose from their mats to stretch and to enjoy the wine as they mingled among each other.

After awhile, the whole party seemed quite intoxicated by Abudamancus' strong wine – that is most everyone but Laotzu, young KoYou and his fiancé Yin Lian.

The dignitaries broke for an intermission and clustered in groups to discuss business and share jokes.

Yin Lian and KoYou took the opportunity to leave Wong Yuen's side and wander over toward Laotzu.

Yin Lian heard the important reference to the issue of 'Se,' to store up the power. To her it seemed like an important point since Laotzu emphasized it quite clearly. Yin Lian whispered to KoYou to ask Laotzu how to store up the power of Tao. She knew she shouldn't ask publicly, for in this formal assembly it wouldn't be right for a young girl to address the prince's guest directly. She could ask Uncle Laotzu her own questions out by the stable, but here inside the palace, it was a different kettle of fish.

KoYou quietly tugged Laotzu's sleeve. Laotzu smiled at the two and motioned for them to come close and sit down.

"Teacher, we want to know more about storing up the Te power," KoYou told him.

The party was so noisy that few listened to Laotzu when he started to answer KoYou's question on how to store up the Te power. Most guests figured that questions from a young and inexperienced boy couldn't be very important and allowed Laotzu to indulge the prince's son while they talked of more important matters.

Chong Zen would have stood by KoYou's side, except Wong Yuen detained him, eager to get to know her future son-in-law's new tutor.

KoWu looked pleased that his son had the initiative to ask the sage a question and nodded from across the room toward KoYou with approval. He then resumed his talk with Abudamancus about the raids the Dazos traveling party endured on their way to China.

Meanwhile, Laotzu held both of the young people's hands. "Son and sweet one, this is a very important issue. Listen closely. You must first bring your body into a relaxed state. Calm your mind and breathe naturally. Second, pay attention to your entire body. Do this slowly, one part of your body at a time, until you can pay attention to your whole body inside and out. Then thirdly, you must use your pure mind to feel the life energy, Chi, flowing naturally throughout your body."

"Pardon me, Master. Could you slow down a bit as you explain, so that I can practice this while I follow your instructions?" asked KoYou. Some nearby guests who'd only been half-listening to Laotzu and the boy now chortled to themselves about some gossip. The party noise all around him made it hard for KoYou to listen and concentrate.

"Of course, son, take your time," Laotzu paused and waved his flywhisk occasionally, smiling at the laughing group of men next to KoYou.

"I feel something now. I feel light and relaxed," KoYou told the sage, with his eyes closed and focused inside.

"Me too!" whispered Yin Lian. "I feel my body becoming more relaxed and warmness spreading on the inside."

"Excellent," smiled Laotzu. "Now the fourth step is to use your undivided mind to bring that feeling inward and shrink or concentrate it into your spine. Be gentle and delicate, but don't let go. Seal in the energy."

"Whoa!" cried the young prince, "What a shock. I feel a warm thrill-like feeling filling my spine and see a flash of light in my head!"

Yin Lian strove to keep her ladylike composure, but she too, could feel the excitement of energy moving into her spine. Other guests continued to chuckle and talk, but Dao An, the visiting monk, also drew closer to Laotzu and listened attentively.

"Very well," Laotzu continued, "hold the feeling, plus now imagine there is rain showering from above." Laotzu raised his right hand and pointed to the ceiling. Closing his eyes, he closed his thumb and last two fingers, leaving only his index and middle fingers extended toward the sky. Pointing upward, he concentrated and went into a meditative trance.

"I feel a sensitive tingling all over my skin," KoYou exclaimed. Dao An, sitting across the floor from KoYou could also feel the chilling effect.

"Son," Laotzu whispered to KoYou and Yin Lian, "absorb that tingling feeling. Pull it into your spine. Store it firmly and do not waste it. Take it all, from your skin into your whole body and then pack it into your spine." **(figure 9)**

Only Dao An could hear what Laotzu taught the two young people, since the clamor of the guests filled the room. All the guests except watchful Dao An figured Laotzu played children's games with the two and paid no attention.

KoYou and Yin Lian could feel a shower of invisible power from all around them, like a drizzling rain landing on the skin of their entire body. They followed Laotzu's instructions faithfully, and absorbed it into their body and pulled it into their spine.

"Store it repeatedly and your Te power will increase in volume and intensity. Then you can use it for a good purpose," Laotzu advised. "But

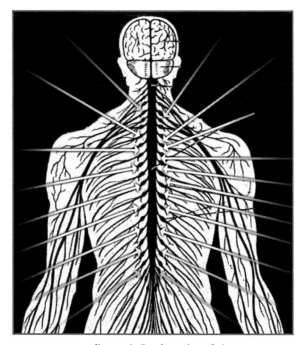

figure 9 *Condense into Spine*

remember to be 'Se!' Be thrifty and do not waste your power of Te. When you use it, it drains fast. When you try to replenish it, it takes it in a penny at a time, bit by bit. So be thrifty. Be 'Se.'"

KoYou and Yin Lian stood and bowed to the sage, then returned back to their seats.

Fa Tingtz only had one cup of wine. As KoWu's spiritual advisor, he spent the evening in sober brooding over Laotzu's teachings. Although he'd studied many old writings, what Laotzu said was new information he hadn't seen before. Each evening Fa Tingtz carefully weighed Laotzu's words. Although he could find no fault with them, he worried that Laotzu might be like those other sorcerers who came into a palace and beguiled its leaders with magic tricks. He'd heard stories of charismatic monks who used their powers to control a king and even drive him to suicide so that they could assume power. Fa Tingtz did not know whether to be alarmed or comforted last night when the palace monks' mischievous spells turned back upon themselves.

Fa Tingtz hailed from a traditional school that believed that the heavens were divided between a good god and an evil god. He had never heard of an all-encompassing power of Tao that created and ruled over both. He worried that this talk of "Tao" might be a trick of the evil god to lure KoWu away from allegiance to just and benevolent action. Fa Tingtz' conservative caution when it came to spiritual matters was one reason KoWu trusted him.

The guests settled back into their places and soon quieted down.

With a great display of prudence and concern, Fa Tingtz asked Laotzu, "Master, every state and every temple all worship gods, ghosts, or the devil. Some of the priests are praying for the power of God to bless and protect their state. Some are even capable of applying the power of the devil to harm other states or specific people. It sounds as if the power of Te is overwhelmingly powerful. Will the power of Te hurt anyone? Or will it cause anyone else to turn the power of the devil on us in return to hurt us?"

Laotzu understood Fa Tingtz' concern and the sincerity underneath it. He knew Fa Tingtz genuinely cared about KoWu and his welfare, so Laotzu wanted to reassure him. "60-1 *Ruling a big country is like cooking a small fish*; be skillful and gentle. When a saintly ruler broadcasts the power of Tao, being skillful and gentle, this will render evil's spiritual power harmless. And since the saint broadcasts the message through his power of Te, and since both evil and people are in the network of the power of Tao, evil and people cannot hurt each other but instead live in perfect harmony.

"Just like cooking a small fish, do not turn or poke unnecessarily. Be gentle, let the heat – or the power of Tao – take its course, until it is done. Cook but do not overcook. When the power of Tao is in action, the spiritual power of evil, which is equally powerful to that of God's spiritual power, will lose its function and harm no one."

The sage continued, "60-2 *Ruling the world with* the broadcasting power of *Tao, evil will lose its power.* 60-3 *It isn't that evil has no spiritual power, but rather evil's spiritual power will become harmless to the people* if the power of Tao prevails in the state.60-4 *Not only will the spiritual power of evil harm no one, the saint* and the message broadcast through the power of Te also *harms no one.* 60-5 *Both powers*, the power of Te broadcast from the true saint, and the evil power exerted by the evil forces within the broadcast power of Tao's network, *cannot hurt each other, and therefore the* power of *Te returns to the original state*: the Tao."

215

"See here, my good man," said Laotzu. The teacher reached for a bamboo twig by the sand pit, which the kneeling servant quickly offered him. Fa Tingtz and several other guests came to the pit to watch as Laotzu drew several circles in the sand. He pointed to each circle to show how the all-encompassing power of Tao enveloped both good and evil power as well as the Te power. He explained how connecting with the power of Tao through the Te allowed a message to penetrate through the entire network of Tao. **(figure 10)**

Fa Tingtz seemed relieved. He hadn't fully understood what the sage tried to tell him, and the circles Laotzu drew in the sand helped him only a little. Yet this sage seemed committed to a path of doing no harm. His teachings might be complex and mysterious, but Fa Tingtz was convinced they were either benevolent signposts, or at worst, harmless conundrums.

KoWu nodded to Fa Tingtz and resumed his place at the center of attention. With yet another question on government, KoWu posed:

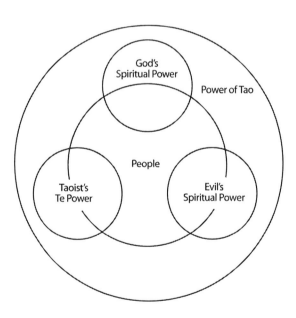

figure 10

"Master, I am ruling the most important frontier city, located at the juncture of many states both large and small. How should I deal with other larger states or a smaller state? There are so many struggles for power, what is the best way? Does the power of Tao also apply to such matters of diplomacy?"

"From the viewpoint of the power of Tao, 61-1 *a large country is like a river delta. Where streams flow to meet is like the mother of the world,*" answered Laotzu.

"*61-2 The female always overcomes the male with stillness, and remains still and lower in position. 61-3 Therefore if a large country takes a lower position than a smaller country, it will conquer the smaller country. 61-4 And if a small country takes a lower position to a large country, it can affiliate with the large country. 61-5 Therefore those who would be great should yield, and those who are great become so by yielding. 61-6 A large country wishes to expand its oversight; a small country needs to serve another. 61-7 If each finds what it wants, then it is right for the large country to yield.*"

All this talk of larger countries made KoWu remember his father, the king. If KoWu had a difficult job, he knew that his father had even more complex problems to contend with. If KoWu could somehow use this great force to benefit his father as well, what a gift that would be!

"Master, can I offer the power of Tao to my superior?" asked KoWu.

Laotzu nodded affirmatively."62-1 *The* power of *Tao is the source of the ten thousand things. 62-2 It is the treasure of the good man, and even also well kept by the bad man. 62-3 Beautiful words can buy honor; deeds that appear honorable can win respect. 62-4 Even if a man is bad, how can anyone abandon it?* Can one abandon the power of Tao? 62-5 *Therefore on the day the emperor takes his throne, or the three ministers of state are installed, do not send a gift of jade and a team of four horses. Instead, stay still and offer the* power of the *Tao to them.*"

His new scholar, Chong Zen, reported to KoWu that he'd found references to a power similar to this Tao among older writings from previous scribes. Chong Zen explained that it was hard to tell from the writings whether the power was evil or good, because all reference to it placed it above such considerations. So KoWu asked, "Master, why in the old days did people, both good and bad, treat the power of Tao with such respect?"

Laotzu answered, 62-6 "*Why did everyone like the power of the Tao so much in the past? Isn't it because you can get what you need and are redeemed when you sin? 62-7 Therefore this is the most valued treasure under heaven.*"

Indeed it seemed to be the world's most valuable treasure, thought KoWu. But how would he find the time to meditate and practice these methods in his demanding life? Somehow he must!

His ninth and final question for the night was one of exasperation. "Master, how difficult is it to practice the power of Tao?"

Laotzu looked KoWu in the eye. He could empathize with this strong prince who must shoulder so many burdens. "Just stay in the power of Tao, 63-1 *practice non-action* power *and execute by non-doing power as if tasting the tasteless.* 63-2 *Regard the small as if it were large, and the few as if it were many.* 63-3 *Counter hostilities with the* power of Te. 63-4 *Plan for difficulties while a situation is still simple to solve, act on big things while they are still small.* 63-5 *In the universe, difficult things start out easy. In the universe, large things arise from the small.*

"63-6 *The saint does not strive to be great, and eventually achieves greatness.*

63-7 *Otherwise, those who make quick promises rarely earn trust. Those who regard things lightly end up with plenty of difficulties.* 63-8 *Because the saint respects difficulties,* and always confronts difficulties with the power of non-action, *as a result he has no difficulties.*"

KoWu nodded. He might not understand the sage fully, but Laotzu did seem to stress that achieving the power of Tao was indeed possible, even for a prince.

The guests nodded too, only they nodded from sleepiness as it grew late and the wine had settled into their bones. KoWu clapped twice to clear everyone's heads and adjourned the evening's festivities by thanking Laotzu and his guests. He gave a special thanks to Abudamancus for both the saffron and the wine, to which all present heartily applauded.

KoYou walked Yin Lian and her mother to the palace gate and advised a guard to see them home.

As he walked back to the cottage to see if Laotzu needed anything before going to sleep, KoYou stopped and stood still under the stars. "Why can't they feel it?" he wondered. "They ask so many questions, but they never stop to just try and feel."

Back in the palace hall, as the dignitaries made their exit bows and filed into the hall, KoWu remained seated, rubbing his chin. He had so much to think about. It seemed clear that this powerful master had much to offer, but why did it confuse him so?

"Even princes need sleep to understand so many things," KoWu reminded himself.

Now alone, he rose quietly to find Dai Dong waiting outside in the hall. Giving his valet the order to prepare his bed, KoWu ran his hand along the stone walls that led back to the family rooms. The cold rock that scraped his hands felt solid and real to his fingers. Somehow it settled the fog swimming in his head.

A candle glowed from his chamber doorway. He saw the figure of his wife asleep on his bed. She must have had a change of heart since their argument this morning, he thought. She hated discord between them as much as he did. She probably wanted to greet him with an apology, but fell fast asleep as the evening grew late.

It was the peaceful time of night when the palace slept – one of the few moments he could exhale and forget he was a prince. He draped his robe across Dai Dong's waiting arms, and dismissed him.

Sliding under the bedcovers next to his wife's warm body, he lay awake for a while staring into the candle flame. What if he'd been born an ordinary man? Or a monk? Could he then have followed Laotzu and learned the ways of Tao and Te? Imagining a simpler life, one free of care and worry, the prince drifted off to sleep.

Chapter Twenty

A Stablegirl and Her Many Teachers

The next morning, Laotzu came to the stable and rounded the corner of the stall where he could see the stable girl Lo Yintz brushing Ox. At only thirteen years old, the girl lived a life of hard work. She was pretty, but not in the way that city boys would notice. Her skin was tanned and her hands rough from labor. She pulled her hair back in a simple knot, and her practical and sturdy clothes did nothing to flatter her slim body or her bright eyes.

Even though she and her father were staying in the palace for these nine days, Dai Dong and the cavalry chief made it clear they must still finish all of their stable chores each day.

Ox contentedly munched hay as Laotzu pointed toward the far end of the stable where they kept the finely decorated harnesses and carts, and the elegant imported horses. "Very luxurious surroundings for one such as this," he said.

She looked up and smiled, running her hand along the ox's bony back. "He can't be very comfortable to ride," she frowned playfully. Ox tossed his head with a grunt, showering them with a litter of hay. She and Laotzu laughed.

Laotzu lifted an eyebrow as he cocked his head at Ox. "We're very well suited to one another. I have no need for speed, and he seems quite satisfied to graze and drink where he can. We meander along together, and as long as we both find what little we need, we are the happiest of companions."

Lo Yintz gave the master a sincere and sweet look, "Uncle Laotzu, it has been so wonderful to have you here, coming and going every day. I can't believe you chose to stay in our cottage instead of the prince's comfortable room."

"Ah," he said, "Comfort is not always what it seems. Every morning I wake to the clear fresh smell of hay, and I can hear you sing softly while you draw water from the well. The birds and the animals stir from their sleep, and your father's tools hammer in the barn. I look out the window and see the rising sun coming up over the sleeping city. What could be more comfortable than this?"

"But the palace guest chambers have servants, and on every wall is a beautiful tapestry. The cushions are made from soft down and trimmed with fur. Musicians play flutes to send you to sleep. It is like a dream!" said Lo Yintz.

"Yes, but haven't you noticed that in the palace they wake stiff from long evenings of drinking and too much food. They cough and fill the air with complaints and disgruntled words. Your every move is planned and attended to and according to schedule. No, Lo Yintz. Your little home is a refuge. I can only be sorry to be leaving it so soon."

"Leaving soon!" she exclaimed, her face falling. "But I had hopes…." Her voiced trailed away. Ox swung his neck around and shoved his head under her arm.

As she absentmindedly petted his soft nose, she continued, "I am not wealthy and educated like KoYou, and I'm certainly not as powerful as the prince. I'm not even as graceful and talented as Yin Lian. I can't even read or write because my father could never afford such teachers. I am ignorant and clumsy. I spend every day working and tending these animals. How could I ever learn the marvelous things you teach? That's why I thought if you stayed here, I might have a chance to at least listen to you talk to the others …" She stopped to wipe her pug nose with her sleeve. Tears fell warm down her tan face.

She opened a wide gate at the back of the stable that opened into a small fenced-in field outside the palace. She led the ox and horses out to graze so that she could clean their stalls. Laotzu helped her hold the gate, and as Ox lumbered by, he swung his tail, hitting Laotzu squarely in the back of the head.

Laotzu rubbed his head and said to Lo Yintz, "May I help you with your chores today? I feel the need to use my arms and legs and to take a break from all this teaching."

Lo Yintz smiled, "Sure. I can show you all the other places you haven't seen yet. My father went to the market this morning to buy tools and oil, so I'm by myself." Her face brightened and her eyes dried at the joy of having her special "Uncle's" company all to herself.

After she securely penned Ox and the prince's horses in the grazing field,

Lo Yintz motioned for Laotzu to follow her. They walked together through the wheelwright's barn, and saw the ornately decorated wooden chariots behind the work yard. There, they could see the cavalry chief and her real uncle training new warhorses.

After a while, they walked behind the work yard to a hidden alcove. Behind a rickety gate was small area where the prince kept his hunting birds. But as she showed Laotzu the bamboo cages holding the prince's falcons and trained birds of prey, a shadow crossed Lo Yintz' face.

"Why do you look so troubled dear one?" asked the master.

"I can't help but be sad when I see them this way," Lo Yintz replied. Over two dozen hawks, peregrines and various large birds sat tethered to their perches with their heads covered by little leather hoods. "They're kept here for days, blind and tied up. Once in a while they're brought out to fly with a trainer or a hunter. Even when the hunter sets them loose, they are trained to fly back to his arm and go back into their cage. They don't even think to fly away." She looked angry now. "I would set them all free if I could."

"You are sad because these birds are not able to express their true nature, but instead are forced to conform to a life not meant for them," said Laotzu.

"That's right. That's exactly right. Once I saw an eagle that did fly away and never came back. It made me so happy. Only princes are allowed to keep eagles because they are so special. A prince should know better than to try to keep an eagle penned!" she replied.

"So some birds have the strong yearning inside to find their true nature no matter what their lives are like?" asked Laotzu.

"That eagle did," answered Lo Yintz.

After Lo Yintz put fresh bits of meat left from the kitchen into each bird's pen, the two friends walked back to the field where the soldiers rode their horses in formation training.

"Do you ever ride horses, little one?" asked Laotzu.

"Oh yes!" cried the girl as her eyes brightened at the thought. "It is the most wonderful thing about working here. My uncle lets me help him train the new horses, and I often ride outside the city with him into the country-side."

"How do you train them?" asked Laotzu.

"Well that's the funny thing," she explained. "A horse can do everything on its own, you know; you really don't have to train it to do anything. It can walk, trot, gallop and leap over streams and logs. The secret is to learn to ride in harmony with their movement and teach them to harmonize with your body and the signals you give them. At first it is very awkward, and you must make your movements very large and do things very slowly so they learn. After a while, you can be more subtle and they learn to listen and respond. You learn to listen to them by feeling them with your whole body and keeping your balance."

"What do you do if the horse goes the wrong way?" Laotzu tested.

"When you are a good rider, you notice very early when they start to head in the wrong direction. So you stay in harmony and gently use the feeling in your body to redirect them. They move very fast and are very big, so you can't turn quickly. You have to make their own force turn by your signal and turn it far enough in advance before you get hurt," explained the stable girl.

"I'll bet you are a good rider. Maybe that's how people work too!" Laotzu said.

"Huh?" asked Lo Yintz. "Oh..ha..ha..ha! Maybe you're right, Uncle!"

They walked along past the cavalry field and into a large shack that stored hay. Every day the girl had to tell the servant at the hay shack how many bales they'd need at the prince's stables. She looked at the bales and selected only the grasses that had no mold or rot. The lesser quality hay went to the cavalry stables.

When she finished her work, Laotzu suggested they rest a bit on a mound of hay outside the shack.

"Do you miss your mother?" Laotzu asked.

"Oh...", she thought for a moment. She hadn't expected the question. Most people didn't dare to ask her about her mother. They didn't want to hurt her feelings. Sometimes it hurt more that no one seemed to care enough to ask.

She looked at Laotzu and said, "Well it's hard to explain. Since she died giving birth to me, I never knew her. I don't have any brothers or sisters to tell me about her. All I know is that my father loved her very much. He tells me stories sometimes. I am not terribly sad about it, since my life is as it is and I know no different. But inside I have a small place that yearns to go back to something, to be in her arms and see her face," Lo Yintz spoke low with her eyes looking far away.

"Funny," said the master, "That's what I try to explain to those scholars."

"What?" asked Lo Yintz.

"Oh nothing, young one," Laotzu replied.

Just then a kitten bolted out of the hay shack. It had gotten itself tangled in a long piece of string it played with. She and Laotzu laughed. The more the kitten struggled to get out of the string the more tangled she became. The kitten's twisting spooked a chicken that pecked for grain outside the shack. The chicken squawked and headed toward the kitten, ready to peck at the young cat in defense.

Laotzu pointed to the kitten, "See that funny kitten. Her mother is lying over there next to the haystack. The other kittens are safe and warm beside her. This stray one wandered off to play with string. The more she played, the farther away from her mother she got. The farther she got, the more tangled she became. Now she's outside the shack and in trouble. That chicken will come and hurt her, or else that kitten will have to run farther away and get lost."

"Should we help it?" asked Lo Yintz.

"Let's watch some more first," said Laotzu. "See, that kitten doesn't know that the farther it goes, the more problems it has. The more she tries to get out of her problems on her own, the more tangled she gets."

"If that kitten went back to its mother, that mother cat would teach that chicken a thing or two!" cried Lo Yintz.

"That's right!" said Laotzu. "But right now that kitten is too far away for the mother to help. If the kitten knew better it would run back to its mother where the mother waits for her. She would find it's safe and warm and enjoy sweet milk to drink. But that silly kitten keeps trying to solve her own problems instead of running back to the mother. What a silly kitten!"

"Oh! I see what you mean. You are talking about people and how they get into trouble when they use their own ways instead of returning to the power of the Tao," Lo Yintz nodded.

"Are you sure you have no tutors? You are a very bright girl!" applauded Laotzu.

Lo Yintz got up and shooed the chicken away. She gently picked up the kitten, unwrapped the string and tenderly set her down by the old gray mother cat near the haystack. The kitten mewed pitifully until the mother's paw pulled it into her breast where it could nuzzle and nurse with the rest of the litter. The mother licked the returning kitten, brushing off the dust and dirt from its misadventure.

Together the man and young girl walked back to the stable. Lo Yintz picked up rags and oil and began polishing the bridles and harnesses that hung on the wall. There hung a bronze tiger facemask that the prince's mount wore when the prince joined a battle. Bridles with bronze dragons alternated with harnesses sporting curling clouds of gold on each side. The girl rubbed and oiled each one until their gleam stood in sharp contrast to the dull wooden walls and dirt floor.

Through the open door Laotzu could see Ox out in the field, legs folded beneath him, contentedly chewing his cud in the shade of a broad tree. The master could hear a gentle buzzing swell and fall as the resident insects talked with one another in the sun-warmed grass.

He turned to the girl and her polishing. "What happens when your horses are taken to war?" Laotzu asked while she concentrated on her task.

She frowned and again her face darkened. "They are not meant for that. They lose their spirit and become only tools for death and destruction. I'm old enough to know that men will be men and we will always have wars. But I still wish it didn't need to be that way."

"What happens when the horses are trained with fear instead of patience?" he continued.

She looked up from the harness, "They still perform in some fashion. But they'll give you their least, not their best. Most people don't know that because they can't tell the difference. If a horse is taught with fear they will stay away from you. Unfortunately, you can never trust those horses, because they are afraid and cannot trust you."

Laotzu walked over and stood next to the young girl. He gently touched her shoulder. She turned around. He looked into her eyes as he told her, "You have been a good student, and you have better teachers than any money could buy. You don't need to travel to learn about the power of Tao. All the lessons you need will come and lay themselves at your feet."

She looked at him, wide-eyed, not quite understanding.

"Put out your hand," he told her. She held out her arm. He held his hand over her arm in a loose pinch. He looked into her eyes and asked, "Can you feel that?" She shook her head.

He focused intently and tried again. After a few seconds she broke into a radiant smile and nodded eagerly. "Yes! It's like a stream running through my arm."

"Good!" Laotzu replied. "That energy is just like your horse. You can learn to feel it and where it will go next. Harmonize with it and you will learn quickly."

Lo Yintz bowed as the teacher made his way toward the back door and the humble stone cottage. As he reached the door he turned back and said, "Horses are really dragons you know, and they know the way to heaven!"

They smiled at each other from a distance. Then, Laotzu disappeared into the only little home the girl had ever known.

Chapter Twenty-One

The Eighth Night with the Taoist Guest

On the eighth night of Master Laotzu's stay, the moon rose under an ominous shadow. The temple priest rang the ritual bells and announced from the steps of the temple that this sign was a portent of trouble. The gods burned with anger at the people and the ruler of West Peace for listening to the old silver-tongued troublemaker Laotzu. The gods would not rest until blood spilled, according to the red shadow on the moon.

Because of the priest's dire warning, few townspeople dared to venture out of their homes to the palace banquet. Although most knew that the priest's warnings rarely bore fruit, they superstitiously heeded him nonetheless. He always predicted doom and gloom with every omen. Yet, with all the strange events of the past week, who would dare risk venturing out on this forbidding night?

When KoWu heard of the priest's warning, he fumed. "That viper! He will stop at nothing to keep the people's minds fettered with fear. If Laotzu stayed in this town, he and his money-sucking temple would soon be finished and he knows it."

Although the kitchen staff had prepared a banquet for fifty, only a dozen or so participants arrived from the outside. Along with the palace regulars, only twenty-one guests filled cushions at the horseshoe table when dinner commenced. There was so much food left over, that KoWu suggested the excess be brought back to the kitchen and that the servants enjoy what remained as a reward for all of their hard work that week.

While last night's party had been truly gay, complete with wine and energetic conversation, this night felt heavy with gloom and reserve. The few guests attending felt inclined to only listen and meekly gave KoWu the floor.

KoWu absolutely refused to allow the brooding atmosphere to infect him. With a bold and buoyant voice, he offered his first question: "Master

Laotzu, for several evenings you have tried to teach us the ways of the power of Tao. As a true holy man, would you please talk more about the proper way to apply the power of Tao to deal with problems around us and the troubles of our lives?"

Laotzu smiled back at him. Equally unaffected by the dour mood around him, and only slightly amused at the priest's prognostication, he rose from his cushion. With his usual habit of waving his flywhisk to and fro, Laotzu walked slowly around the room. He answered, "While applying the power of Tao, the timing is critical. 64-1 *It is easy to maintain a situation while it is still at peace.* You should *plan for change before it happens.* 64-2 *While still weak, it is easy to be shattered; while it is still small, it is easily scattered.* 64-3 *Act on it before it happens. Create order before it becomes chaos.* This is the best way to prevent small troubles from growing into big problems.

"But when faced with a difficult situation, you must know the fact that 64-4 *a tree so big that it takes many men to embrace it starts from a tiny shoot;* 64-5 *A nine-story terrace rises from a bucket of earth; a journey of a thousand miles starts beneath one's feet.* So it is also with practicing the power of Tao. Every small moment of calm and progress in your meditation puts you closer to that moment when you can connect to the power of Tao with the Te inside you.

"Whenever you are faced with a troublesome situation, always remain aware of non-action power; otherwise, 64-6 *whoever tries to act on it will ruin it; whoever tries to hold on to it loses it.* 64-7 *The saint performs non-action power and so is never defeated.* With the right mentality, 64-8 *he does not have to own and therefore he does not have to lose.*

"Otherwise, 64-9 *people usually ruin things right when they are on the verge of success.* 64-10 *So be just as careful at the end as you were at the beginning, and you'll have no failure.*"

Laotzu continued, "It helps to pay more attention to your practice than to spend the time in fruitless worry about the problems of your life. Most importantly, you should not fret, and plan, and strategize and act rashly. Instead, you must prepare your spirit, your mind, your life energy — the Chi, and your body to be pure, like a baby. Free from pollutants and distractions, you must dedicate your true feeling to feel your power of Te to connect with the power of Tao. Without interruption, open and empty, you let the power of Tao enter your body, mind, Chi and spirit.

"64-11 *Therefore the saint seeks not to desire and does not value precious goods.* 64-12 *He learns how to not need to learn — to avoid repeating others' mistakes.*

64-13 *He uses non-action power to help the ten thousand things find their own nature, but dares not take conventional action."*

"Master, I have two questions. The people today seem to run their lives on fear and superstition. Can I use the power of Te to educate people? Second, I find people are so hard to govern when they listen to the silly ideas of others. What is the proper way to rule them?" asked the prince. Everyone in the room knew KoWu referred to the priest and his effect on the citizens that very night.

Laotzu gave him a knowing nod. "I understand your frustration. However, **65-1** *In ancient times those who knew the* power of *Tao did not try to* use the power of Tao to *enlighten others, but rather tried to keep them simple.*

"**65-2** *Why are people so hard to govern? Because they are too clever.* **65-3** *Rulers who depend on cleverness to rule, harm the state. Those who rule without depending on cleverness are instead a benefit to the state.* **65-4** *These are the two alternatives. Understanding the difference between the two is knowing how to employ the Great Te.*

"**65-5** *The Great Te comes from a deep source and is therefore powerful and far-reaching.* **65-6** *The* power of *Te works by making everything return to its original state and eventually will make everything return to a state of great harmony."*

KoWu got up and began to walk around the room opposite Laotzu. Like two ends of a pivot, they circled the room. "Master, I know you've tried to tell me over and over again to rule without the force of action. Doesn't a ruler need to take at least some action to lead? Even a little?"

Laotzu empathized, "I understand that this is hard for you to grasp. Let me use another analogy. To be a true leader, instead of trying to take heroic actions, you should understand and follow the principle of how the power of Tao works. The true leader should behave like water; follow and yield, instead of act and confront. Look, **66-1** *the reason why oceans are the kings of a hundred streams is because they lie below them. Therefore an ocean is able to be the king of a hundred streams.*

"**66-2** *If the ruler would like to guide the people, his words must be humble.* **66-3** *If he would like to lead them, he must follow behind them.* **66-4** *In this way when the ruler leads, the people will not feel burdened;* **66-5** *When he stands in front of them, he poses no obstruction to them.* **66-6** *The whole world will support him happily and will not tire of him.* **66-7** *Because he* stays in the power of Tao, applies the power of Te, and exercises non-action power, he can broadcast his message with the correct mind-set of being humble, low, yielding, gentle and weak. Through the power of Tao, this brings all people into harmony with his message. Everything is in order and takes its natural course. All being in harmony, he *does not confront them, so he does not meet with confrontation."*

"Master, the people all say that the power of Tao you talk about is powerful, but too hard to understand. It would be almost impossible for me to give your wisdom to my people after you are gone. Do you have something easier to understand and more practical to follow for the people in their daily lives?" asked the prince.

Laotzu sighed, "67-1 *The whole world says that my* power of *Tao is great and is like nothing else.* 67-2 *It is because it is great that it seems to stand apart. If it did not stand apart, it would have become insignificant long ago.*

"For those who cannot connect to the power of Tao, but would like to start to practice to get ready to do so, 67-3 *I have three types of practical messages that I hold and treasure. The first is mercy; the second is storing up; the third is* yielding and *not being ahead of others.* 67-4 *From mercy comes courage* to accept the way the power of Tao prevails; *from storing up* the power of Tao *comes immensity; from yielding comes leadership.*

"67-5 *Instead, nowadays men give up mercy yet try to be courageous. They forsake storing up, but try to pretend immensity. They do not believe in yielding, and instead always try to be first.* They certainly would receive no power of Tao. 67-6 *This is sure to end in death.*

"67-7 *For mercy will* broadcast the power of Tao to *win any battle and strengthen defense.* For the means by which the power of Tao of *heaven prevails and protects is with mercy.*

"If you can explain this to the people, and they can apply it even a little, then their understanding will grow," said the sage.

"Master, the other night you spoke very clearly to my generals that instruments of war should be avoided. But if I were under attack, what should I do? I can't survive merely by being merciful. Don't I fight back?" KoWu challenged.

Laotzu shook his finger and wagged his head. "68-1 *A top gentleman does not depend on martial action. A superior warrior never fights with rage.* 68-2 *He who always overcomes never confronts. He who always leads is ever humble.* 68-3 *This is known as the Te of non-confrontation.* 68-4 *This is known as the ability to borrow other's forces. If you can behave like this,* 68-5 *this is so-called 'matching with the power of heaven' that was known since ancient times."*

Guests gather around Laotzu

"Master, nevertheless, if I must confront my enemy with force, what should I do? This is a frontier city, bordering the barbarians. Sometimes it's a choice to kill or be killed."

Laotzu finding himself near his cushion again, decided to sit down. KoWu likewise grabbed a cushion and sat down opposite Laotzu at the sage's personal table. A few of the others brought their cushions over as well. It seemed silly to remain so spread out through the cavernous palace hall when there were so few of them. So they gathered around the sage like a school of youngsters around their tutor.

Laotzu held out his hands to those on the floor in front of him, "69-1 *There is a saying among soldiers: I dare not make the first move but would rather respond secondly; I dare not advance an inch but instead retreat a foot.* Actually, while exercising the power of Tao, 69-2 *this is called not needing to line-up to face the enemy, no need to lift an arm, no need to confront the enemy, no need to hold a weapon.*

"69-3 *There is no greater disaster than underestimating the enemy. By underestimating the enemy, you may forget my precious advice.* Then, you may lose your chance to exercise the power of Tao and to broadcast the three power messages of mercy, storing and yielding.

"69-4 *Therefore when the battle is between two equal armies, the side* broadcasting the Tao's message *of mercy will win.*"

Prince KoWu asked, "Master, why is it that so few can understand your powerful ideas?"

Laotzu looked down at the ground mournfully, shaking his head. "*70-1 My words appear very easy to understand and appear very easy to practice, yet no one in the world understands or practices them. 70-2 All my words refer to* great power from *ancient beginnings. All my actions follow the Lord's will.*

"*70-3 Because people have no true knowledge, they therefore cannot understand what I am talking about. 70-4 Those that know what I am talking about are few; those that can follow what I am talking about are lucky.*

"*70-5 Just like someone wearing coarse clothing yet holding a precious jewel against his chest*, so too the true saint cannot be truly appreciated."

"Master, indeed your idea of Tao is hard to understand," confessed the prince with all humility, "Even we who have education and experience do not know your power."

"You're not so bad off, my friend. It is indeed very difficult to truly know the power of Tao," the master replied. "But *71-1 to know you don't know is strength. Not to know yet think you know is a handicap. 71-2 If one knows he is flawed, then he is not flawed. 71-3 The saint is not flawed because he knows he is flawed. Therefore he is without flaw.*"

"Master, I try to rule with force to make subjects fear me, but sometimes they still are not afraid of me. They have no respect for the power of the law. Why?" asked Prince KoWu.

"Just apply your power of Te. Then, *72-1 when people lack a sense of authority, there will come the great authority.*

"To rule with the power of Te, *72-2 there is no need to restrict their home lives. You do not need to exploit them at work. Simply because you do not need to oppress them, they will not weary of you.*

"*72-3 Therefore the saint knows self and his own power of Te and does not need to appear and act; he treasures self and his own power of Te instead of exalting himself. 72-4 He rejects after and chooses the front*: rejects action and chooses to depend on the power of Te...."

Just then, a commotion in the doorway startled the group. Laotzu abruptly stopped his talk, as Dai Dong and the captain of the civil guard asked permission to enter. A small company of guardsmen followed the two. With hands on their swords, the guard marched into the room and bowed to KoWu.

Dai Dong informed KoWu there had been a theft in the palace. He explained that shortly after the evening meal, the servants discovered that the most valuable treasure in the guest quarters was gone – the jade vase and the delicate metalwork flowers set with jewels. Not wishing to bother the prince and his guests, Dai Dong explained that he himself had summoned the guard who now held the stableman and his daughter in the guest room. The guard awaited further orders.

Dai Dong bid the prince's permission to have the stableman and the girl moved to prison cells at the rear of the palace.

KoWu, red with anger, nodded to the captain of the guard, and two guardsmen drew their swords and left to fulfill the order.

Murmurs now traversed the room. "How could they be so ungrateful?" "The sage put them into the way of temptation." "Servants are all thieves if you don't watch them closely."

Some guests even commented to themselves that perhaps the temple priest was right after all. This certainly proved to be an ill-fated night, and blood would soon be spilled if the prince called a public trial for theft in the morning.

Yin Lian and KoYou turned pale and searched Laotzu's face for answers. Laotzu met their eyes with a serious look that conveyed that he, too, did not believe Lo Han and Lo Yintz could steal.

The evening's lessons adjourned quickly. The guests knew there would be a public trial at noon the next day. Theft of palace property was a capital crime. Criminals found guilty of such theft faced public beheading.

KoWu, stern and grave, stared at the floor as he stormed out of the room.

Yin Lian, KoYou and Laotzu found themselves alone together in the main hall. Yin Lian pleaded, "Uncle Laotzu, I know this can't be true. Lo Han would never steal. Neither would Lo Yintz. We must help them."

"My father will not be lenient," said KoYou. "That vase is one of his favorite treasures since the metal work is so rare. It was a special gift from his father the king."

"I know they did not steal that treasure," Laotzu comforted them. "Sometimes a bad turn of events happens for a reason." His voice sounded sad and serious. He placed a fatherly hand on each of the young shoulders to comfort them. It would be a long and troubled night for many of his palace friends.

Chapter Twenty-Two

Thieves are Captured and Punished

Instead of another night in the luxurious guest quarters, Lo Yintz spent the night on the cold ground leaning against the stone wall of her small prison cell. The wall adjoined the cell that held her father Lo Han. With no window in either of the filthy small hovels, they could only weep together and comfort each other through the cracks in the stone. The same civil guardsman that had taken Lo Han and Lo Yintz away now guarded the thick wooden cell doors.

While two simple souls struggled inside their cells to understand the sad turn of fate that now ripped their lives apart, other guards ransacked the stable, looking under every mound of grass, every pail, and in every cubby hole for the missing treasured vase and flowers. The guardsmen even asked Laotzu to stand outside while they meticulously combed through every inch of the small stone hut. The captain of the guard reasoned that the clever stableman might have hidden the treasure back in his cottage, figuring nobody would disturb the honored guest Laotzu to look for it.

But the guards found nothing. The captain finally presumed that the stable man must have buried or sold it, so he sent the guards home for the night.

The whole city lay in a fitful sleep.

As the cold starlight shone down on the troubled palace, Laotzu secretly and noiselessly approached the prison area. The watchful guard paced back and forth in front of the cells that held his two friends.

Laotzu closed his eyes and stretched his palms outward. The guard paced more slowly. Finally, he sat down against the prison wall. His head grew heavier and heavier, and soon rested on his shoulder.

The sleepy guard dozed peacefully as Laotzu, stealthful and silent, made his way over the gate and toward the cell doors without disturbing him.

"Lo Yintz, Lo Han!" he whispered.

Lo Yintz managed a snuffled cry, "Uncle Laotzu, is that you?"

"Yes, young lady, it's me," Laotzu whispered in reply

"My soul, what will happen to us? They will kill us both tomorrow Master," cried Lo Han from the next cell. Laotzu hushed them both as they wept in their separate confinements.

"I stole nothing, Teacher," Lo Han's muffled voice cried through the heavy wooden door. "I swear to you I didn't."

"I know you didn't," assured the sage.

"All my life I have been a good man and now I must die and know that my daughter dies needlessly," sobbed Lo Han.

"Don't worry, all will be well," assured Laotzu. "I do not feel tomorrow is your day to die. But no matter what happens, you must have faith in your heart that what I say is true. Do you hear what I tell you, little one?"

"Yes, Master," wept Lo Yintz from her cell.

The guard coughed and started to rouse. Laotzu gave a final "Shhhh...." and said, "I must leave now."

When the guard finally opened his sleepy eyes, he could have sworn he saw the shadow of a man leap over the locked gate that barred the prison area from the rest of the palace.

"Must have been a dream," he said. "That gate's eight feet high!" He rubbed his eyes and resumed his watch.

*   *   *

The cock's crow at dawn sounded shrill and dry in the prince's ear as he turned in his warm morning bed. The morning of a public trial always felt raw and chill. KoWu delayed as long as he could underneath his covers. His wife lay sleeping on the cushion across the room. He didn't bother to wake her, as he knew she wouldn't come today. She could never bear to watch his somber duty as judge. She'd seen enough of killing in her day, she told him.

Breakfast was a silent and formal affair for the palace staff. The prince ate alone, attended by Dai Dong. On their way out to the courtyard, they passed by the vacant guest chambers. The prince could see the empty cedar pedestal where his treasured vase and flowers once sat. How would he explain the missing treasure to his father, the king? The lost vase would be a source of deep shame for KoWu.

He felt responsible somehow for the bitter turn of events. He, after all, had agreed to the sage's crazy notion of letting peasants sleep amidst such a display of wealth. How could they not be tempted?

"That simple, stupid stableman," thought KoWu. "If he'd been smart, he could have stolen several small items, like serving spoons or jade rings from the cushions. Such small treasures would have provided the peasant with handsome profit in the marketplace, and never been missed. But to take the palace prize treasure? The poor man probably thought the piece was commonplace."

While Dai Dong brought the special robes KoWu wore and the staff that the prince carried during a trial, the rest of the palace began to stir. Quietly and somberly, advisors and guards prepared for their roles in the day's sad duty.

Before the sun peaked over the eastern wall, townspeople already filled the marketplace, some pretending to shop or gossip. News in West Peace traveled fast, and word of a public trial was on everybody's lips. While few enjoyed watching an execution, the suspense and tragedy drew them in. It is a strange quirk of human nature that a crowd could watch and even cheer a gruesome death in the name of justice.

When the sun rose over the city walls, a large gong sounded from the palace doors. KoWu, accompanied by select officials, made his slow and serious procession out of the palace gate and to the center of the square in front of the palace walls.

The prince took his place on a large platform in front of the main palace gate. Dai Dong stood behind the platform in attendance. Several guardsmen with drawn swords flanked the platform, as a line of the prince's advisors filed up the stairs to take their places, kneeling in a line behind their ruler.

On cue, a large gong rang once more. From the front row of the gathered crowd, Laotzu, Yin Lian and KoYou could see the side palace gate open as four guards shoved their friends Lo Han and Lo Yintz toward the clearing below the platform. Their wrists were tied together with coarse rope, and they wore no shoes. They were dirty from the grimy cells, their faces streaked with tears.

When the prisoners finally stood below the platform to face the prince, the captain of the guard stepped forward. In a loud voice, he announced the charge of thievery. The crowd burst into bellows and boos.

The prince's judicial advisor, Po Fu, stepped forward and shouted a public report of how the Lo household had scorned great favor shown by Prince KoWu and his guest Laotzu. The prince and his guest had allowed them, mere peasants, to stay in the palace itself. Their ingratitude and evil hearts had led them to return such gracious favor with theft.

The crowd hissed and booed again, and somebody threw a piece of rotten fruit at Lo Han.

Yin Lian's eyes stared wide in disbelief. But she fixed them on Lo Yintz to give Lo Yintz something to look at that offered support, instead of the disdain of the crowds. She held both hands in front of her heart and then stretched them to Lo Yintz in a gesture of friendship. Lo Yintz returned her gaze with deep eyes flooded with tears.

KoYou watched his father, the judge. He couldn't believe that a trial for a man's life was so short, and death so swift. The convicted had no chance to even plead their case. He knew his father did not enjoy this role as judge. For days after an execution, his father's mood was usually foul and cantankerous. Once, when he was alone with him afterwards, he saw his father vomit after an execution.

But KoYou also knew that his father executed harsh justice as a means to keep the restless city under control. Someday, KoYou would have to do the same. This was the only form of justice West Peace had known for a hundred years or more.

KoYou could never see himself standing on that platform and giving the order for the guardsman's knife to go down on some poor wretch's neck. He knew, then and there, in that marketplace, that his father's path was no longer the path he wanted for himself. How could he grow up to be so callous and cruel? But how could he avoid it if he followed in his father's footsteps?

Although the proceedings were all too swift, to KoYou, everything seemed to move in slow motion. The guardsman now read the sentence, "Death by beheading."

The crowd let out a strange and collective sigh of horror and approval. Some hecklers in the back rows even offered distasteful applause and whistles.

Laotzu, from the moment he took his place in the front of the throng, remained in deep meditation with his arms stretched down to the side at an angle. His palms faced the platform, but his eyes remained closed.

Laotzu's eyes opened now as guards brought Lo Han and Lo Yintz to kneel in front of the prince's platform. The side gate opened again as a huge guardsman with a thick curved saber walked solemnly toward the platform. The guard forced Lo Han and Lo Yintz, now kneeling, to stretch and bow their necks.

In a solemn gesture of respect, the executioner offered the saber to the prince. It was always the prince's prerogative to avenge himself with enemies of the palace. The prince, in this case, waved the saber away, indicating he'd charge the executioner with the task.

The muscled guard moved to the side of Lo Han and whetted his blade on a long flat stone. The crowd grew silent.

With her last bit of strength, Lo Yintz jerked free of the guard's hand that held her neck down and turned her head to look at Laotzu, crying "Master, please help us!"

Laotzu's eyes snapped open. At that moment, the executioner's hand froze around his saber. His face paled as he realized that no matter how hard he tried, he could not move the blade from the whetting stone.

A deeper layer of stillness surrounded the already silent crowd. Not a bird crowed, nor did a horse so much as bray. The advisors on the platform tried to talk to each other but found their voices hoarse and their tongues frozen. It seemed that both sound and time stood still. Every living being turned to stone.

Suddenly, Laotzu stepped forward and yelled "KoWu!" He pointed to the prince, who stood helpless, holding his throat. KoWu dropped his hands and stepped to the front of the platform. Suddenly, all but the executioner's arm was unfrozen and could move again. The advisors on the platform coughed and blinked in their confusion. The crowd murmured.

"Master Laotzu," replied the prince, sputtering and coughing. "Why do you stand forward? Why does your power interfere? This is a trial. What business is this of yours?"

"I only stand forward to inquire as to whether you've found the stolen treasure," replied the sage. "I can't see how killing the two before they've revealed where the vase is will help you retrieve it."

A captain of the guard stepped forward from the rear of the platform and answered: "We interrogated them last night. They maintain they do not know where the vase is. We conclude they must have buried it or sold it before we found them."

"Would there be any other way to find the treasure first before executing these two peasants?" asked Laotzu. "If you truly believe Lo Han knows, then won't you be sending his secret to the grave with him?"

KoWu looked down at Lo Han. Laotzu was right. He should try to wrench the hiding place from the thief before he killed him.

The prince thought for a moment and then nodded. He looked down at the prisoners and cried, "Stable man. Will you now confess where you hid or sold the palace treasure? If you reveal to me where it is, I will be merciful and kill you both at once. If you still refuse, I will execute your daughter first before your eyes."

The crowd gasped while Laotzu frowned even more deeply at KoWu.

Poor Lo Han could stand no more. Even though he already kneeled, his body collapsed in the dust while he screamed, "I don't know, I don't know!"

Laotzu walked forward toward Lo Han and stood between him and the executioner's blade, which was still frozen to the whetstone. He called the prince again. "KoWu, you have presented this man with such a hellish fate, and yet he still will not reveal where the treasure is. What use would carrying this secret to his grave be to him? Can you still not believe he doesn't know?"

The prince stood silently. The crowd held its breath. Nobody had ever dared to challenge the prince in his performance of justice. No one could understand why the guest Laotzu confronted the prince so brashly, and flaunted his powers on behalf of two thieves. Such disrespect could cost Laotzu his own head under West Peace law.

All of a sudden, the silence broke. At the back of the crowd, from the street where the caravans gathered, a commotion erupted. A small group pushed its way through the crowd and toward the platform. Those at the front turned around to see what was going on. From the royal platform, the prince and his advisors could spy Abudamancus' tall figure, head and shoulders above the rest, pushing through the crowd, calling out furiously "Hold the trial! Hold the trial!"

KoWu motioned the guards to push the crowd aside and waited for Abudamancus to make his way through the throng and into the clearing.

Each of the giant's meaty hands held the scruff of a man's neck. One man looked strangely familiar to KoWu, and the other had the facial features and dress of Bou Yang. Lying to the East, Bou Yang had always coveted the wealth of West Peace and often fought skirmishes with KoWu's father.

Abudamancus' servants withdrew the knives they held at the two men's throats so Abudamancus could thrust the two forward on their faces in the ground. There they lay in the center of the clearing next to Lo Yintz and Lo Han.

"Honorable Prince KoWu," Abudamancus cried. "I have found the real thieves!"

The crowd now let out a collective "Ohhh...?" as word flew from mouth to ear through the mob. The new development created quite a stir.

"This man," Abudamancus now kicked the local man whose face was buried in the dust, "came to me trying to sell me this!" KoWu's tall friend drew the precious jade vase and its flowers out from a heavy tapestry bag slung around his broad back. "He figured I, being from far away, would not recognize the treasure. But Prince, you have shown it to me many times, and so I knew at once that this man was a thief."

KoWu commanded that the man's face be lifted from the dust. "Who is this man? Do I know him?" KoWu demanded. Dai Dong stepped around from the back of the platform and bowed to his master.

"My Prince," Dai Dong said in a low voice, heavy with shame, "it is my very brother."

"Your brother?" inquired the prince. That's why this man looked so familiar to him. His eyes now flashed with rage at his trusted valet.

"He had no part in this, I swear," screamed Dai Lon from the ground, before a guard kicked him in the chest to silence him.

"Your majesty," Dai Dong knelt with his forehead flat on the wooden platform, "He tells the truth, I did not know."

"But that's not all," interrupted Abudamancus. "I knew that this thief was not too bright, otherwise he would never have tried to sell this treasure inside this city. If he had any brains at all, he would have taken it to another state to pawn. So I suspected there was more to this story. I had my servants threaten him until he talked. That's why I am able to bring you this other villain."

Abudamancus grabbed the second man's hair. Placing a knife at the man's throat, he pulled the foreigner's face up from the dirt for the prince to see. The captured villain looked wild-eyed with fear.

Thrusting the man's head back down into the dust, Abudamancus let his servants guard the foreigner who lay in the dirt, while he stepped forward to the platform to tell his story.

Abudamancus explained to the prince and his advisors that Dai Dong's brother merely did the dirty work for the other man, a foreign spy from the city of Bou Yang. Bou Yang sent the spy to cause mischief and embarrassment for KoWu, and to keep the palace unsettled while their king, Lu Kuang, planned an invasion to claim West Peace as his own territory.

"My father's oldest enemy! I should have known he'd have spies here," cried KoWu.

It turned out that the spy came to West Peace seeking an accomplice who would have access to the palace. Dai Lon proved easy to seduce.

Dai Lon had spent his life watching enviously as intelligent and hard-working Dai Dong rose from the ranks of peasantry to the right hand of the prince. No one else in the family merited a palace appointment. Dai Dong would return to the family home once in a while and regale his family with tales of palace life and luxury. His brother cringed every time Dai Dong would say goodbye to the family home and toss gold coins behind him. It was so condescending, so arrogant.

He vowed to his mother that he would rise to a good position someday and do as well as Dai Dong. Their mother never believed Dai Lon's promises, and Dai Lon tired of living a life of shame.

When the spy from Bou Yang offered Dai Lon a handsome sum of gold and the promise of high employment in the palace of Lu Kuang, Dai Dong's brother's prayers were answered. Although he would have to move to Bou Yang, he could prove to his mother that he, too, was worthy of honor, if only in a foreign kingdom. He could send back gold to his mother as proof.

Dai Lon only needed to perform a few tasks for the spy to earn the foreign position. The Bou Yang spy gave him specific instructions that Dai Lon followed to the letter.

Using Dai Dong's name, he entered the palace the previous night while the servants and guests listened to the visiting sage far down the hall. Through the empty corridors, Dai Lon found his way to the guest chamber that Dai Dong had described to his family so many times.

When he came to the guest chambers, he posed as Dai Dong's assistant and asked the stable man and his daughter to please step into the courtyard to enjoy the cool evening as he prepared their beds. Lo Han and Lo Yintz had no way of knowing that this man posing as a servant was an imposter, and so did what he asked.

While Lo Han and his daughter strolled out into the courtyard, Dai Lon had enough time to slip the heavy vase and its flowers into a strong tapestry bag hidden under his full robe and leap out the open window.

When Lo Han and Lo Yintz returned to their room, they wondered why their bed wasn't made up. They hadn't even noticed the missing vase when the real servant came in to prepare their bedchamber.

The real servant noticed that the vase was missing and saw that the two peasants seemed confused and ill at ease. She had seen Lo Han and Lo Yintz returning from the outside courtyard just moments before. Suspecting the worst, she ran down the hall calling the alarm for guards to come.

By the time Dai Dong and the guard arrived at the guest chambers, Dai Dong's brother was long gone, hidden by darkness as he made his way back to deliver the treasure to the spy.

Dai Lon returned with the vase to the agreed rendezvous point, but he couldn't find the spy. He waited for what seemed like an eternity. Scared and worried that the spy had tricked him and that he might now be found with the palace treasure, Dai Lon panicked and decided he needed to be rid of it.

Quickly, Dai Lon sought out the caravan that had come from the farthest distance. Surely those traders would have never heard of the vase, and would pay a handsome price and take the contraband. Then he could hide for a while until the whole matter died down, Dai Lon thought.

That is how he came to Abudamancus' tent in the middle of the night.

When Abudamancus identified the vase and seized Dai Lon, it took little effort to pry out the whole story and have Dai Lon lead them to the spy's regular haunts. In a drinking house, they finally found the Bou Yang spy carousing with a local prostitute, and seized him as well.

The whole convoluted tale unfolded by Abudamancus allowed KoWu to command Lo Han and Lo Yintz' release. Once KoWu announced their innocence, Laotzu pointed to the executioner, who could suddenly release the heavy blade that had rested immovably against his whetstone since the commotion began. Shocked and exhausted, the executioner let the saber fall to the ground.

As guards cut their bonds, the stableman and his daughter embraced, shaking with sobs of abated terror and joy.

Yin Lian and KoYou ran to their friends and took their arms to help them back to the palace. Prince KoWu announced his formal apology to the stable hand and his daughter and commanded that they be restored to their room in the palace for the last night of the sage's stay. He ordered that his palace servants attend to their needs for clean clothes and warm food.

Laotzu stepped forward to address the prince once more. "This tragedy turned into a stroke of good fortune for you, Prince KoWu," observed Laotzu. "You not only have your treasure back, and avoided the killing of innocent people, but you uncovered a very dangerous spy who would have brought even greater harm to your city."

KoWu bowed. "You speak true words, Master. I now can execute the true thieves and send a message to my enemy, Lu Kuang."

The sage raised his hand in caution. "If you do, you may again proceed too hastily," Laotzu advised. "If this spy is killed, word will get back to his king. Lu Kuang will defend himself, saying that this man was not a spy. He will use the excuse that you killed an innocent man and attack your walls under the pretence of saving his kingdom's honor.

"And the other man you wish to kill?" Laotzu continued. "The poor misguided thief is the brother of a valued servant whose loyalty you have enjoyed and may wish to rely on in future years. What will it pay you to make him watch his brother die? You have your treasure back, surely there is some other way to punish the two."

"In my country," boasted Abudamancus, "we put thieves and spies to work in the quarries as slaves. I would get at least fifty pieces of gold for these two."

KoWu felt paralyzed. He knew the sage spoke the truth. An execution would send a strong message, but it might backfire in the long run by injecting a slow poison into his personal and international affairs.

Prince KoWu conferred privately with his advisors. In a few moments the prince returned. He announced to the crowd that the two culprits would be turned over to the harsh punishment of Abudamancus. They would be exiled as slaves, and Abudamancus, in return for his excellent work in uncovering the thieves, could collect any premium offered for the men's lives back in Dazos.

At that, the tall caravan leader ordered that two be bound together and taken away. Abudamancus' servants tied the two men's wrists and stretched a lead rope between them. Abudamancus himself attached the rope to another lead wrapped around a pack-camel's neck. The two would walk with the caravan in fetters to Dazos where a life of slavery awaited them.

And yet, because he spared their heads that day, they bowed to the prince for his act of mercy.

Dai Dong too, bowed and touched his forehead to his master's feet, sobbing in gratitude for the mercy shown to him and his brother. The prince assured his valet that he held no doubt of his innocence in the unfortunate affair. He let Dai Dong return to the palace with the full responsibilities of his previous duties.

The crowd murmured noisily, trying to understand the full ramifications of the day's events.

As the city hummed, the prince conferred with his advisors once more on the platform. The group on the platform exchanged heated words with each other and then summoned military generals for advice.

After some deliberation, the prince announced that an armed party would accompany an envoy to the king of Bou Yang. Their message would be that Lu Kuang's spy had been exiled to Dazos, and in return for such espionage, all trade routes between Bou Yang and West Peace would be closed under military order. Such a move before winter would certainly choke Lu Kuang into submission, and engender a formal apology within weeks. Similarly, messengers would bring news of the matter to the capital city and KoWu's father, the king.

The crowd hesitated, and then reluctantly applauded the move. Merchants and caravan leaders groused among themselves and left the square to reconsider their trade and travel plans given the closing of the roads to Bou Yang.

Without adjourning the day's unusual assembly, the prince stormed off the platform to retire to his palace. He gruffly pushed aside his own guard and left the generals to work out their own details.

When he arrived back to the palace, KoWu waved his advisors away. His head ached. Confounded by the twisting and turning of events, he'd maintained his composure long enough. He must find a quiet room to think and sort through all that had just transpired. He needed privacy.

He found a small room just inside the palace main hall. He ordered the servants to leave him alone. When they finally left, his knees buckled as he sat down on a cushion by a low window. Looking out the window, KoWu rubbed his forehead and tried to calm himself.

He was angry. Angry that Lu Kuang had spies that could access even his own palace. He was relieved. Relieved that he didn't have to execute the poor stable hand and the girl. He was worried. Worried that his act of mercy toward the two thieves would make some think him soft and ineffective. The jumble of thoughts and feelings left him exhausted. How did everything become so confused?

He'd certainly have questions for Laotzu tonight. That sage made it all sound so simple – governing a country with the power of Tao. What did a sage know about hard decisions? Where was the power of Tao today? How was this simple?

But the sage was right. Ultimately, every strange chapter in the day's events unfolded for the best. If matters had not resolved themselves in such curious ways, the spy would still be working mischief.

What strange irony haunted the lives of men? Was that Laotzu's power of Tao at work?

Three small girls peeked shiny familiar faces around the curtain. "Daddy, daddy…." They ran into his arms. Even KoWu's brooding couldn't stop the small bit of warmth that spread through his chest – the warmth his small daughters always brought with their smiles and hugs. He spent a rare moment alone with them to hear about their day's lessons and their squabbles. Where had he been all week, that he didn't think to visit his darlings?

As he hugged them, his own words echoed in the back of his mind. Did he really threaten the stableman that he would kill his daughter before his own eyes?

Then Dai Dong arrived, penitent and solemn, to tell the prince that they must plan for the sage's final evening reception.

Chapter Twenty-Three

The Ninth Night with
The Taoist Guest

In contrast to the previous night, the palace hall filled to the rafters on the ninth and final night of Master Laotzu's stay. Citizens had no fear since the strange outcome of today's trial and the exposure of a spy seemed to explain last night's moon shadow. The temple priest's prognostication of disaster came close enough to describing the odd twists of the day's events, so he suffered no loss of reputation.

However, most clear-headed people refused to believe the priest's view of Laotzu as a dangerous influence. To all who filled the city square during the trial, it seemed clear that Laotzu's interruptions bought precious time for the innocent peasants and allowed the exposure of the true thief and a dangerous spy. The visiting sage obviously brought justice, peace and good fortune to those close to him.

Even a few of the generals ventured back into the hall, impressed by the routing of the foreign spy, and anxious to hear what the final questions and answers might yield in terms of information on the precarious situation between West Peace the enemy state of Bou Yang.

Because of the crowd, extra tables lined all four walls of the hall. Guests sat by rank, with Prince KoWu, his son KoYou, and the palace generals at the head table. Prominent city nobles, palace advisors and foreign diplomats sat at the side tables, while those of lower rank sat in the back of the hall. Laotzu's private table remained in the center.

As a gesture of both apology and forgiveness, the prince invited Lo Han and Lo Yintz to sit at the back tables with the other guests of low rank. The prince made sure that they were given appropriate attire to wear, and Dai Dong seated them personally. Other guests didn't quite know how to receive the two, and greeted the peasants' entry with awkward silence. They were ill-fated celebrities given their close call at this morning's trial.

But any awkwardness between Lo Yintz and Lo Han and the other guests instantly melted away when Laotzu himself got up from his seat and walked to the back table to greet the two, clasping both of their hands with a warm smile.

Although the kitchen prepared a great number of dishes for the final banquet, there were too many people to offer every guest a taste of every dish. The preferential seating allowed the servants to bring the choicest dishes to the ranking officials and Laotzu first, and then to the side tables. Those sitting at the rear received only the remaining rice, cooked beans and a bit of stewed deer meat. Spirits were high, however, and nobody complained.

Most of the dinner conversation focused on Bou Yang. Would there be war? Would Lu Kuang endeavor to attack West Peace? Would the closing of the trade routes force negotiations? Were there other spies in their midst?

Even as the guests ate, everyone knew at that very moment an armed envoy rode with its message to Lu Kuang. What would that king do? Submit? Kill the envoy, thus declaring war? Send the envoy back in a stalemate?

Clearly these matters also weighed heavily on KoWu's mind. Barely containing his ire and drive for revenge, his first question was, "Master, why does my enemy hate me and want to kill me? I swear to you that when I encounter Lu Kuang, I will be brave and kill him!"

Laotzu paused for an extended time allowing the din in the room to settle into silence. The silence also forced KoWu to reflect on the impetuous tone of his question, especially when Laotzu responded with a voice a gentle as rain. "To face the enemy it is better to follow the power of Tao.73-1 *If one is simply brave and daring he will be killed.* 73-2 *One who is brave enough admits to what he will not dare to do.* Turning to the power of Tao, *he will stay alive.*

"73-3 *In these two cases, one is good and the other is harmful.*73-4 *Heaven hates some things. Who knows the reason why?* But I know one thing for certain; follow the power of Tao and you will never go wrong.

"Look, 73-5 *the* power of *Tao from heaven does not need to strive, and yet it always overcomes.* The power of Tao 73-6 *does not need to speak, and yet is well answered.* The power of Tao 73-7 *does not need to summon, yet is supplied with all its needs.* The power of Tao 73-8 *seems slow, yet follows a good plan.* The power of 73-9 *heaven's net is ever large and wide. Though its meshes are coarse, yet nothing slips through.*"

KoWu continued, "Master, you had the unfortunate opportunity to witness a public trial this morning. It appeared that our local customs may have offended you. It is a tradition that enemies of the palace be tried and condemned immediately. I, as prince, have the right to choose whether to wield the beheading knife myself whenever a crime is committed within the palace.

This has been our way for many generations. I find it is a bold and effective deterrent to would-be traitors if I execute the serious offenders myself. Do I offend the power of Tao while I personally kill these criminals?"

Laotzu frowned and shook his head, "Death as a deterrent is a tricky matter. It will usually do no good for those who truly hate you. 74-1 *If people are not afraid of death, it is of no use to threaten them with death. 74-2 And if people live in constant fear of death, and if acting contrary to society means a man will be killed, who will dare break the law?*

"As for wielding the beheading knife yourself, 74-3 *there is always an executioner in charge of killing. If you try to kill in his place, it is like trying to take the place of a master carpenter at cutting wood. 74-4 If you try to cut wood like a master carpenter, you will cut your own hand.* In this instance, your actions are not following the power of Tao."

KoWu partially agreed with the sage. "Master, you are right that it is a tricky thing to use death as a deterrent. In some cases it is not a deterrent at all. Among the lower classes who steal because they are hungry, their crimes continue no matter what laws or penalties apply – even death. But they must understand that a city needs to maintain order somehow. What else can I do?"

Laotzu offered no words of comfort, instead he scoffed, "75-1 *The people are starving because the rulers eat up too much from taxes. That's why the people are starving. 75-2 The people are difficult to rule because the rulers like to act and interfere. That's why they are hard to rule. 75-3 The people take death lightly because the rulers demand too much of their own life. That's why the people take death lightly.*

"75-4 *Nevertheless, those who cannot value their life are smarter than those who value their lives overly much.*"

The prince recoiled with a frown, pondering the sage's hard-hitting words. "Again you rebuke me, Teacher. But I do respect your wisdom and will consider what you say. You undoubtedly think me harsh and cruel for asking these things. Such forcefulness would go against your advice of being tender and merciful. But Master, why does the power of Te work only when there is softness and weakness?"

Laotzu gave him an assuring glance, "I don't seek to rebuke you, but merely wish to answer your questions as best I can. This morning you ended the trial showing a good deal of mercy, after only a small bit of guidance."

The sage got up from his table so that he could turn and address the full circumference of the hall. "But back to your question," he began. "The Te works when there is softness and weakness because this is also the way the power of Tao works. Life and death are separated by the way life energy flows.

"*76-1 When people are born, they are gentle and weak. At death they are hard and stiff. 76-2 Green plants are pliant and tender while living. When they're dead they are withered and dried. 76-3 Therefore the stiff and unbending follow death. The supple and yielding follow life.*

"*76-4 Thus an army depending only on its strength never wins a battle. 76-5 A tree that is stiff is easily broken. 76-6 The hard and strong will prove inferior. The supple and weak will prove superior.*"

KoWu seemed to understand. He thought for a bit while the crowd remained silent. Everyone in the hall instinctively understood that on this final night, it would be the prince alone who would speak to the sage. Nobody else dared to venture a question, especially given the events of the day that placed their ruler on the brink of declaring war with Bou Yang.

Prince KoWu finally collected his thoughts and asked Laotzu, "What then is the difference between following the power of Tao to rule and following the will and knowledge of men to rule? If I were an observer looking from the outside, I wonder if I could tell the difference between a good ruler and one who ruled with the Power of Tao."

"*77-1 The power of Tao in heaven acts like the drawing of a bow,*" Laotzu replied. "*To aim at the goal, the high is lowered and the low is raised. In applying force to pull the string, 77-2 if there is excess tension, the archer makes sure it is reduced: if there is not enough tension, the archer makes sure it is increased. 77-3 The power of Tao in heaven works to take from what's excessive and give where there is deficiency.*

"*77-4 The Tao of man works differently: He takes from those who lack in order to give to those who already have too much.*

"*77-5 Who can have more than enough and give it to the whole world? Only the man possessing the power of Tao.*

"*77-6 Therefore the saint works* with his power of Tao *behind the scene. He achieves what has to be done without claim. He does not even show his true knowledge.*"

Prince KoWu knew that he only had a few questions remaining to him. He decided that tonight, he wanted more specific advice from the sage. Impending war was a real problem that required a real solution.

KoWu pressed Laotzu for more direct answers by asking, "Master, my city suffered great insult today by the presence of this spy. Other leaders will say I was weak not to declare war on Bou Yang immediately. Closing the trade routes is just a temporary measure. If Lu Kuang does not apologize for his actions, and I still do not declare war, I will definitely be seen as weak among the leaders of other states. Appearing weak, other states will consider West Peace vulnerable, and no longer a leader among cities. How can I, if I don't take a firm stand in situations such as this one, be a leader to the world?"

But the teacher wouldn't give KoWu the direct answer to his problem that he looked for. Instead the sage responded in his usual preference for metaphor. "*78-1 In the whole world, nothing is softer or more yielding than water. Yet for attacking the hard and strong, nothing can do better. It is irreplaceable.*

"*78-2 The weak power always overcomes the strong power; the supple eventually overcomes the unbending.78-3 Everyone in the world knows this fact, yet no one can put it into practice.*

"*78-4 Therefore the saint says: 'One who burdens himself with the humiliation of the nation is fit to rule the people's daily affairs.78-5 One who assumes responsibility for the country's disasters deserves to be king of the world.'*"

"You always give abstract answers that sound confusing, Master," KoWu gave a sigh of resignation.

Laotzu laughed, "*78-6 True words often sound backwards.*"

The prince pressed on, continuing his questions using the current tension between West Peace and Bou Yang as a model. "My decision today to close the trade routes could bring any of several outcomes. Lu Kuang could submit or declare war. The trouble could be left unresolved and the bitterness drag out for generations. At any rate, it is hard to see how we could be anything but enemies for years to come. What attitude should I adopt to create lasting peace in an impossible situation?"

"Resolving conflict is not easy," Laotzu agreed. "Remember what I said last night about thwarting trouble before it begins? This is because even

79-1 *after resolving a bitter quarrel, some resentment is bound to remain. How can this be considered good?* 79-2 *Therefore the saint keeps his loan receipt but does not push for repayment.*

"79-3 *A man with the* power of *Te performs as if he has a loan receipt but does not push for repayment,* in other words, he only has to broadcast his power of Te, he does not have to take action. *One without the* power of *Te always requires others to pay what they owe,* he always has to take action with people. He acts *as if he is a tax collector.*

"79-4 *The* power of *Tao in heaven is fair. It blesses good men all the time.*"

"Master, if I and my son, and my son's son, followed all of your advice and only governed from the power of non-action and the power of Tao, our city would no doubt become an ideal empire. If it were so, how would it be different than it is today?" asked KoWu.

Laotzu tried to paint a picture of the ideal state for KoWu. "With rulers who continue practicing the power of Tao, broadcasting the power of Te, an ideal empire is 80-1 *small,* that is *the size of the country, and few, the number of people.* 80-2 *Though there are all kinds of tools and equipment available* to make life easier, *they are not needed.*

"Such rulers 80-3 *make people take life seriously and do not migrate far.* 80-4 *Though they have boats and carriages, nobody uses them. Though they have armor and weapons, nobody displays them.* 80-5 *People return to the knotting of rope to keep records.* 80-6 *They enjoy their plain food, they consider their clothes beautiful, they feel safe and secure in their homes. They are happy with the way that they live.* 80-7 *Though they can see adjoining states, and the sounds of cocks and barking dogs can be heard across the border, they will nonetheless grow old and die without ever bothering to visit them.*"

"Goodness! What an ideal state. It is obvious that we all have much to learn and a long way to go before our city resembles your description," said KoWu. Muffled laughter filled the hall. The sage's ideal state and West Peace couldn't be more dissimilar.

"Master, I am so humble from all the wisdom that you have given me and my guests these past nine nights. It seems that eighty-one questions, even with the other questions my friends and advisors offered, still cannot plumb the depths of your knowledge. For my last question I will offer you the chance to evaluate my very own weaknesses. Will you please give me final advice, the advice that I need most?" the prince concluded.

Laotzu looked around the room; he especially looked at the faces of the prince's proud advisors. His answer was brief. "*81-1 Words of faith are not beautiful. Beautiful words are not faithful. 81-2 Good men offer no skillful words. Those who talk skillfully are not good. 81-3 Those who know the truth possess no knowledge. Those who possess knowledge do not know the truth.*

"*81-4 The saint never tries to accumulate. The more he does for others* with his power of Te, *the more he has. The more he gives to others* with his power of Te, *the greater his returns.*

"Remember, *81-5 the* power of *Tao in heaven is very powerful but does no harm. 81-6 The* power of *Tao possessed by the saint is performing work without confrontation.*"

The sage lifted his palms toward the ceiling. He closed his eyes as if to listen to the silence in the room. Suddenly, he abruptly turned his back on the hall and walked over behind a side table to the open window where he craned his neck to gaze at the stars.

Hushed murmurs flowed across the low tables as the audience realized the sage's teaching had ended. Prince KoWu rose and bowed deeply to

Wei Lon asks Laotzu to name the scrolls

Laotzu, even though the sage's back was turned. All of the palace guests rose as well, and followed the prince's example by bowing to the sage's back together in silence.

When KoWu extended his arm toward the door, his guests knew they must take their leave. They would have many new ideas to mull over during the long winter in West Peace. It took more time than usual for the crowd to empty out of the palace hall and head back to their homes.

Once they'd left, Laotzu remained alone, still perched at his window. Prince KoWu looked on him with admiration. He knew the sage had kept his agreement most generously. The old master had answered all of KoWu's questions just as he'd promised to do, and more. While KoWu knew that this "Tao" Laotzu spoke of still eluded him, he also knew he had enough understanding to begin practicing as Laotzu described. The notes from the nine nights of teaching would guide him on his way.

"Pen Hei!" the prince summoned his chief scribe. "Wei Lon!" he called as an afterthought to the records keeper, who had just come in to take the evening's bundle of bamboo carvings from Pen Hei. The two men gently laid the bundle of precious notes on the low carving table and approached the prince with several deep bows.

"Did you record every word?" inquired the prince.

"Yes, your majesty," Pen Hei assured, "we did our best. You can see that in these bundles of carvings are the important answers that Master Laotzu gave to your majesty. I stayed up until morning each of these nine nights, carving everything I could remember." At this, Pen Hei showed the prince his blistered hands, raw from the pressure of the carving knife.

"Take this order," said the prince. "This is the most valuable teaching we have in our palace. Have your keeper Wei Lon make several copies and keep them safe. I will call on you from time to time when I wish to review these teachings. Wei Lon, take the bundle of carvings from this night and show them to our venerable sage guest."

Wei Lon bent down and gently cradled the armload of bamboo slats. He walked tentatively toward the window and stood quietly behind the sage until Laotzu, sensing his presence, turned to face him. As Laotzu turned around, Wei Lon bowed deeply and gently tipped his head toward the table, motioning for Laotzu to follow. As Wei Lon spread the evening's notes across the tabletop for inspection by the prince and the sage, Laotzu nodded and smiled with approval. "Very good job. But remember to keep these words only as a reminder. The most important thing to do is practice."

Again Wei Lon gathered his bundle, while Pen Hei brought a covering of heavy silk to wrap the precious planks until he and Wei Lon could polish and tie them properly when they returned to the records storage cellar. The two men scurried out with their package, leaving the prince and Laotzu alone.

"Master," asked Prince KoWu, "Since you insist on leaving tomorrow, what shall I do when I have questions while I practice your power of Tao?"

"All the answers you need are in what I told you to practice. Meditate with what I have said and you will gain your spiritual power and reach the power of Tao – someday," encouraged Laotzu. "Meanwhile, I have taught several disciples over the years, and more than one of them will pass through here in the future. You will know them when you see them and can ask them your questions."

At the curtained doorway, Wei Lon bowed for permission to re-enter. He'd obviously forgotten something. "Master Laotzu, your majesty," apologized Wei Lon. "My esteemed chief Pen Hei asks what title we should give to this script from these last nine evenings?"

KoWu bowed to Laotzu, deferring the answer to the sage. Laotzu stared upwards briefly as if the answer would come from the palace ceiling. Then, returning a kindly gaze to the records-keeper, Laotzu offered: "You may call it Tao Te Ching, the Classic of Tao and Te."

Chapter Twenty-Four

The Sage Must Bid Farewell to West Peace

Cool and crisp, the autumn dawn spread its clear sunshine over the palace on the last morning of Laotzu's visit to West Peace. The servants hurried through their chores as usual, preparing morning pails of water for washing and setting out food for delivery to the various palace living quarters.

Without warning, the prince burst from his bedchamber and without addressing anyone, turned immediately down the corridor toward the stable yard. Startled servants rushed to offer their assistance, but KoWu waved them away. He had a determined look on his brow and quickness to his step. "I must persuade this teacher to stay longer!" thought the prince. He walked quickly so as to deter any questions or followers. He wanted to be the first to see Laotzu this morning and wanted to see him alone.

KoWu had a strange dream during the night that a great war erupted with Bou Yang, and that many soldiers died. The faces of mothers and wives, children and old people all cried to him, "Why?" In the dream KoWu couldn't answer, and although he tried to run, he couldn't move to get away from the haunting, pleading faces. Instead he looked down to see his arms and legs bound by a golden cord.

At the banquet's end last night, KoWu could confidently conclude the sage's visit, grateful for the nine nights of teaching. But when he woke up this morning, especially after such an eerie dream, KoWu felt differently. He would do anything to induce the sage to stay, even beg if need be.

A thin column of smoke curled upward from the stone hut's chimney. KoWu rapped on the door. His faced paled when he looked down and noticed the golden cord from the first day tied around the latch. It was the same cord from his dream.

The teacher's face, looking older today than yesterday, peered around the edge of the door as it slowly opened.

"Come in, come in," beckoned Laotzu. "You're just in time for breakfast."

A plain clay pot bubbled on the stove, steaming with barley and the fragrance of an herb that tapped at KoWu's boyhood memories. It was one of the mountain herbs his own mother brewed on cold mornings when he was a child, but that was so long ago, he couldn't remember its name.

While Laotzu set out two bowls and scooped hot gruel into each, KoWu cleared his throat trying to get the sage's full attention.

"I've come to this small house as humbly as I can to do what a ruler will not usually do," explained the prince. "I come to beg you to stay and be my most high advisor, master and teacher." At this, KoWu fell to one knee and bowed his head.

"Stand now or you'll spill your porridge," scolded Laotzu. "It remains as before. I have no choice in the matter. I must go." Laotzu turned to put the clay pot back on the stone hearth. He motioned for KoWu to sit down on the plain straw cushion, as he moved KoWu's bowl closer across the flat log that served as a table.

Laotzu looked Kowu straight in the eye. "You are a good prince. By your questions I know that you care for your people and you wish to be the best ruler you can be," the sage assured KoWu. Both men paused to waft the steam over the surface of their bowls. "But you have many years ahead of you, and some of them will be full of trials. You will remember what I said, and some day you will find the secret to practicing the power of Tao."

KoWu sighed and resettled himself farther back on his cushion, leaning his back against the cool stone wall. He confessed to the sage, "Sometimes I feel as if I'm torn in two. I would love to ride with you to the Kunlun Mountain and spend the rest of my days learning heaven's secrets. But I also love this city and know that I have a destiny and a duty to serve as prince. That is why I begged you to stay, for if you stay, then I might be able to fulfill both of my heart's two callings at once."

Laotzu also sighed. "I know that, but I feel the energy going west, over a thousand miles. I, too, might wish to stay if I could. It will be a very long and cold journey. Many months my ox and I must ride together. Beyond Kunlun there is a small kingdom with a prince a little like you. He too had two hearts, one that pulled him toward learning the truth and one that wanted to help his people. This prince chose the way of truth, and has meditated for many years. He feels that if he finds what he seeks, he will be able to rid the people of their suffering. He is now very frustrated since all his seeking proves fruitless. His parents, the king and queen, now beg him to return to his palace instead of drifting and suffering outdoors. He continues to refuse and single-mindedly pursues the true way."

Laotzu turned around to spit out the matted herbs floating on the surface of his cereal. "I have already told you much more than this foreign prince has ever heard about the secret of the Tao. Had he heard even a small portion of what I've given to you, he would have found his answer. That's why he needs my help. You don't need me here to practice what I told you. I must answer this call I hear from the sky and leave today." Laotzu nodded and looked down into his teacup.

KoWu rose without tasting the gruel. He was overcome with conflicting emotions. Grateful beyond measure for the gift of Laotzu's teachings, and moved by Laotzu's encouraging words, KoWu nonetheless felt unworthy and rejected by the teacher's insistence on leaving so soon – and leaving in favor of another prince who had already rejected his kingdom, no less.

Pacing the dirt floor, KoWu wanted to speak but couldn't find the words. He realized that he didn't need to, for when he looked over at the sage he could see that Laotzu was clearly finished listening.

Laotzu sat still and straight, looking down as he stirred his porridge slowly with a piece of dried straw. The sage acted as if KoWu was no longer there.

The sage would say no more.

Prince KoWu bowed and left the stone hut without troubling the sage further. He returned to the palace alone.

A short while later, Dai Dong knocked on the stone hut's door with four large bags of provisions for Laotzu's trip. "Master Laotzu, we know you usually accept no gifts, but we give you these traveling supplies so that you will not hunger or suffer cold on your journey." Laotzu smiled and thanked the valet, instructing him to place the bags near the ox's stall so he wouldn't forget them.

No sooner had Dai Dong left than two robed figures entered the small courtyard at the back of the stable and waved toward Laotzu's doorway. "Master!" called KoYou. He walked toward the stone hut with his new tutor Chong Zen. Laotzu came to the doorway and met the two in the yard outside the hut.

The two bowed to Laotzu and also begged him to stay in West Peace, at least for the winter. Laotzu again explained that he had a mission to help a prince in a kingdom west of Kunlun Mountain and north of Tianzu *(an ancient name for today's India).*

"How do you know he needs help if he lives so far away?" asked KoYou.

Laotzu smiled, "Because this prince has sincerity. He uses his true heart to call out for help. That vibration echoes and reaches the sky like the string of a musical instrument. I can hear it."

"But I am sincere, and I too, will be forced to become a prince when I am older whether I wish to be a prince or not. Why don't you stay and help me?" KoYou pleaded.

"Why do you need help?" the old master tested KoYou.

"Because, after I watched you doing the 'moving-slow-dance,' I tried to follow you a few times. I felt something strange inside my body. Something flowed like a stream inside and around me. I don't know what this is or what to do next. Only you can help me learn," explained the youth.

Laotzu stern face broke into a loud laugh, "Excellent! You are a good boy. You have a good heart. You deserve it. I will help you!"

"So you'll stay longer?" KoYou's eyes lit up like two candles.

"No, son," Laotzu patted KoYou's shoulder with affection. "Sit down right here in the grass. I can't stay longer, but I can help you."

KoYou sat in the courtyard at Laotzu's feet. Chong Zen also knelt beside him, anxious to hear what the sage's final words to the boy might be.

Laotzu advised KoYou to sit with his eyes closed, relax and think about his navel area. Chong Zen slid from his knees into a seated posture in the grass as well, also following Laotzu's instructions.

While the two sat still, he continued to bid them to relax as much as possible, both mentally and physically. Laotzu told them he would now give them a fast course, many years of practice compressed into a few minutes, to let them experience the power of Tao first hand.

"Every night I answered your father, Prince KoWu's questions. I also answered all of his staff, advisors, scholars, priests and guests about how to practice the power of Tao. Each of them were only interested in a goal of how to achieve something – to use the Tao to get what they wanted. They may know about the Tao, but they don't have first hand experience of the power of Tao."

While KoYou and Chong Zen sat quietly, Laotzu closed his eyes and again began his slow and soft instructions: "First, breathe naturally. Do not force your breath. Second, close your eyes and look at your lower stomach area from within."

Laotzu raised his left arm with his index and middle finger pointing up to heaven. His thumb and last two fingers touched together. Then he placed his right palm forward and down pointing toward KoYou and Chong Zen. In a short while, KoYou, with his eyes closed, could sense Laotzu's palm shooting and radiating some sort of energy toward his face, head and then his entire body. It was a warm, soothing pressure like a beam of sunshine entering his very flesh.

Suddenly, KoYou could no longer feel his body. Instead, he saw light inside his head and his stomach.

"Wow," he cried, "this is tremendous, Master. What is it?"

"It is the power of Tao, the most pure force of the universe. I am burning my own Te power to create a pull force. I then allow the power of Tao to come into my body. Then I guide it through my arms. One arm becomes Yin power, and one arm becomes Yang power.

"When this is beamed at you, it recombines back into the power of Tao to charge up your life energy. I will feed you enough power so that you can take over from here to practice this."

Chong Zen could feel something too, although he did not see the light inside. Yet the scholar knew that this was no theory or philosophy that he witnessed: it was the real power of Tao. He reached out with his hands and heart attempting to soak up the energy around him.

"Wow, Master," KoYou cried again with his eyes still closed. "I felt my body disappear. It's amazing. I am floating. Master, I feel like I am flying away."

"That is enough," Laotzu dropped both palms and the power subsided. "Continue to close your eyes and let this energy settle into your body for a while. After this direct charge up, you may follow my instructions from these last nine nights. You will be able to develop a powerful ability to broadcast the power to help people.

"If you use this ability to broadcast the power of Tao with a good message – like kindness, soothing, nourishing, caring and love – you connect to the power of good God. You can help many people, generation to generation."

KoYou listened with his eyes still closed. He was still overwhelmed by the power of Tao.

"However, if you use this ability to broadcast a bad message," continued Laotzu, "such as destruction, hurting people, hate and distrust – you will connect to the power of bad God, the Devil. You will hurt both others and yourself."

With the power still radiating through his body, mind and soul, KoYou uncannily understood every word of what Laotzu said. Not only could he understand these words in the courtyard, but suddenly everything Laotzu had taught for the past nine nights became crystal clear in KoYou's understanding. All the talk of Tao and Te now made sense.

Chong Zen, moved by the power around and within him, placed his head on the ground. With tears in his eyes, bowing deeply to Laotzu, Chong Zen said softly, "Now I truly understand what Confucius really meant when he said that if he learned the skill of Tao's power in the morning, he wouldn't mind if he died in the evening. Thank you so much, Master."

Laotzu infuses KoYou and Chong Zen with the Power of Tao

Laotzu pinched the sleeve of the scholar's robe and looked squarely into his eyes. "Do not thank me. We are all offspring of the mother power of Tao. It is the ignorance clogging up our mind with manmade knowledge that blocks our connecting back to the original power of the universe. As soon as you remove the blockage, the pollution of artificial thought, you can 'see' the truth instantly."

"Master," KoYou slowly got up and bowed to Laotzu. "I feel so wonderful, it is truly amazing. I do not want anything else. I want to be in the power of Tao always. Can we do it again?"

"No, my son," Laotzu replied. "You had enough for you to start on your own. From now on, just follow my instructions recorded by the scribes. Listen to the power within your own body. Move and flow to let your power grow. When your own Te power grows strong enough, you will be able to connect with the Tao power on your own and do many great things.

"Furthermore," Laotzu warned, "it is tempting to abuse your ability. You must restrain the desire to use it for trifling things. You may weaken and leak, draining your power too quickly and become just a normal person again – no longer a Tao person. Be mindful!"

Chong Zen could feel the subtle movement of energy within his body. He let go of his mind, and for once did not analyze the situation. Instead he followed the power and found that he too began to do the slow dance he had seen the sage do a few mornings before.

Now it was Laotzu's turn to bow. Leaving the two to explore their newfound awareness, he went back into the small hut to gather his few belongings. As he closed the door on the tidy stone cottage, he raised his palm as if to bless the home.

In the stable, Ox was not alone. Lo Han and Lo Yintz waited with big smiles and damp eyes in the ox' stall. Ox now sported a dozen silk ribbons on its tail of all the colors of the rainbow. Lo Han draped a beautiful red woolen blanket across the ox' back. "My mother wove this blanket," explained Lo Yintz. "It is our most precious possession. We want to send it with you to the Kunlun Mountain so that you and Ox will be warm."

Laotzu moved his hand to refuse the generous gift, but Lo Han interrupted "Master, you must take this gift. You saved our very lives. We would forever live in sorrow if you refused to let us honor you in the small way we can."

Laotzu nodded. "It is a most beautiful blanket. It will make the long journey more comfortable for both me and my friend." He patted the ox' back through the thick soft wool.

Lo Yintz could restrain herself no longer. She ran to Laotzu and threw her arms around his neck, whispering "Good bye, Uncle Laotzu. I'll never forget what you taught me."

Laotzu stepped back and reached over with his sleeve to dry the girl's tears. "You keep that father of yours out of trouble!"

They helped hoist the bags of provisions across the ox' shoulders and Laotzu mounted the tall animal lithely as if his own body were weightless.

When they led Laotzu's ox out of the stable doors, he could see the entire royal household assembled in the courtyard in his honor. They followed the ox through the palace gates and down into the street where the entire city of West Peace had come to make its farewell with song and celebration. Tumblers went before the ox, while children skipped alongside Laotzu. He could see Abudamancus and his caravan across the square, the big man waving furiously with a gleaming smile. He spied the widow Wong Yuen and her attendants who held a great canopy over their wealthy mistress to shield her from the sun. Curiously, Yin Lian was not by her mother's side.

As Laotzu finally came to the great gates of the city walls, he met Prince KoWu himself standing with the gatekeeper at his post. Surprisingly, even his wife, Zhu Xiao Hua, stood by him this morning, although her eyes demurely stared at the ground. Three little princesses, dressed in their finest gowns stood in a row beside their mother. But where was KoYou, the sage wondered? Was he still back in the courtyard after all this time?

"I thank you again, Master, for your stay, and your precious teaching. Please know that this city will always be your home and that I will always be your humble student." KoWu bowed formally, as Laotzu nodded in return. He and KoWu looked into each other's eyes for the last time. They knew they would never forget each other.

The same escort troop of West Peace soldiers that brought Laotzu through the gates when he arrived, waited outside the gate now to accompany Laotzu as far as he would allow them. The prince gave them orders to go even to the Kunlun Mountains if the sage permitted them. But Laotzu said he would bid them farewell at the city's edge, for he had the protection of the One Power that was always with him.

So the escort troop rode proudly by his side to the outskirts of the city. At Laotzu's command they turned back, giving the sage their royal salute.

Laotzu was again as he'd arrived – traveling alone on a long and dusty road on his ox. The autumn sun gave a gold glow to the dry landscape. It might be summer before he reached the mountains.

Ox ambled uphill until it reached the crest of a plateau. Laotzu looked back to see the City of West Peace below him on the eastern horizon. It looked like a small fortress of sand that a child might build.

Yet as Laotzu looked, he saw a small cloud of dust moving quickly toward him on the road. Soon he could hear the distant pounding of horse's hooves. He smiled to himself.

A few minutes later, he could hear them calling, "Master Laotzu! Master Laotzu!"

Behind him rode KoYou and Yin Lian. They'd missed the parade at Laotzu's farewell because they'd been packing their riding-sacks and stealing horses from the royal stables. They had to make their way out of a side gate so as not to be seen.

Laotzu laughed. The youths' faces burned red with excitement, and their eyes grew wide with wonder at the daring decision they'd made. "We've come to be your disciples!" announced KoYou.

"What made you decide to do such a thing?" asked Laotzu, beaming back at them.

"The other trader spit!" said KoYou. He looked at Yin Lian and they laughed together.

Laotzu scratched his head and shrugged. "Well, come along then," motioned Laotzu with his flywhisk from atop Ox. "Just slow down a little or my poor ox will wear out!"

Resources

DVDS BY MASTER WAYSUN LIAO:

Complete Single Form Library

This 12 dvd archive features Master Liao's personal demonstration and instruction. Filmed several years ago on location at the Tai Chi Tao Center, this rare footage preserves the entire sequence of single forms leading up to and including the Taichi Long Form, breathing and meditation techniques, as well as two-person practice forms. Purchase the complete set, or build your collection by purchasing each disc individually. (also available on vhs)

"How To Develop Chi" Series

Follow along while Master Liao explains key single forms, their refinements and how to flow the energy in each form for maximum chi development. This 15 disc collection is a must in every Taichi practitioner's library. (also available on vhs)

BOOKS BY MASTER WAYSUN LIAO:

CHI - How To Feel Your Life Energy

Master Liao takes you on a step-by-step journey allowing you to reconnect with your feeling of life energy. Once you can feel your Chi, you can learn to flow and strengthen it. Armed with the truth about Chi, you can regain your lost connection to your life energy and restore your True Self.

Tai Chi Classics

For over thirty years, Master Liao's *Tai Chi Classics* remains the only book with a clear discussion of internal power and the art of Taichi. Master Liao translates the works of three centuries-old Chinese masters, and gives a practical commentary on each to help the reader apply each principle in practice.

Essence of Tai Chi

This pocket-sized book is an abridged version of *Tai Chi Classics*, and makes a great gift.

Nine Nights With the Taoist Master - Deluxe Study Edition

If you liked this book, you'll enjoy the Deluxe Study Edition, which provides valuable and in-depth perspective on the mystical teachings of Lao Tzu's *Tao Te Ching*. The Deluxe Study Edition includes an expanded preface, an interview with Master Waysun Liao, a complete stand-alone translation of the *Tao TeChing*, a Chinese version of the *Tao Te Ching*, and an instructive glossary of key terms used by Lao Tzu and their application to Tao meditation practice.

For more information on books, videos, dvds, and seminars featuring the teaching of Master Waysun Liao, contact:

Taichi Center

433 South Boulevard

Oak Park, IL 60302

708-386-0266

www.taichitaocenter.com